Microcomputer Systems

Microcomputer Systems

Richard C. Seals
BSc(Hons), PhD, CEng, MIEE

Principal Lecturer
School of Engineering, University of Greenwich

Stanley Thornes (Publishers) Ltd

First published in 1993 by:
Stanley Thornes (Publishers) Ltd
Ellenborough House
Wellington Street
CHELTENHAM
GL50 1YD
England

A catalogue record for this book is available from the British Library

ISBN 0 7487 1532 0

Typeset by Florencetype Ltd, Kewstoke, Avon
Printed and bound in Great Britain by The Bath Press, Avon

Contents

Preface

Increasingly, computers are no longer regarded as individual stand-alone products, but as part of larger systems; they are becoming microcomputer systems. This text considers some of the requirements, methods and implications of designing and programming such microcomputer systems. It follows the syllabus for the BTEC unit of the same name and is also suitable for second and final year students on Electronic, Electrical/Electronic and other degree courses which include microcomputer system design and programming. The text will be popular with students as it contains many example programs and a considerable amount of detailed information and theory of operation of the component parts of computer systems and programming languages.

No particular microprocessor is featured throughout the text although the Intel range of microprocessor products is considered in some of the more detailed examples as are the **8088/6 microprocessor** and **PC/XT and PC/AT compatible systems** in several of the programming examples.

Throughout the text, emphasis is placed on 'doing', rather than just reading or listening to a lecturer, which is achieved through worked examples. The reader is encouraged to collect, process and apply information as a prelude to gaining 'hands-on' experience. This process acts as an aid to learning how to solve problems which will be applicable in other areas of knowledge.

The book encourages the ability to think clearly about a problem or a design specification by using a system or 'black box' approach to define a solution and then to find ways of implementing it. Some of the hardware and software solutions are considered in detail with many **example algorithms** and **program listings** written in **8086 assembler, Pascal and C**. The general philosophy of design, documentation and testing is maintained alongside the detailed applications to confirm to the reader that the design method is only loosely coupled to the components finally used. At times, the reader is invited to supply material and ideas considered to be the most suitable for their own systems.

Chapter 1 is a brief introduction to microcomputer systems explaining in more detail what they are. **Chapter 2** is a description of the main factors which influence design such as cost, reliability, etc., with **Chapter 3** being a detailed case study of the design of hardware and software of a simple personal computer and how it interacts with the operating system.

Chapter 4 considers a number of 'state-of-the-art' concepts: multi-Master bus systems, multi-tasking systems and co-processors with **Chapter 5** concentrating on advanced concepts such as: memory management systems, parallel processing using the Transputer and Occam as examples, and the design and programming of Reduced Instruction Set Computers (RISC).

Chapters 6 and 7 concentrate on Software Development, with **Chapter 6** considering the operation and use of development systems, simple software design methods such as algorithms and flowcharts, and the documentation of program listings. **Chapter 7** deals with two major High Level computer programming languages; namely Pascal and C, with a case study comparing the design and implementation of a simple problem (matrix multiplication) in both languages. There is then a case study of a significant problem, which is implementing the design of a Pascal program to control the non-volatile CMOS memory used in the 'set-up' of Personal Computers. (Warning: the use of this program is not for the inexperienced or faint-hearted!)

Acknowledgements

With thanks to my Mum and Dad who let me keep on learning when I was young.

Trademarks

Intel is a registered trademark of Intel Corporation. IBM is a registered trademark and PC/AT and PC/XT are trademarks of International Business Machines Corporation. Microsoft and MS-DOS are registered trademarks of Microsoft Corporation.

Disclaimer

All the programs, examples and data used in this text are for illustration only and no responsibility is accepted by the author for any errors, mistakes or problems caused by using this information. The full technical information and data can be obtained from the appropriate technical and data manuals, which will also contain the most up-to-date information.

R. C. Seals
February, 1993

ONE

Introduction

1.1 THE AIM OF THIS BOOK

The aim of this book is to formalise the process of designing microcomputer systems, from the specification stage through to hardware and software solutions. Due to the wide variety of microprocessors and computer languages available, no specific solutions are used throughout, but rather a variety of solutions are used to show that the design method is only loosely coupled to the actual devices used.

In addition the book is laid out in a top-down format, starting with the system design concepts. These are then expanded into techniques of specification and hardware/software design. Some of the ideas and concepts raised in the previous section, are covered in more detail but still attempting to be as general as possible. In this section some of the possible avenues have not been fully investigated, as they require a larger treatment than is possible, or they are covered in other books in the series. Alternatively, the user is invited to supply material and ideas considered to be the most suitable.

Several case studies are followed through from the initial design to the most practical specific solutions in both hardware and software. There should be no difficulty in adapting these case studies and providing alternative microprocessor or language solutions not mentioned. The major case study involves the design of an IBM PC compatible computer.

Throughout the text, emphasis will be placed on 'doing' rather than just reading or listening to a lecturer, in line with the new BTEC policy. This will be through worked examples in the book, and examples to be performed on the preferred development system. There will be information within the book to provide the reader with sufficient knowledge to perform all the specified assignments as 'paper exercises'. Ideally, this knowledge should then be considerably reinforced with as much practical experience as possible, of writing and executing programs on specific hardware.

The aim of the book is for students to gain knowledge and practical experience concerning the specification, design and testing of reprogrammable electronic systems. These will consist of both hardware and software sections with the major emphasis on the software design and testing. Only the functional blocks of the hardware designs will be considered, although sufficient detail will be given to enable correct programs to be designed. That is, the hardware will be considered to exist already, or to be capable of being made to the desired specification, so that only the programming of the hardware need be considered.

In order to meet the aim of this book, several sequential processes need to be performed.

1) Information Gathering. This book will form the majority of the information gathering, supplemented with some additional lectures. However, because most topics are covered without being too specific to a particular microprocessor, there is the need for the additional detailed information, concerning the programming and hardware design of the particular microprocessor being used.

2) Information Processing. Once the information has been gathered then it must be used, or processed, in order to apply it to particular problems. The best method for this is to use examples, which can be supplied either by the lecturer, or can be based on the case studies and examples in this book.

3) Information Application. The final process once the information has been gathered and processed to produce paper designs, is the practical implementation. Obviously this book cannot provide 'hands-on' experience, but the general operation of software development systems will be considered.

These will illustrate the basic operation of assemblers, linkers, tracers and simulators.

1.2 TASK-ORIENTATED LEARNING

The learning method of this book is by 'doing' so that the emphasis is upon the solution of practical problems at all times. This can be achieved through a method known as Task-Orientated Learning (TOL). This method requires that the information to be learnt is identified and a 'task' set which will require the acquisition of that knowledge in order that the task is completed.

The tasks set are known as TOL's and can be undertaken with little previous knowledge. The aim is always to identify the knowledge required to solve the problem from a consideration of the boundary conditions, rather than just to gain certain knowledge and then apply it.

Once this method has been learnt, the ability to solve problems does not end if the area of knowledge is changed.

What is required is the ability to think clearly about what the problem specification is, using a system or black box approach. Then, identify a system solution and finally find methods and ways of implementing the system solution.

Philosophy

Although in general, the hardware will only be considered in block form, some of the software/hardware interfaces will be considered in some detail in order to allow 'realistic' and complete programs to be designed.

Software will also be considered in block form, but will then be expanded to include more detail. Programs, or the appropriate program fragments will be written in 8086, 68000 assembler or Pascal. Usually only a simplified subset of the language will be used, in order to be applicable to as many other systems as possible.

Alongside the detailed design, there will be the general philosophy of design, documentation, testing, and so on.

System Design

The major TOL routine which will be used throughout this book is the design of a system which has the capability to produce, save and execute computer programs which perform useful control of data processing functions. This will be designed to be as compatible as possible with an IBM PC.

The initial system solution will be considered in the first chapter, and then various more specialised concepts will be considered in detail in later chapters.

TWO

Design considerations

2.1 INTRODUCTION

The process of design has one aim which is to convert the inputs of a system into the outputs as illustrated in *Figure 2.1*. The inputs in this particular design process can vary from physical quantities such as sand and cement, to less tangible items such as data and information. The process then converts the input quantities into the output quantities so that the sand and cement might be converted into concrete and the data and information into money. Stated in this way it seems simple but unfortunately this is not so, as there is a nearly infinite set of possible solutions ranging from those which have already been implemented, tested and verified, to those which have not been thought of.

A design technique used by many engineers is to look at the specified inputs and decide which of the known previous designs already produces the maximum number of outputs required. The design is then adapted, extended, reduced and altered until the product is able to produce the required outputs.

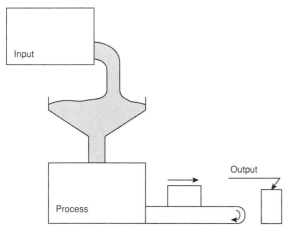

Figure 2.1 The design process

This may seem haphazard but is based on the common sense idea that if it worked before it will work again.

This produces a slow but steady increase in knowledge and experience and an engineer uses past experiences of a variety of different solutions to previous problems and then fits them together like a jigsaw puzzle to solve the present problem. It may not be possible to form a complete solution from past designs and there may be gaps in the solution. It is the gaps the engineer fills by considering the surrounding boundary conditions and looking for a solution which will meet them. This may require a completely new idea which may be obtained from various sources of information, such as journals, books or other engineers.

Although the basic concept may be based on previous successful solutions it is still necessary to work to a set of design rules and procedures, to ensure compatibility between similar products and product designs likely to be correct. The majority of engineering solutions are based on previous solutions which at some point in their history were original ideas, considered against the background of engineering theory and concepts such as stress, reliability, and so on. Therefore those basic theoretical concepts do not need to be considered again for the present design. For example, the mathematical theories behind numbers and arithmetic is not often considered but it is known that such theories exist and are satisfactory. Because of this, calculus, theorems, trigonometry, etc., are used without having to verify that number theory is still valid. Engineering theories do have to be reconsidered occasionally when a limit is reached at which existing designs falter, called the **boundary condition** and this is illustrated in *Figure 2.2*. When a boundary condition is reached the basic principles of the problem are considered and this may take place in the development laboratory or the research

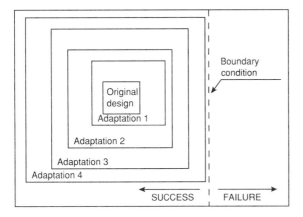

Figure 2.2 Reaching the boundary condition

laboratory. Research laboratories investigate fundamental physical laws and have access to sophisticated production and testing equipment. The ideas and concepts produced are then published in technical journals and gradually propagate through to engineering design departments and development laboratories. In the development laboratories the new ideas are incorporated into products to overcome the failure boundary.

For example, the development of optical fibres for use in communication systems instead of copper wires occurred in research laboratories, whereas the development laboratories use the optical fibre to produce a 100 MHz Local Area Network communication link and protocol.

2.2 DESIGN INFLUENCES

There are many influences on the design process and generally there is no single solution to a specific design problem, but rather a series of alternative solutions which have different characteristics and parameters. The aim of a design technique is to identify which solutions are possible and then which is the optimum. The optimum solution is the best attainable for a set of parameters, such as cost, speed, flexibility, expandability, and so on. It may be possible to design a central heating controller which maintains the temperature within 0.01°C but it would be expensive. A better solution is one which maintains the temperature within 1°C or 2°C, and is compatible with existing central heating systems. This is cheaper and the user will not be able to detect any significant deterioration in comfort caused by the reduction in accuracy of temperature control.

Therefore, before the designer begins specifying

the design parameters, contraints other than the purely technical ones, need to be identified in order to arrive at the optimum solution. For the central heating controller example, the problem specification deals mainly with technical aspects, such as being compatible with existing systems, maintaining the temperature to within 1°C, the number of rooms, thermostats, controllable valves and so on. Other design parameters are cost, ergonomics, speed of introduction into shops and the life-time of the model. These might not be directly connected with the technical aspects of the design but they do have a significant influence on the final product.

The following sections discuss some of the major technical considerations when optimising designs and attempts to show how they are related.

2.3 THE SOFTWARE AND HARDWARE

Most products contain several programmable elements, i.e. those whose function can be modified in some way without physically re-soldering or remaking anything. This programmability enables a division to be made between the software and the hardware. The whole concept of design can be considered as a spectrum of solutions, see *Figure 2.3*, where the position in the spectrum indicates the mixture of hardware and software, the actual division being decided by considering the requirements, constraints and optimisations to be applied.

No solution consists completely of software as any program requires some computer hardware to execute it. However, there is a minimal hardware solution where many tasks which could be performed by the hardware are instead performed by the software.

Similarly, there is no solution consisting totally of hardware, although this is not so immediately

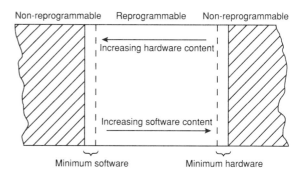

Figure 2.3 The design spectrum

obvious. It is possible to propose solutions which appear to have no programmability and therefore no program. However, in those instances the program is considered to be stored directly as a hardware circuit layout. This becomes clearer in the simple design shown in *Figure 2.4*, where four NAND gates are arranged to produce two outputs from five inputs and the result is therefore a product suitable for applying design techniques. The four logic gates can be obtained using TTL logic gates such as the 74LS00. The outputs P and Q can be formulated using Boolean algebra to become:

P = NOT(NOT(A AND B) AND (NOT(B AND C)))

Q = NOT(D AND E)

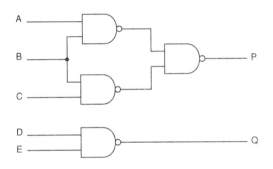

Figure 2.4 Hardware programming using NAND gates

By changing the hardware the Boolean equations have changed and hence the unit can be considered to have been re-programmed. This type of programmability is limited and would not normally be a viable or practicable method of programming if standard components are used, as in this example. However, the widespread use of **Programmable Logic Devices** (PLD's) and **Application Specific Integrated Circuits** (ASIC's) provides an easy method of

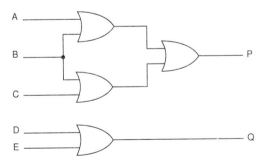

Figure 2.5 Hardware programming using OR gates

programming using the hardware. These devices have many pins, typically between 40 and 84 which can be internally reassigned. Therefore, although the hardware has been fixed in terms of the IC package and PCB space occupied, some programmability is possible.

A Simple Case Study of the Hardware/Software Divide

An example of the hardware/software divide is a serial communication link between a PC and another device. A serial link transfers one bit of information at a time from one computer to another. There is a mainly software solution and a mainly hardware solution.

A Mainly Software Solution

At least two signals are required to make a bi-directional serial link to produce an electrical connection between devices. The communication of data is internationally standardised at fixed transmission frequencies called the Baud rate, which specifies how many binary digits are to be transmitted. There are 10 bits required to transmit an 8 bit byte of data with 1 start bit and 1 stop bit. One alphanumeric character occupies one byte so that this sentence containing 160 characters, requires 160 bytes to transfer it as spaces count as a character.

The encoding and subsequent decoding of the byte of data is implemented using software to control the signal lines, to send and receive bytes at the specified Baud rate with the specified bits per character. This requires the software to be continuously monitoring the data values on the input and output signals in order to transmit and receive bytes of data correctly. The following algorithm will transmit the sentence and indicates that a large amount of processing time is spent in delay loops where no useful instructions can be executed.

Example algorithm

(1) Get the byte;
(2) Output the start bit;
(3) Wait for one bit period;
(4) Output a bit of data from the selected byte;
(5) Wait for one bit period;
(6) Repeat from step (4) until all the bits in the byte have been transmitted;
(7) Output the stop bit;
(8) Wait for one bit period;
(9) Repeat from step (1) until the end of the sentence.

If another process or function is involved which is to be controlled there is a conflict, as the processing unit is required to perform two or more functions simultaneously. This can be achieved by making use of the periods when the processing unit is performing a timing loop. This is illustrated in the top line of *Figure 2.6* where the straight line between the serial link indicates that a timing loop is being executed as the serial link signals do not require active control. Instead of executing timing loops a second, and possibly subsequent, function can be executed and provided that the timing required for the serial link is maintained when executing the other function instead of the original timing loops, there will be no problems. This can be difficult to achieve if the additional functions have variable execution times. From *Figure 2.6* it can be seen that further processes can be performed in any unused time periods. There are difficulties in swapping between several different processes and this approach is not normally taken if it can be avoided. Sometimes there is no viable alternative and a great deal of time, effort and care is taken to ensure the systems operate correctly.

A Mostly Hardware Solution

By adding hardware to deal with the majority of the serial link control requirements, the processing unit no longer performs all the low level actions such as timing loops and bit outputting as these are performed by the hardware. Only the input or output of bytes of data to the hardware is required and the processor time previously wasted in waiting loops can be used to execute additional functions.

Adding the additional hardware introduces further requirements. For example, the hardware requires a clock signal which is a multiple of the Baud rate being used which is used to perform the timing loops

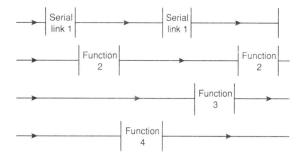

Figure 2.6 The use of vacant time to perform additional functions

and this is usually difficult to obtain from the system clock. Therefore either a special Baud rate generator or a general-purpose programmable timer device must also be added.

It is also necessary to consider the manner in which the additional hardware is controlled and two main techniques are available. The first uses the hardware to produce a signal whenever a byte is received or can be transmitted, which interrupts whatever the processor is executing to perform some action required by the serial link. Alternatively, the processing unit periodically interrogates the hardware to determine whether a character has been received or whether one can be transmitted and then to take the appropriate actions.

These design decisions are introduced when the extra hardware is added so that decisions about the hardware and software division affect the software part of the system by placing restrictions or introducing extra design decisions. These ideas may or may not be identifiable in the specification before the design process begins depending on the specification detail.

2.4 REAL-TIME PROGRAMMING

This introduces the concept of real-time and real-time programming. In the physical world, time is measured in seconds, the length of which is independent of where or when the measurement is made. However, for control purposes, time becomes relative to the process being controlled and real-time can be said to be in operation when there is no user-perceivable delay between an input and the response. For example, a person sitting in front of a Visual Display Unit (VDU) presses a key and the character appears on the screen within 200–300 milliseconds, so no delay is noticed and the display is said to be operating in the user's real-time. These characters are transmitted from the VDU to the computer system. As a person cannot press the keys at high repetition rates the computer has to wait between characters when it is doing nothing of importance and the VDU is **not** operating in the computer's real-time. Therefore the VDU is performing in real-time with one user but not with another and a priority is assigned to determine the most important real-time.

It is possible to make use of the waiting time in computer systems to perform other tasks. This could involve connecting more VDUs to the computer to produce a time-shared computer system where each VDU is allocated a small section of the time of the processing unit. This is similar to the functions illustrated in *Figure 2.6* with each one being allocated sufficient time to perform the VDU operations of character transmission and reception. In this way many VDUs can appear to be simultaneously connected to the computer. The computer system then operates in its real-time with the set of VDUs and each separate VDU operates in the user's real-time.

2.5 MAXIMUM CAPABILITY VERSUS EXPANDABILITY

When designing a product there is usually a subconscious desire to produce a system which performs exactly to the specification. This is because once a problem is specified and the boundary conditions given, it is natural only to produce what is specifically asked for. This approach is satisfactory if the product will never be re-designed or used for anything else which is not true for the majority of products. Most products have a limited life-time and are continually re-designed to control new situations and include desirable enhancements. If the product is designed only to fulfil the specification originally given, it can be difficult to include the enhancements without re-designing the entire product. The limitations of designing to meet the specification can be reduced to a certain extent by producing a more thorough specification that incorporates possible future enhancements. Such eventualities are allowed for then in the internal product structure, so that re-designing and enhancements follow in an orderly structured manner.

For new designs, once the design process is completed and the product manufactured it is possible to reconsider the specification and identify areas which could be re-designed. The re-design may be to improve one of the parameters of the product, such as reducing power consumption or PCB area. This may be something the manufacturer is keen to implement but is not able to consider until the complete design is in production.

For the personal computer being designed throughout this book, there are a variety of improvements that could be made once the initial designs have been completed. Power consumption can be reduced by using CMOS or other low power versions of the components. This in turn reduces the size of the power supply required and the amount of heat generated, leading to a reduction in the amount of cooling required.

In addition, by designing custom components such as ASICs it is possible to combine large numbers of standard components into a smaller number of special components leading to a further reduction in the power requirement, which reduces the size of the PCB, which in turn reduces the size of the enclosure and again reduces the cost. Reducing the number of components also increases the reliability of the product, assuming all other things remain constant. All these actions add to the attractive qualities of the final PC as it requires less space on the user's desk, is lighter, makes less noise and is cheaper.

Figure 2.7 illustrates the concept of designing for future enhancements with the perfect inner circle representing the design of a product which meets the original specification. This is the centre of both designs with *Figure 2.7(a)* indicating that enhancements have been considered in the initial design stage, even though they might not have been explicitly stated in the specification. The first closely dotted ring indicates the enhancements that are immediately possible and have been considered in some detail. The widely spaced dotted circle indicates those enhancements that have been considered in outline, which might be possible once the initial enhancements have been implemented. For the PC, one possible enhancement might be a new type of video display which when the PC was initially designed was not envisaged.

On a PC where there was a design for enhancements, it would probably be a standard interface for video display adapters. This enables new types of display to be designed and by matching the standard interface they can be included. There is always some loss in performance when using a standard interface of this nature, but this is compensated for by increased flexibility. After several enhancements have been implemented the product could be viewed as in *Figure 2.8* showing that as the additions continue, the less well specified enhancements

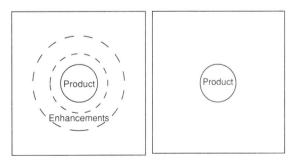

Figure 2.7 Products at initial design stage

become specified with new enhancements identified at the new perimeter.

On a PC not designed for future enhancements the video display would have been designed as an integrated part of the basic system and there would be little possibility of changing this to accommodate the new display. If improvements could be made

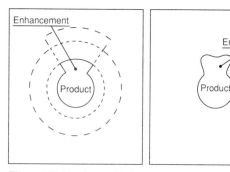

Figure 2.8 Products with first enhancement

they would generally be of an untidy, unwieldy and possibly unreliable nature, as illustrated in *Figure 2.8(b). Figures 2.8(b) and 2.9(b)* illustrate the addition of enhancements to a product where future or alternative uses were not considered. Initially the enhancements can be made but they produce malformed structures, as they are forced to fit products for which they are not ideally suited. Later enhancements become even more difficult to add and eventually a point is reached at which no more enhancements can be added because part of a previous enhancement overlaps or obscures an area necessary for the new enhancement.

The disadvantage of designing for enhancements is the cost, as anything requiring extra components or extra design costs more. This results in each of the manufactured products containing a cost element not directly related to the product function but

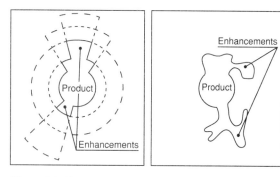

Figure 2.9 Products with further enhancements

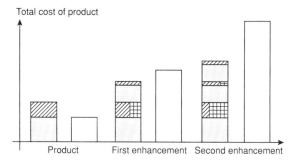

Figure 2.10 The benefits of designing for enhancements

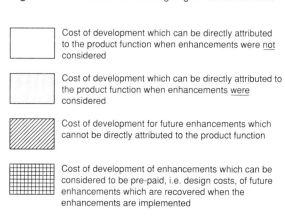

☐	Cost of development which can be directly attributed to the product function when enhancements were <u>not</u> considered
☐	Cost of development which can be directly attributed to the product function when enhancements <u>were</u> considered
▨	Cost of development for future enhancements which cannot be directly attributed to the product function
▦	Cost of development of enhancements which can be considered to be pre-paid, i.e. design costs, of future enhancements which are recovered when the enhancements are implemented

Figure 2.11 Explanation of bar chart Fig 2.10

to possible future enhancements. *Figure 2.10* illustrates a breakdown of the cost with the use of bar charts, indicating how the costs vary as enhancements are added for the two techniques, of designing for enhancement and not designing for enhancements. The cost initially is higher for products designed for expansion but future products become cheaper.

Designing for expansion is no guarantee that the extra costs will be recovered and it is possible to over-design a product such that the costs of designing for future enhancements are large and will never be recovered. The ideal design enables any enhancements to be implemented but the optimum design only allows those enhancements most likely to be required, to be included in the original design. Any enhancements not covered must then be added as best possible.

2.6 MAXIMUM FLEXIBILITY, MINIMUM HARDWARE

Often the initial specification is incomplete and could consist of a requirement for a microcomputer of some indeterminate capability which is to control functions not yet defined. Also, it may be known that the initial product will have a short life-span but that certain sub-component designs such as the floppy disk controller board will be used again in subsequent models. The same basic controller is to be used in all the PCs to reduce design costs, design time, and the number of spares required by the dealer and service personnel.

An additional influence when designing programmable products is that it is **easier to change the software** than the hardware and this results in the hardware being minimised. Minimum hardware for a microcontroller would consist of some form of input/output, program storage and a method of transferring data, information or status to the user.

Maximum flexibility can be achieved by minimising hardware and maximising software. Maximising software content introduces the concept of **the universal product**. This is a minimum hardware product that can be altered to fulfil a wide variety of control and design purposes by changing the software. In addition, by the use of some standard interface, further hardware functions can be added. Minimum hardware does not mean that there is no possibility of expansion or very little hardware and the universal product is not necessarily the smallest or cheapest solution. Universality requires a suitable number and variety of hardware functions, which for a microcomputer might be 24 I/O lines, two serial communication links and 32 kbytes of ROM and RAM. If the function being implemented requires 2 I/O lines, 2 kbytes of ROM and no serial links, then the universal component might not be the best selection. Alternatively, if more hardware facilities are required than are available on the universal component, for example, 48 I/O lines when only 24 are available, a special design may be preferred as illustrated in *Figure 2.12*.

The concept of the universal design can be extended further by using modular hardware and universal interfaces. This concept requires minimum hardware containing one or more general interfaces which allow other hardware sub-modules to be added as required. For a PC the minimum hardware is the power supply, a motherboard consisting of several multi-pin connectors connected in parallel and a case. Sub-modules might be a data processing board, a temporary data variable board, a display driver and a secondary mass storage board such as a floppy disk drive controller, as illustrated in *Figure 2.13*. If this arrangement did not meet the specification any or all of the sub-modules could be removed

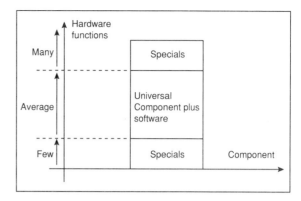

Figure 2.12 The selection of special or universal Components

and additional ones inserted until the correct hardware configuration was achieved.

The demand for universal products which produce subsequent savings on design, proto-typing and production costs, has lead to a variety of universal programmable components. These are called single chip microprocessors and contain the majority of required facilities within a single integrated circuit package, as illustrated in *Figure 2.14*.

2.7 STANDARD OR CUSTOM COMPONENTS

When designing re-programmable micro-electronic products there are two main types of components that can be used, standard or specially designed custom components. Standard components are those produced by manufacturers which are designed to be used in a general area and are not targeted for specific products. This requires the components to be as general purpose as possible

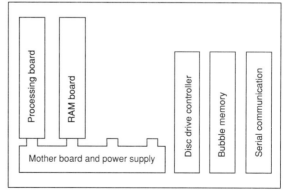

Figure 2.13 Motherboard and hardware modules

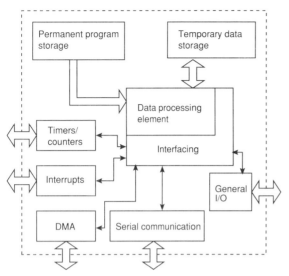

Figure 2.14   Integrated (single chip) micro-controller

with as many functions as possible. The designer then selects from the available components those which, when correctly connected, will implement his own product specification.

If custom components are used, the specification can be implemented directly by designing-in a component which is specific to the applications. Such devices are known as **Application Specific Integrated Circuits** (**ASICs'**) and are being increasingly used in new products due to their many advantages.

There is also a variety of intermediate solutions ranging between only standard and only custom components by including a mixture of both, or using semi-custom components. Semi-custom components include a variety of standard sub-functions which can be internally connected as required for a specific product. Different products then have different internal connections so that the semi-custom components are adapted for each new product.

The Advantages of Standard Components

Standard components tend to be produced by several different manufacturers, particularly if large numbers of them are sold. This provides a user with what is known as second sourcing and means a user is not restricted to a particular manufacturer. In addition the supply of the component is more reliable and dependable and competition will generally maintain prices as low as possible. This enables a greater confidence in the possibility of maintaining

future supplies, allowing lower stocks to be held and reducing the product material costs. This gives the product a potentially longer life-time without re-design and ensures a continuing supply of replacement components for maintenance.

Proto-typing time can be reduced as the components are immediately available, have established parameters and performance and the reliability of the components is high and inter-connection techniques are known and defined. There is often documented or previous experience of using the wide variety of standard components which reduces the demand on the designer's skills and enables automated techniques of design to be used to increase productivity. These include automatically designing a PCB layout from the circuit diagram, a range of development aids such as **In-Circuit Emulators** (ICE) for the hardware and assemblers, compilers, linkers and so on for the software. This promotes increased productivity, especially if several designs will be produced using the same standard range of components.

The Disadvantages of Standard Components

Products containing standard components generally contain more of them, due to the redundancy inherent in general components which are designed to fulfil many functions, some of which are almost certain not to be used in every product. This decreases reliability as reliability is approximately proportional to the number of components and the number of soldered connections. The standard components also occupy more PCB area and require larger overall power supply currents than custom devices. Another disadvantage is the lower operating speeds due to the general purpose internal architecture.

For large production runs the cost of using standard components may be higher than custom ones as the discounting structure is less favourable due to the fact that very large numbers are already being sold at a discounted price. Competitors may also use the same components to produce similar products, at a lower price. This is possible as the design costs may be negligible due to the design already having been performed elsewhere.

The Advantages of Custom Components

When custom components are used the redundancy in the product is reduced as the internal operation is specifically designed for the application, producing parameters that are faster, smaller, use less power

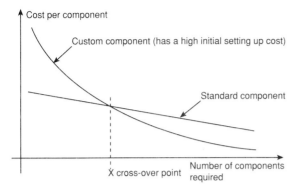

Figure 2.15 The cross-over point between custom and standard components

and are more reliable than a product designed using standard components. For large production runs the initial costs of setting up the manufacture of the custom solution can be recouped over a larger number of components tending to make the initial costs worthwhile, as illustrated in *Figure 2.15*. If cost is the major consideration and if the number of components required is less than the point at which the two curves cross, standard devices should be used.

Other considerations such as high speed, small space or low power, may require the use of custom components in order to meet the design specifications. The higher initial cost of producing the custom component is the penalty of this requirement.

The increased speed of operation is a major advantage and a 10- or 20-fold increase in speed over designs using standard components is possible.

As many of the solder connections are eliminated and the number of components is reduced, the reliability of the product is increased. For example, a special component with a total of 40 solder connections may replace four or five standard components with a total of up to 200 solder connections, increasing the reliability of the connections by a factor of 4 or 5. In addition, production costs for assembling custom components into the product are less due to the reduced number of pieces.

The Disadvantages of Custom Components

There are two major disadvantages of custom components: cost and the inflexibility of the design. There are high setting-up costs because of the specialised nature of the components, although various techniques for reducing these high initial

manufacturing setting-up and production costs are available. These alter the position of the cross-over point (X) so that it occurs at lower numbers of components required. One technique is to use semi-custom devices. One example of semi-custom is **Programmable Logic Arrays** (PLA) which are arrays of standard logic cells interconnected in standard methodologies by programmable links on the inputs and outputs of the standard cells. This allows the outputs to be customised combinations of the inputs as illustrated in *Figure 2.16*, and this type of device can be considered as a standard component. The programming equipment is simple and cheap and programmed devices can be produced from the initial specification within a few hours.

For more sophisticated components there are larger arrays of standard logic cell functions produced from combinations of NAND's, NOR's and so on, from which the final metallic interconnections of the cells have been omitted. Such devices come under the heading of **Uncommitted Logic Arrays** (ULA). The final metalisation layout is then designed to produce the customized functions. The equipment required to design the final interconnection mask is complicated and expensive, consisting of various CAD packages for routing the metalisation connections between the cells. Usually the manufacturer of the ULAs offers this design service to the

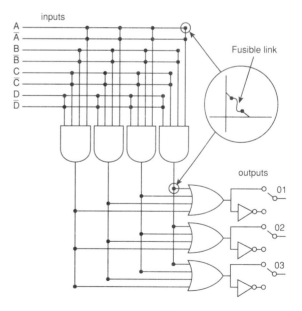

Figure 2.16 A Programmable Logic Array with 4 inputs and 3 outputs

user as part of the component fee. An average time to produce a component implemented on a ULA can be as little as 6–8 weeks with quantities as low as 20–30 at prices of £20–40 each.

The final method of producing custom components is one which designs all the internal layout of the component from the product specification. There are no existing cells already constructed but the design process makes use of standard cell design layouts in order to reduce the design period. The component is constructed from basic semiconductor materials with a turn-round time of up to six months or more where several test prototypes are necessary before a satisfactory device is produced. This method of construction is only used when large numbers of components are required and where long development times are possible. A close collaboration between the custom component manufacturer who has all the expensive design facilities and the user is necessary to ensure that a correctly functioning component is obtained.

2.8 DESIGNING FOR MAXIMUM RELIABILITY

The reliability of microprocessor-based products is often not seriously considered when the functional and logical operation is being designed because of the high reliability of micro-electronic devices. These components are designed to be electrically and functionally as reliable and as compatible as possible. New products from the same manufacturer tend to be compatible with existing components and can be included in new designs without much consideration, see *Figure 2.17*. The design emphasis so far has been one of functional and logical compatibility with the specification, without much thought to the reliability.

If components from different manufacturers are used additional hardware interfaces may be required to glue the different devices together, as illustrated in *Figure 2.18*. If the disk drive controller from manufacturer A is to be fitted to the microcomputer designed from components produced by manufacturer B, the 'glue' of interface and logic devices can sometimes be difficult to design.

This mixing of different manufacturers' components can reduce the reliability of the finished product as the components have different electrical characteristics, leading to premature ageing, complete failure or reduced resistance to errors caused by electrical noise.

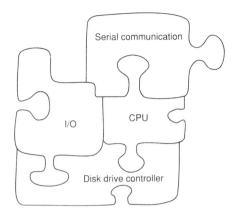

Figure 2.17   A system from manufacturer A

Failure of a Product

There are a variety of reasons why a product fails and the three major factors are:

(1) Incorrect or poor design;
(2) Incorrect assembly;
(3) Ageing.

Incorrect design. Most reprogrammable products are prototyped before being manufactured in quantity to look for failures caused by incorrect design. However, there are several reasons why not all the failures are detected such as the test conditions may not be sufficiently complete to induce all the failure modes. Often this is not because of poor test sequences but because the product is used in ways that were not envisaged and hence not tested for. Another reason for the testing failing to detect failure

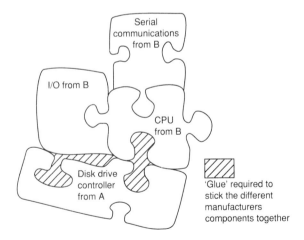

Figure 2.18   Linking components from different manufacturers

modes is that the testing environment is free of failure-inducing situations such as power line spikes and power surges, which may be common in situations where the product is used.

In complex products there are many possible sequences of actions depending upon the input conditions and the order in which they occur. This is illustrated in *Figure 2.19* for a simple product which has three inputs which occur sequentially, resulting in one of twenty-two output actions. To ensure that the product performs correctly, tests should be performed to check the operation after every input, to ensure that all the results are valid and correct. Therefore, the first input requires three tests, the second level seven tests and the third level twenty-two tests, to make a total of thirty-two tests. For products that have hundreds of inputs and operate continuously, the number of tests required is very large. It is not practical to perform all these tests as the cost and time required would be excessive.

Instead, representative tests are made which reduce the number of tests by:

(1) Grouping the outputs together;
(2) Checking the boundary conditions operate correctly;
(3) Ignoring unlikely combinations of inputs.

In addition there are failure modes which only occur when the hardware and software are performing the designed task and these are known as real-time run errors, as they can only occur when the system is being used at the specified speed. This is because the real data being processed is different from the test data used to verify system operation. For example, there might be more data than

originally thought, causing the memory to become full and corrupt the processing of that data.

Often, the failure modes cannot be detected until the product is produced and being used. There would then be a revision of the design with the aim of eliminating all the known failure modes. The decision to re-design is taken with care as nobody wants to buy products requiring post-production modifications, nor do they want to buy products which do not operate correctly and the updates themselves may introduce additional failure modes. The result is that as the product matures and failure modes are eliminated, the reliability increases. This is one of the reasons why micro-electronic components are reliable because the initial spate of failure modes has been detected and corrected in later versions. New types of micro-electronic components are sometimes still discovered to have obscure failure modes.

Incorrect assembly. The second main reason for failures is that a percentage of the products has been incorrectly assembled. There are many different product faults, with a common failing being poor solder connections varying from no electrical connection to poor connections with a short lifetime which then become high impedance. Assuming that any open circuit connections are discovered by testing and quality assurance procedures, the remaining short life-time connections can be uncovered by soak-testing. This exercises the functions of the manufactured products before they leave the production facility and is performed at higher temperatures to speed up the ageing process and discover the poor connections. This results in products which are more reliable but cost more due to the additional testing period.

Ageing. The final area of failure is ageing, where failures begin to occur because the components reach the end of their lifetime. The failed components can be replaced but at this stage it does not significantly increase the lifetime of the product as the remaining original components are still at the end of their lifetime and subsequent failures are likely. Replacing a worn-out component with a new component normally decreases the remaining lifetime of the rest of the components as they introduce a step change in the internal parameters, such as current, voltage or temperature, due to the differences between aged and new components. Step changes in parameters cause additional stresses and accelerate the ageing process leading to further

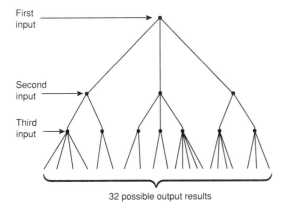

Figure 2.19 Production action sequences requiring testing

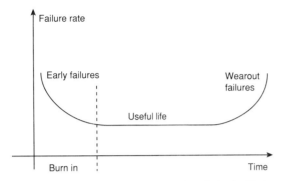

Figure 2.20   The failure rate of a product during its lifetime

Table 2.1 Some General Failure Rates

Item	Failures per million hours	
	(min)	*(max)*
Alternator	1	9
Battery (lead acid)	0.5	1.5
Battery charger (simple)	2	
Ball bearing (light)	0.1	1
Busbars (11 kV)	0.02	0.2
(415 kV)	0.5	2
Capacitors (metallised poly)	0.001	0.04
(mica silvered)	0.03	
(ceramic)	0.001	0.04
(electrolytic)	0.1	0.5
(tantalum solid)	0.2	
Clutch (friction)	0.5	3
Computer (mainframe)	4000	8000
(mini)	100	800
(micro)	30	100
Connections (hand solder)	0.001	0.02
(flow solder)	0.0005	0.002
(wire wrapped)	0.00005	0.0005
(crimped)	0.001	0.004
Connectors (coaxial)	0.2	0.6
(PCB)	0.001	0.1
(DIL)	0.0006	
Crystal (quartz)	0.05	0.2
Fuse	0.1	0.2
Generator (ac)	30	
Inductor	0.3	0.5
Lamp (filament)	0.05	1
LCD character	0.05	
LED character	0.01	
Loudspeaker	10	
PCB (single sided)	0.03	0.05
(double sided)	0.04	0.09
(multilayer)	0.04	0.1
Resistors (carbon film)	0.001	0.05
(metal oxide)	0.001	0.004
(wire wound)	0.001	0.005
Stepper motor	0.5	5
Switches (micro)	0.3	1.3
(DIL)	0.2	1.8
(pushbutton)	0.2	1
Thermocouple	3	10
Transformers (main)	0.2	0.3
TV receiver	2.3	
VDU	100	600

failures within a shorter period of time. Attempting to repair a product which is reaching the end of its lifetime is generally not cost-effective and a better option is to replace the entire product with a new one.

The effect of these different reasons for failure on the failure rate of a product is the so-called bath tub curve, see *Figure 2.20*.

Determining the Failure Rate

It is possible to determine some average failure rates for electrical and electronic components in order that comparisons of reliability between different designs and methods of construction can be made, see *Table 2.1*. *Table 2.2* gives failure rates for a variety of micro-electronic devices and illustrates the increasing ageing effect of higher temperatures, indicating that a product is best operated at room temperatures to obtain the maximum lifetime. For example, the 4 kbyte CMOS RAM component has as a 50-fold increase in failure rate when the operating temperature is increased from 30°C to 100°C. Temperatures of over 60°C can easily occur when semiconductors are operated for long periods in enclosures.

Failure Rate Comparison

Supposing a 16 kbyte RAM module is being designed for an existing motherboard system. This requires 4×4 kbyte Bipolar RAM, 24-pin components and one 50-logic gate, 14-pin digital logic decoding component. A 64-pin PCB connector is used to connect the module into the mother-board. *Table 2.3* gives a summary of the component failure rates and a predicted assembled module failure rate.

The major source of failure is the 4 kbyte Bipolar RAM component and at higher temperatures the failure rate becomes due almost entirely to this device. Replacing the memory components with a single 16 kbyte RAM device reduces the product failure rate considerably.

The second major source of failures is the solder joints themselves, where the large number of solder connections multiplies the failure rate of an individual joint. Therefore, the fewer the solder links, the more reliable the product and it should be noted that this causes each component to contribute to the

Table 2.2 Micro-electronic failure rates

Type	No. of transistors	Gates	Max failure rate at a temperature of:			
			30°C	50°C	75°C	100°C
Bipolar, linear	5		0.15	0.15	0.30	0.75
	25		0.15	0.15	0.30	0.80
	100		0.35	0.40	0.70	2.00
Bipolar, digital		50	0.10	0.15	0.20	0.30
		500	0.20	0.30	0.50	0.80
		1000	0.40	0.50	0.80	1.50
Bipolar, RAM		4 k	0.35	0.80	2.00	5.00
		16 k	0.80	1.50	4.50	10.0
NMOS RAM		4 k	0.30	0.70	3.00	15.00
		16 k	0.80	1.50	7.00	35.00
CMOS RAM		4 k	0.25	0.40	1.50	7.50

Table 2.3 An example of failure rate calculation

Component	Failure rate	Number required	Total
4 k RAM	0.1	4	0.4
50-gate logic (30°C)	0.03	1	0.03
PCB connection	0.001	64	0.064
Solder joint	0.0005	164	0.082
Overall (failures per million hours) 1.246			

failure figures twice, first because there is an inherent component failure rate and second because of its solder connection failures. This effect can be minimised by reducing the number of connections and using the most reliable method of connection.

The assessment of reliability is achieved by referring to the **Mean Time Between Failure** (MTBF) which is the predicted time between two successive failures of a product. The MTBF can be calculated for individual components but it is more usual to produce this figure for the complete product and may include both hardware and software. The MTBF is an average figure obtained from statistical analysis indicating the average time between failures for a large number of products. As it is a statistical evaluation of what will happen it does not guarantee when failures will occur. It is useful when comparing the reliability of similar products from different manufacturers. The values obtained can be calculated from the measured and theoretical failure rates of the components and sub-assemblies and if the product is mature enough, from an analysis of actual product failures.

2.9 OPTIMISING THE COST

Cost as a design parameter is considered throughout the preceding sections and this section will summarise the concepts in order to identify the effect on the cost of making a design decision concerning a different parameter. Specific cost evaluations cannot be made unless a particular product and its parameters are specified and accurate costing's made. Instead, relative comparisons are made and general trends indicated.

Six important parameters have been selected and the relative unit cost, high or low, indicated for the two boundary conditions that are most appropriate:

	Low cost	High cost
(1) The number to be made	Many	Few
(2) Reliability	Low	High
(3) Enhancements required	No	Yes
(4) Speed of operation	Low	High
(5) Number of functions required	Few	Many
(6) Life-time	Short	Long

2.10 THE IDEAL PARAMETERS

The ideal parameters are the same for any product and are listed below. These are default parameters if they are not explicitly defined in the specification and order does not imply any priority:

(1) Low cost;
(2) High reliability;
(3) High speed of operation;
(4) Maximum flexibility and enhancements possible;
(5) Maximum number of functions;
(6) Large numbers produced and sold;
(7) A long-term future.

The list of ideal parameters is representative rather than exclusive. Although each parameter is listed separately they are not independent with the level of dependency being specific to the product. However, it can easily be seen that the cost is a function of all these parameters and to obtain the lowest cost the parameters' boundaries would change from:

(1) High reliability, to low reliability;
(2) High speed of operation, to low speed;
(3) Maximum flexibility, to minimum flexibility;
(4) Larger numbers produced, to unchanged numbers;
(5) A longer-term future, to unchanged life-time.

This illustrates that the design parameters are not independent and that altering one affects the others to a varying degree. The exact relationship between them is different for every product and is not always easy to determine.

If the ideal parameters of the design do not meet

the specification, they are changed from the ideal to the optimum. Some parameter boundaries will be given in the specification and these cannot be varied from the ideal. The optimum solution is then obtained by varying the unspecified parameters, or alternatively, relaxing one or more of the specified parameters. For example, reliability might be allowed to be lowered in order to maintain a low cost, or alternatively, a higher cost might have to be accepted in order to meet the specification of all other parameters. Optimising the design becomes a process of balancing high priority parameter gains against low priority losses.

If a parameter is not assigned a high priority rating the designer does not automatically attempt to achieve the opposite. If low cost is the major priority, a product with a low reliability and large numbers made would not necessarily be designed because these parameters are less expensive. However, it may be that the product designed does have a low reliability and is made in large numbers. An example of this is the plastic teaspoon, where the reliability is reduced to the spoon being used for just one cup of tea and large numbers are made, resulting in the final product being cheap. The lifetime of this product is sacrificed to maintain the number one priority of low cost. To continue this example, if a more reliable teaspoon is required a stainless steel one could be made. This increases the unit cost by 100 or more but increases the reliability by much more, as a stainless steel teaspoon is expected to stir more than 100 cups of tea. The range of functions of the teaspoon is also increased, ice cream can be scooped, paint can lids removed and so on.

THREE

Designing the microcomputer

3.1 INTRODUCTION

This section will consider a complete design which will incorporate information from other chapters in the book. The aim is to demonstrate how complex designing is, being much more than simply connecting together a few components, but rather a synthesis and optimisation of many different and conflicting requirements, such as:

(1) Cost;
(2) Technical function;
(3) Ergonomics;
(4) Saleability;
(5) Market trends and situation;
(6) Publicity;
(7) Selling points.

There are several different design techniques that can be used for designs such as this, but a simplified top-down approach will be used. The details of the top-down approach will not be considered as the reader will be able to 'pick-up' the essence of the technique by following the method in which it is applied.

The method separates common actions and functions into self-contained blocks with defined interfaces to the other blocks. Each block is then subjected to a top-down design which considers the actions required of each block. These actions are then broken down into smaller sub-actions which are effectively simpler blocks with simpler interfaces. These simpler blocks are then broken down into even simpler blocks. This process is repeated until the blocks being produced contain only single actions which can be implemented directly. As the

blocks are all completely defined as are all the interfaces between blocks, by implementing the lowest level of blocks, the complete product is also automatically implemented.

Before the design can start, the specification has to be produced and some would call this the first step in the design process. The specification is obtained by considering the inputs the product will have and what the correct response to each of them will be, which includes possible sequences of actions as well as individual actions.

The basic functions of a microcomputer are listed below:

(1) Executing user programs;
(2) Manipulating and saving data;
(3) Displaying results;
(4) Responding to user intervention.

Each of the functions must also contain information on what to do if incorrect input data is used, or if a fault or error condition is detected during the product operation, caused by things other than incorrect input data.

Part of the specification will detail the communication required between different functions, parts and layers of the product, as the use of well-structured communication interfaces produces error-free, robust and reliable links.

For a microcomputer, many functions can be implemented using either hardware, software, or a combination of hardware and software.

The exact solution is generally determined by the response time required by each function, which needs to be defined in the specification in order that the correct design be obtained.

3.2 CASE STUDY: A MICROCOMPUTER DESIGN

A general-purpose computer will be designed that is capable of executing user-defined programs. The functional specification for such a product is not simple and a realistic specification would occupy several hundred pages. Therefore, in addition to not considering the practical implementation of the final design in terms of the power supply, printed circuit board, etc., a simplified functional specification will be used.

The programmable peripherals that will be selected for the final design are all compatible with an IBM PC. The programming sequences required to initialise and use them will not always be included in order to avoid unnecessary detail. This detail can easily be obtained from the appropriate data sheets and manuals.

3.3 THE FUNCTIONAL SPECIFICATION

The main aim of the product is to execute user programs, which leads to the following list of major requirements:

(1) Storage of user programs;
(2) Execution of user programs;
(3) User interaction with programs.

These are illustrated in *Figure 3.1*. The following practical requirements of the microcomputer circuit have been deduced from this, as follows:

(1) Secondary mass storage, probably a floppy disk drive;
(2) Fast transfer between secondary storage and execution memory using DMA transfers;
(3) Large execution memory to enable the widest range of user programs to be executed, Read/Write Memory;

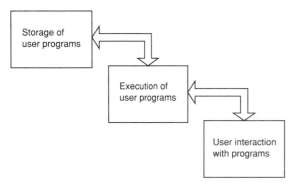

Figure 3.1 Basic microcomputer functions

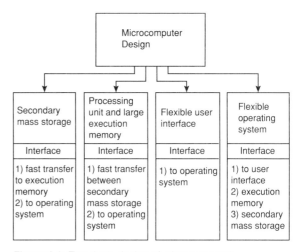

Figure 3.2 Top-down design of microcomputer

(4) Flexible user interface allowing a wide variety of input and output devices ;
(5) A flexible operating system providing control over the hardware while the user program is transferred to and from the secondary mass storage and access to system services for the user program via the Disk Operating System.

This expanded specification is illustrated in *Figure 3.2* and comprises the first level of the top-down design.

3.4 THE SECONDARY MASS STORAGE

Secondary mass storage is a mechanism for saving user programs, data and results using a non-volatile medium, such as floppy disks. The floppy disks fit into a mechanical read and write mechanism called the floppy disk drive, controlled by the **Floppy Disk**

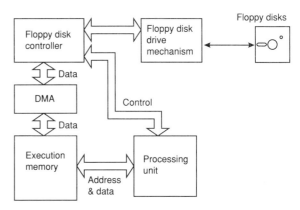

Figure 3.3 Secondary mass storage

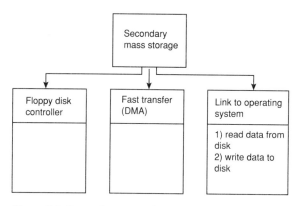

Figure 3.4 Secondary mass storage

Controller (FDC) connected to the processing unit, as illustrated in *Figure 3.3*.

The FDC is programmed and controlled by the processor to transfer data between the floppy disk and the **execution memory**. This is an interface shown from *Figure 3.2* and uses **Direct Memory Access** (DMA) to achieve the maximum speed of transfer as specified in the interface, see *Figure 3.4*.

The two main operations required of the FDC are:

(1) Read a block of data from the floppy disk;
(2) Write a block of data to the floppy disk.

These are performed using the link to the operating system. The user will specify the block of data to

be transferred by supplying the filename. This forms the second interface specified which is the link to the operating system, as shown in *Figure 3.4*.

3.5 THE FLOPPY DISK CONTROLLER

The operation and programming of the FDC is briefly described below. The actions of a FDC fall into one of three categories:

(1) Reading data from the floppy disk to memory;
(2) Writing data from memory to the floppy disk;
(3) Initialising the floppy disk drive and floppy disk.

Because this device is designed for mass storage, the data transferred is in large blocks and to obtain the maximum performance DMA transfers are performed. The system must therefore, also contain a DMA controller.

The FDC can be used in either a polled or an interrupt-driven mode. In an interrupt-driven mode there is an interrupt signal which is used to indicate that the presently-executing command has completed; if this is used a **Programmable Interrupt Controller** (PIC) will also be required, see *Figure 3.5*.

Data is accessed on the floppy disk in terms of the head used, the track number and the sector number. The record/playback head is physically moved to place it directly over the selected track, and then pressed against the track, in order to be able to read or write data.

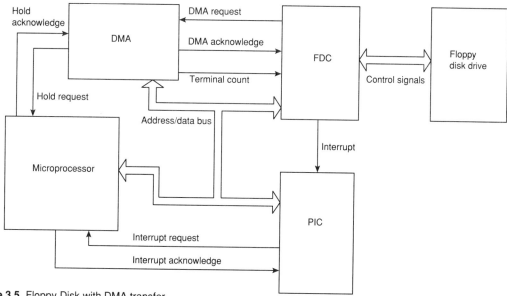

Figure 3.5 Floppy Disk with DMA transfer

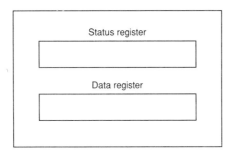

Figure 3.6 Programmers' model of a FDC

The sectors are all the same length and this is fixed when the disk was formatted. A typical value would be 512 bytes per sector, as used by the IBM PC. However, the actual number of bytes of data stored in a sector can vary from 1 to 512, as any unused byte locations are set to the null character. This can result in a 1-byte file occupying 512 bytes on the floppy disk and if the program or data is longer than 512 bytes then several sectors are used.

Other disk formats can be used with higher densities and 720-kbyte and 1.2-Mbyte floppy disks are common. To the user, the floppy disk format used is not of great importance, except in how it affects the program used to program the FDC.

Track 0 of side 0 of the floppy disk is used to contain the directory which is a list of the files containing user programs and data that are stored on the disk. The directory also contains information which indicates where each file is physically stored on the disk, in terms of side, track and sector. The FDC has a special method of accessing track 0 of side 0 in order to obtain this very important information.

The general programmer's model for a FDC is shown in *Figure 3.6* and consists of the status and data registers.

The FDC is different to most other peripheral components in that it does not require a programmed initialisation, as the correct initialisation takes place internally whenever there is a hardware reset.

The FDC is similar to a simple co-processor as it is programmed by writing successive command bytes to the data register. The number of bytes written to the data register for a single operation can vary from one to nine bytes. The FDC independently executes the specified operation which may involve positioning the head over the correct track, loading the head and writing or reading the selected sectors. This sequence can take up to 60 or 70 ms, during which time the main microprocessor is free to perform other actions. Once the operation has been completed, the FDC has several bytes of status information which the microprocessor can read from the data register.

The data register acts as the entry point to a pop-up and push-down queue. When a data byte has been written, it is automatically popped-down and another byte can be written. When the complete sequence has been transferred the operation executes and when complete the status information is available by reading from the data register. The first byte is read from the data register and the next byte is automatically popped-up ready to be read. This process is repeated until all the status bytes have been read by the microprocessor. The FDC repeatedly executes the sequence:

(1) Program the required floppy disk operation;
(2) Execute the programmed operation;
(3) Obtain the results of selected operation.

The FDC is designed to transfer the data between execution memory and the floppy disk using DMA, as this is the fastest method of transferring large blocks of data. It is possible to transfer each byte one at a time under direct microprocessor control but this is not recommended as it takes many times longer and does not have any advantages.

As most transfers will be in DMA mode, the DMA handshaking signals are provided automatically and the data is not written to the data register. The data is transferred directly between execution memory and the floppy disk via the FDC. The DMA transfers take place between an I/O port and a block of execution memory locations. No I/O address is specified as during DMA transfers only the active I/O device is connected to the data bus. The DMA controller controls the memory address value and control signals, and this frees the FDC from the need to be programmed with this information.

Most FDC's have the ability to transfer data to any one of four floppy disk drives and some additional decoding may be required to select the correct drive as only one drive can be active at any one time.

A typical sequence of bytes required to perform a data write operation might be:

(1) The write data operation command byte;
(2) The selected drive byte;
(3) The selected track number byte;
(4) The selected head number byte;
(5) The starting sector number byte;
(6) The number of bytes per sector;
(7) The total number of bytes to be transferred.

Following the writing of the last byte of step (7), the FDC moves the head until it is over the track specified in step (3), on the drive selected in step (2). The two heads are physically dependent so they both move together until they are over the selected track, on each side of the floppy disk. This simplifies the mechanics of the floppy disk drive but it does mean that data can only be accessed from one side of the floppy disk at any one time. The selected head would then be loaded. A DMA request would be made by the FDC, and the data would be transferred to the floppy disk a sector at a time, starting with the sector specified in step (5). When a complete sector has been transferred the next sector is selected and used. Only complete sectors can be transferred, so that the total number of bytes, as given in step (7), divided by the number of bytes per sector step (6), must be an integer with no remainder. If incomplete sector transfers are required then a special format of the previous command is used.

It is the responsibility of the programmer to ensure that only complete sectors are transferred. If more than one sector of data is to be transferred then the FDC will automatically increment the sector number, so that multiple sector transfers can be automatically implemented. However, there are restrictions to this automatic sector incrementing. One restriction is that the sectors being transferred must be sequentially adjacent on the same track, so that if three sectors are to be transferred to the floppy disk starting at sector three, then sectors four and five must not contain valid data from other files, or they will be over-written. If reading, the same operation must ensure that the data in sectors four and five logically follows that in sector three. The information regarding the position of sectors which constitute a multiple-sector file, is maintained in the floppy disk directory and any alteration to the disk contents affecting sector positioning has to be reflected in the directory to ensure correct operation. This checking is the responsibility of the programmer, although for the majority of users, this task can be left to the **Disk Operating System** (DOS), as is the organisation of the data so that it is correctly transferred to the tracks and sectors without errors.

In addition, the sector number cannot be automatically incremented past the last sector on a track, so that if, for example, the starting sector was seven, then a maximum of two sectors could be transferred in one operation using automatic sector incrementing before the end of the track was reached. Any remaining sectors in the data would have to be

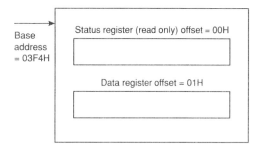

Figure 3.7 Programmers' model of the 8272A FDC

transferred in a completely new operation which would specify the next free track and sector.

The Intel 8272A Floppy Disk Controller

The Intel 8272A FDC is almost exactly the same as the FDC used in the IBM PC, and the programmer's model shown in *Figure 3.7* is similar to the general model outlined previously. The base address of the FDC in the PC/XT is 03F4H, with the status register having an offset of 00H and the data register an offset of 01H, to give a status register address of 03F4H and a data register address of 03F5H.

An initialisation sequence is not required for this FDC, although in the complete microcomputer system it is advisable to check that the floppy disk drive is operating correctly, by performing a simple series of tests when the power is first applied.

8272A FDC Commands available

The 8272A FDC can execute the 15 commands listed below and detailed information on these commands can be obtained from the appropriate Intel data manuals.

(1) Read data
(2) Read deleted data
(3) Write data
(4) Write deleted data
(5) Read a track
(6) Read identification
(7) Format a track
(8) Scan equal
(9) Scan low or equal
(10) Scan high or equal
(11) Recalibrate
(12) Sense interrupt status
(13) Specify parameters
(14) Sense drive status
(15) Seek

Only the recalibrate, sense interrupt status, seek, read and write commands will be considered in

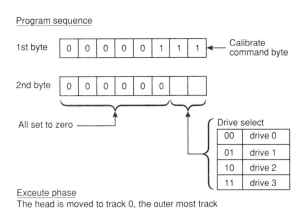

Program sequence

1st byte | 0 | 0 | 0 | 0 | 0 | 1 | 1 | 1 | ← Calibrate command byte

2nd byte | 0 | 0 | 0 | 0 | 0 | 0 | | |

All set to zero

Drive select

00	drive 0
01	drive 1
10	drive 2
11	drive 3

Exceute phase
The head is moved to track 0, the outer most track

Figure 3.8 Recalibrate command

detail as these are the minimum operands that are required by all systems, and allow 8086 assembler language programs to be written. These programs will control the transfer of data between memory and a previously-formatted floppy disk.

3.6 THE RECALIBRATE OPERATION

The recalibrate operation is a test that is usually performed after a system reset to ensure that the floppy disk drive can correctly position the head over the selected track. After a reset the FDC has no information regarding the track position of the heads of the floppy disk drive. To obtain the head track position, the head is moved towards track 0 on the floppy disk, a track at a time, until the track 0 sense switch on the floppy disk drive is activated. Once the track 0 sense switch has been activated the physical position of the head over track 0 is known, and this information is then available to the FDC for all future track positioning commands. If the FDC loses the correct head position the floppy disk drive will have to be recalibrated. For any position of the head after a system reset, 40 or less track steps will be needed before the track 0 sense switch is activated. If more steps are required an error has occurred.

Figure 3.8 shows the two bytes required to program the calibration operation. There are no status bytes returned after completion. However, several bits in the status bytes of other commands are affected, for example, see the seek command.

The FDC has a special handshaking method of transferring the sequence of command bytes to the data register and the sequence of result bytes from the data register, which involves the status register.

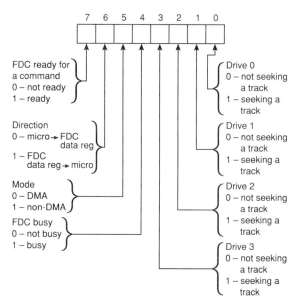

Figure 3.9 The status register

The **status register**, as illustrated in *Figure 3.9*, contains information about the complete FDC rather than just the local status information obtained from the data register after a command has completed. Before a new sequence of command bytes can be transferred to the FDC, the FDC busy bit, bit 4 of the status register, is checked for 'not busy'. When the FDC is not busy (bit 4 = 0) the FDC ready bit, bit 7, is checked. When the FDC is ready (bit 7 = 1) the next byte in the command sequence can be transferred. This status bit becomes inactive after each byte transfer to enable the FDC to implement each specific part of the command. Therefore this bit has to be checked for the ready state before the next byte can be transferred.

The direction status bit is used in conjunction with the ready status bit to determine whether the FDC is being programmed with a command, (direction status bit = 0), or reading the status results, (the direction status bit = 1).

Example algorithm

An algorithm which would implement the calibrate command would contain the following sequence of actions:

(1) Check the FDC is not busy;
(2) Check the direction is correct for programming the FDC;
(3) Check the FDC is ready for the command byte;
(4) Transfer the first byte to the FDC;

(5) Wait until the FDC is ready for the next byte ;

(6) Transfer the second byte of the recalibrate command.

This operation does not return any status bytes when completed. Unless another command is then issued, such as sense interrupt status, the operation is always assumed to have executed correctly if the FDC exits from the busy state within a fixed time period. After this command has completed, the read/write head can be assumed to be positioned over track 0.

For most operations the interrupt signal indicates the beginning of the results stage when status registers can be read. As the calibrate command does not have any status registers to read, the interrupt signal indicates that the calibrate operation has completed. A separate sense interrupt status command is used to obtain some status information to verify that the calibrate operation has completed successfully.

Program sequence

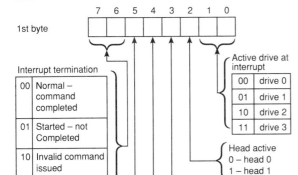

Exceute sequence
None

Results sequence

Figure 3.10 Sense interrupt command

3.7 SENSE INTERRUPT STATUS COMMAND

The sense interrupt status command programming sequence consists of a single byte of value 08H, and a result sequence of two bytes. The first result byte indicates the contents of the status register and the second results byte, the present track position of the head, see *Figure 3.10*. These values enable the calibrate operation to be checked for correct termination, to ensure that there are no faults, that track 0 has been found and that the operation terminated normally.

Example algorithm

The transfer of the command byte sequence to the FDC can be represented by the following algorithm.

(1) Check that the FDC is not busy;

(2) Check that the direction is correct for programming;

(3) Send the sense interrupt status command byte sequence;

(4) Read the status information;

(5) Check the status information for correct termination;

(6) Check that the floppy disk drive is functioning correctly;

(7) Save the head position.

3.8 POSITIONING THE HEAD OVER THE TRACK (SEEK)

The calibrate command will only position the head over track 0, and an alternative command, called seek, is used to position the head over any selected track, including track 0. Some additional information is required by the seek operation: the head to be used, indicating which side of the disk, and the track to be moved to, called the **New Track Position** (NTP). These values were not required for calibrate as track 0 of side 0 is always assumed. These values form a three-byte command sequence, see *Figure 3.11*, with a straightforward construction.

The execution phase of this command causes the head to move from its present track position to the designated new track position. Again, there are no result status bytes for this command and the sense interrupt status command is used to confirm that the seek command has correctly terminated.

It is important to remember that the position of the head is maintained internally in the FDC and is not a measurement of the physical position of the

Command sequence

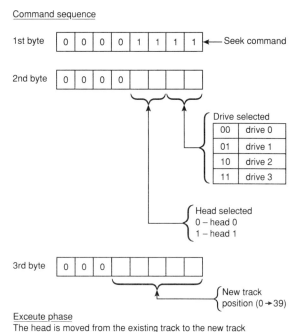

Excecute phase
The head is moved from the existing track to the new track

Results phase
None

Figure 3.11 Seek command

head over the track. If the physical position of the head were to become different from the value maintained by the FDC, then incorrect data would be transferred. Vibration caused by excessive physical movement can cause this to happen and this is one reason why floppy disk drives are only used on stationary computers. A more robust system can be obtained by performing a read track number command after the seek to ensure that the correct track is found. The syntax of this command can be found in the appropriate Intel data manual.

Example algorithm

The following algorithm indicates the sequence of actions required to perform a seek command:

(1) Check the FDC is not busy;
(2) Check direction is correct for programming the FDC;
(3) Send the seek command sequence of bytes;
(4) Check the head is positioned correctly;
(5) Check for any errors.

This would be performed immediately after a calibrate command to ensure that the head is positioned over track zero.

Command sequence

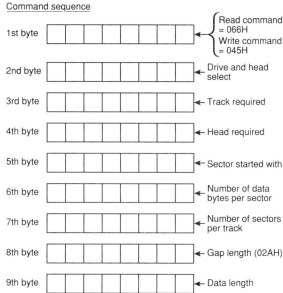

Excecute phase
- The head is loaded (it must already be correctly positioned)
- The correct sector is identified (this information is contained on the track itself) and complete sectors are transferred until the DMA transfer is complete
- The head is unloaded after the transfer is complete

The results sequence

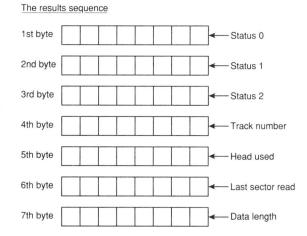

Figure 3.12 The read (and write) command structure

3.9 THE READ AND WRITE COMMANDS

The previous commands have been concerned with positioning the head over the required track. The read and write commands are used to transfer the data between the floppy disk and the microcomputer memory under DMA control, via the FDC. The read and write commands are the most complex of the FDC operations and have a 9-byte programming sequence and a 7-byte result and status sequence, see *Figure 3.12*. Only the initial command byte value varies from 066H for the read operation and 045H for the write operation. The status information obtained at the end of the operation is also the same, except that if the disk is write-protected, the write operation will not be performed and the appropriate status bits set.

The commands assume that the head is already correctly positioned so that a seek command to the selected track must first be executed. This is followed by the associated sense interrupt status command to ensure that the positioning of the head over the correct track was achieved.

The first byte of the read/write sequence of command bytes selects the read (066H) or the write (045H) operation. The following four bytes select the drive, track, head and the starting sector. The sixth byte selects the number of bytes per sector and Table 3.1 contains some possible values used with the IBM PC. The seventh byte indicates the number of sectors per track and the eighth byte contains some technical information about how the data is laid out on the track. To be compatible with the IBM PC a value of 02AH is used. If the number of bytes per sector (byte six) is set to zero, the ninth byte must contain the number to be used. This is used in single-sector transfers when a sector is being transferred which is not a complete sector. If a non-zero number of bytes per sector is selected the ninth byte is ignored, but it must still be sent.

Table 3.1 Bytes per sector

N	Bytes per sector
02	512
03	1024
00	Number given in data length byte of programming sequence

Note 1. Assumes 8 sectors per track.
Note 2. Other values of N are possible but they relate to disks which have a different number of sectors per track.

Once the 9 bytes have been sequentially written to the data register, the programming phase is complete and the operation will begin to execute. The first action to be performed is to load the head, that is, press it against the floppy disk. The head will already have been positioned over the required track using a previous seek operation. A settling time of approximately 15 milliseconds is allowed before data transfer begins, to allow any mechanical vibrations caused by the head movement to disappear.

Track information which identifies the track and the sector is then read and compared with that specified in the command and is used by the FDC to verify correct head positioning. If the head is not correctly positioned the operation is terminated and an error indicated.

If the track is correct the head continues to read the sector identifiers until the sector identified in the programming sequence is reached. The FDC then transfers data between the floppy disk and the the the microprocessor, under DMA control, until the DMA controller indicates the transfer has been completed. The DMA controller must therefore be programmed with the amount of data to be transferred before the operation is started.

The FDC will identify if the head reads past the last sector on the track and signify an error in the status bytes when the operation terminates. However, the termination of the operation has to be performed by the DMA controller and an error in programming the DMA controller could lead to a locked-up system.

After the read or write operation has completed, the FDC will have the result status byte sequence available. This is a 7-byte sequence of which the first 3 bytes contain status information and the next 4 contain position and data information. The first status byte, called status 0, contains the same information as the status byte in the sense interrupt status command. The remaining two status bytes called status 1 and status 2 contain information on 13 additional parameters, as outlined in *Figures 3.13 and 3.14*, and if the operation was

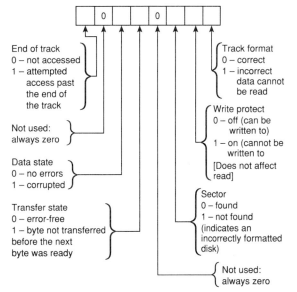

End of track
0 – not accessed
1 – attempted access past the end of the track

Not used: always zero

Data state
0 – no errors
1 – corrupted

Transfer state
0 – error-free
1 – byte not transferred before the next byte was ready

Track format
0 – correct
1 – incorrect data cannot be read

Write protect
0 – off (can be written to)
1 – on (cannot be written to
[Does not affect read]

Sector
0 – found
1 – not found
(indicates an incorrectly formatted disk)

Not used: always zero

Figure 3.13 Status 1

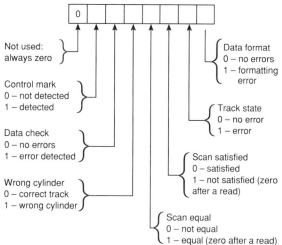

Figure 3.14 Status 2

correctly executed both these status bytes will be zero. If the floppy disk is write-protected then the write protect bit, bit 1 of status 1, will be set to a logic 1 to indicate this for write operations and the operation will terminate without writing the data. Read operations on write-protected floppy disks are not affected. If more details of the other errors represented by these bytes are required, consult the appropriate Intel data manual. To simplify the example program which follows, these status bytes will be assumed to be zero for correct operations and any other values will indicate an error of some sort.

The last four bytes of the result status byte sequence contain information on the track accessed, the head last used and the last sector accessed. If the track accessed is different to that in the programming command byte sequence, an error will already have been flagged in the status bytes.

The head last used should be the same as that in the programming command byte sequence, but on double-sided disks it is possible to access sectors automatically from both sides of the disk. Normally this will not happen and the last head used will be the same as that programmed.

The last sector transferred is used to verify that a multi-sector operation has accessed to the correct sectors.

Full Programming Information

The remaining FDC commands, how they are programmed, the execution and result stages and more detailed information on the commands discussed previously, can be obtained from the appropriate Intel data manuals.

3.10 A DMA CONTROLLER

The operations and techniques being designed means that additional components will be required in order to enable DMA transfers. A DMA controller and a **Programmable Interrupt Controller** (PIC) will be required. The initialisation and use of these devices is explained below.

One of the major requirements of a microcomputer is the transfer of large blocks of data from one location in the system to another. This may be from an I/O port to memory, memory to an I/O port, or from memory to memory. It is unusual to transfer from an I/O port to another I/O port. A typical I/O port would be a floppy disk controller, or some other mass storage media. Typical applications would be the loading of programs from the floppy disk into memory ready for execution, or saving programs or data to floppy disk.

Removing the microprocessor from the control of the transfer and using a faster, dedicated transfer method enables a faster transfer rate to be achieved. This dedicated memory to I/O data transfer method is known as **Direct Memory Access** (DMA), as the reading and writing to memory is directly controlled. A special component, known as a DMA controller, is used to implement this direct transfer method; this is essentially a dedicated device for executing a similar program to that shown above.

In normal operation the microprocessor controls the address, data and control buses, but in DMA mode the DMA controller assumes control of these buses. This requires a method of bus arbitration between the two bus masters. The DMA controller has to request the use of the bus system from the microprocessor and then wait until that request is granted. Normally the microprocessor is organised to respond to a bus control request as quickly as possible, so that the DMA transfers will take place as quickly as possible.

As the DMA transfers involve the I/O port, it is more efficient to use the I/O port to start the transfer when it is ready. This is because the I/O port may require a period of time before it is capable of handling the data. This can be illustrated by the floppy disk controller, which has to wait between 20–60 milliseconds for the physical head movement before the data becomes available. Therefore the I/O port will have the ability to make a DMA request to the DMA controller, which will be acknowledged when the DMA controller has been granted control of the bus system by the microprocessor.

When the microprocessor has released control of

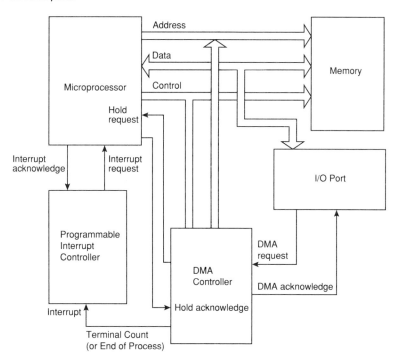

Figure 3.15 A system with a DMA controller

the bus, it automatically puts itself into a frozen state known as hold. The microprocessor will remain in the hold state while the hold request is maintained by the DMA controller. When the hold is removed the microprocessor will continue executing instructions. Alternatively, an interrupt can be used to force the microprocessor to exit from the hold state, although care has to be taken to ensure that it does not immediately re-enter the state by removing the hold request signal. An interrupt is usually produced by the DMA controller once the complete block of data has been transferred and this is called the **Terminal Count** (TC).

Figure 3.15 indicates how a DMA controller is connected to a microprocessor system. It is connected in parallel to the address and data buses and some of the control signals. The I/O port is also connected to the data bus but is controlled by the DMA device. The hold request and hold grant signals enable the DMA controller to gain control of the bus system, and the DMA request and DMA grant enable the I/O port to initiate a transfer. The TC signal is used to interrupt the microprocessor when the transfer is completed.

When the microprocessor is controlling the address, data and control buses, the DMA controller

is quiescent and does not affect these signals. However, when a direct memory to I/O port transfer is to be made, the microprocessor programs the DMA controller which, when ready, requests control of the bus system. At this stage two things must happen. The I/O device, which must have been pre-programmed to perform a DMA transfer, makes a DMA transfer request to the DMA controller, using the DMA request signal. The DMA controller then has to obtain full control of the address, data and control bus, which it does by making a hold request to the microprocessor using the hold signal. The microprocessor then completes the presently-executing instruction, activates the hold acknowledge signal and disconnects itself from the address, data and some of the control bus.

The DMA controller then has complete control of the bus and performs a DMA request acknowledge to the I/O device. The DMA controller then uses the two DMA handshaking signals, DMA request and DMA acknowledge, to transfer data between the I/O device and memory.

The DMA controller has to perform two actions simultaneously, either memory read and I/O write, or I/O read and memory write.

The DMA controller will only transfer blocks of

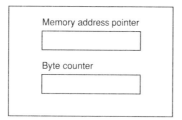

Figure 3.16 A simple model of an ideal DMA controller

data to and from consecutive memory locations. If non-consecutive memory locations are to be accessed, each one has to be separately programmed as a complete DMA block transfer, perhaps of only one byte. In this situation the DMA technique has no advantages. Therefore, for block transfers the DMA controller only needs programming with two quantities, the starting address in memory and a counter containing the number of bytes to be transferred. This results in the programmer's model of the DMA controller shown in *Figure 3.16*.

The I/O port does not need to be programmed as it is assumed that the I/O port being used will already have been activated and will be the only I/O port that is activated at that time. This means that only I/O ports with DMA capability, such as a FDC, can be used in this way. The TC signal can be used to complete the transfer so there is no need for a status register. The microprocessor loads the starting address of the block into the DMA memory address pointer, and the number of bytes into the byte counter. The I/O device is then programmed to perform a DMA transfer.

Every time a byte is successfully transferred, the memory address pointer is incremented and the byte counter decremented. This continues until the complete block has been transferred and the byte counter is zero. At this point the DMA controller relinquishes control of the address, data and control buses. The microprocessor must then be removed from the holding state it was put into by the DMA controller's hold request by deactivating the hold request. The microprocessor then re-asserts control over the address, data and control buses.

When the byte counter reaches zero, a signal is generated which indicates that the block transfer has been completed. This is in addition to the removal of the hold signal and is required for some DMA transfers, such as cycle stealing and transparent transfers, when a deactivated hold request does not indicate the end of the transfer. The terminal count signal is used as an interrupt to restart the microprocessor at the 'end of the DMA block transfer' part of the program. *Figure 3.17* illustrates a typical sequence of events for a DMA block transfer.

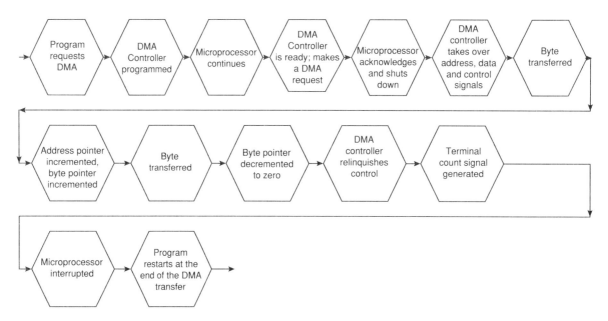

Figure 3.17 DMA sequence of events

For an 8086-based system the DMA controller will transfer a byte every 4 or 5 clock cycles.

Programmer's Model of a DMA Controller (Intel 8237A)

The use of a DMA controller may be better understood by using the programmer's model of a specific device and writing a program which will perform a block DMA transfer. The device chosen is the Intel 8237A which is a readily-available component and is suitable for use in personal computers such as the IBM PC.

Because of the complexity of DMA transfers and the need to reduce the number of separate addresses required to program the DMA controller, the programmer's model of the 8237A is much more complex and awkward to use than the general programmer's model. This is because the DMA controller is not an independent microprocessor, but merely an extension of the microprocessor contained in the system and therefore the minimum number of addressable locations must be used in order to allow as much flexibility in the number and type of other programmable components added to the system. *Figure 3.18* shows a simplified programmer's model of the 8237A DMA controller which consists of 8×16-bit registers and 8×8-bit registers.

All of these registers are accessed through only 16 locations which are treated as 16 **write only registers** and 16 **read only registers**. Only those details necessary to program a block burst transfer will be explained: programming information for the other modes of operation and full technical information can be obtained from the appropriate Intel data books.

Also, the DMA controller is only capable of generating a 16-bit address, whereas most 16-bit microprocessors have a 20-bit or larger, address bus. These extra bits of address can be provided by using a separate address latch, which provides the extra 4 bits required for the 20-bit 8086 address bus. Although this produces the required size of address bus, as only 16 bits are under the direct control of the DMA controller, this limits the maximum block size that can be transferred in a single operation, to 64 kbytes. A similar latch would be required for each of the four DMA channels the 8237A provides.

As illustrated in the programmer's model of the 8237A the DMA controller provides four channels, although only one can be transferring data at any one time. Because of the requirement to perform hardware-controlled handshaking to ensure correct

transfer, a dedicated DMA channel is required for every I/O component capable of supporting DMA transfers. By having four channels, up to four components can be used with the minimum of handshaking. The IBM PC uses one DMA channel for refreshing the DRAM, and one for the floppy disk transfers which leaves two DMA channels for general purpose use and these are connected to the PC expansion bus.

The 16 addressable locations in the DMA controller can be divided into distinct types, address and count registers which are 16-bit registers, and command and status registers which are 8-bit.

3.11 WRITING TO BASE AND CURRENT REGISTERS

The 16-bit registers can be controlled in a similar manner, although the requirements are slightly different. The 16-bit registers are used to hold two quantities, the starting address of the block of data in memory, and the size of the block to be transferred in the count register.

When a write is made to one of the address registers it is actually written into two registers, the base

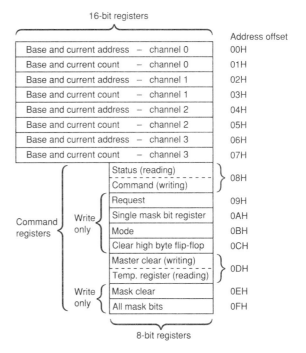

Figure 3.18 DMA registers and offsets

address register and the current address register. The same process happens when writing to a count register. However, when a read to the selected register is made, only the value in the current address or count register is transferred. The base address register is only used to save the starting address or the starting count value of the memory block and can be used to shorten the initialisation program code required if the same DMA transfer is to be repeated. This is achieved by simply transferring from the base registers into the current registers, thereby saving all the programming of the register contents, one at a time, by the microprocessor.

This sort of function would be useful for operations such as transferring data to and from a floppy disk controller. The floppy disk I/O address is fixed and a block of memory called a file buffer is set aside which has a fixed starting address. Whenever the program performs a disk-to-memory DMA transfer it is always between the file buffer and the floppy disk controller I/O address. As the address of the file buffer and the I/O port do not change, the transfer from base to current registers simplifies everything.

A program may have more than one file I/O buffer in use, as not all files are disk-based and most programs have several active at any one time for keyboard, display, data from disk, results to disk, etc. This can reduce the usefulness of the base registers for DMA transfers if different buffers are used each time.

3.12 READING FROM BASE AND CURRENT REGISTERS

When a read operation is performed on a base or current register, only the value of the current register is transferred. It is not usually necessary to obtain the starting address as this should be available to the program. However, it may be necessary to obtain the next address that data is to be transferred to at some time in the program, or possibly what was the address of the last byte transferred.

The base and current address and count registers are 16-bit registers which are accessed through 8-bit I/O port locations. This is achieved by performing two consecutive 8-bit reads (or writes) to the same register address. An internal flip-flop called the high byte flip-flop is used to distinguish which of the two bytes is being transferred.

High Byte Flip-Flop

One of the command registers of the programmer's model is called clear high byte flip-flop. The data written to this command register is irrelevant as the writing to that register address clears the high byte flip-flop. This operation is performed before each 16-bit read or write in order to obtain a correct 16-bit transfer.

Example algorithm

The following algorithm indicates how the address and count values for a DMA transfer using channel 0 are programmed:

(1) Clear high byte flip-flop (write to clear high byte flip-flop register);
(2) Write low byte to address register (channel 0 low byte);
(3) Write high byte to address register (channel 0 high byte);
(4) Clear high byte flip-flop (write to clear high byte flip-flop register);
(5) Write low byte to count register (channel 0 low byte);
(6) Write high byte to count register (channel 0 high byte).

The terminal count signal is generated when the active count register underflows from 0000H to 0FFFFH. One side-effect of this is that one byte extra to the value specified in the base count register is transferred. This should be taken into account by the program before the DMA transfer is programmed and the appropriate adjustments made.

3.13 COMMAND REGISTERS

There are 8 command registers, six of which are write only, used to select the type of operation to be performed and to program some of the DMA functions.

The Command Register

The bits in this register control 5 basic DMA parameters, as illustrated in *Figure 3.19*. Bits 0 and 1 are used if memory-to-memory, rather than memory-to-I/O or I/O-to-memory, DMA transfers are required. This is a special technique requiring two channels to be used and will not be explained here. This technique is disabled by setting both bits to zero. The complete controller can be disabled by setting bit 2

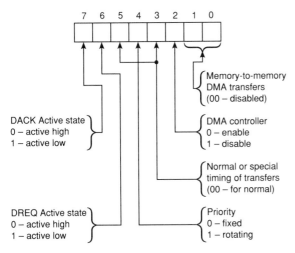

Figure 3.19 Command register

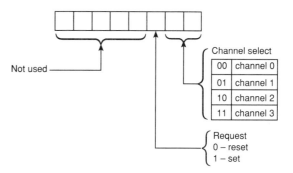

Figure 3.20 The request register (write only)

equal to a logic 1. This can be used to prevent any DMA operations occurring during the initialisation or programming sequences. Normal operation is obtained by setting this bit to logic 0. It is possible to change the priority of the four channels after each one has performed a DMA transfer by using the rotating priority feature. This feature will not be explained as normal operation is with a fixed priority, obtained by setting bit 4 to logic 0.

The state of the two DMA handshaking signals, **DMA request** (DREQ) and **DMA acknowledge** (DACK) are controlled by bits 6 and 7, as some microprocessors have different active states. For Intel microprocessors the normal states are:

> DREQ active high
> DACK active low

obtained by setting bits 6 and 7 to logic 0.

This results in a normal disable DMA control byte value of 04H (bit 2 is a logic 1) and a normal enable byte of 00H.

The Request Register

A DMA transfer, once programmed, can be started by the I/O port hardware using the DMA request signal (DREQ). Alternatively, software can write to the request register to initiate the DMA transfer. Once the DMA transfer has been initiated, the DMA controller performs a **hold request** (HOLD) to the microprocessor and then waits until it has control of the bus, by the **hold acknowledge** (HOLDA) signal being activated.

Only three bits of this register are used, see *Figure 3.20*, with bits 0 and 1 indicating which channel is

presently being programmed and bit 2 indicating whether the DMA transfer request is being initiated (bit 2 = logic 1) or terminated (bit 2 = logic 0).

Although only one DMA channel can be actively controlling the system bus, it is possible to have between 1 and 4 channels in the process of performing transfers and just waiting for control of the bus. If four channels are active then a separate write to the request register would be required for each channel.

The Mask Registers

It is possible to disable the DMA requests for individual channels without disabling the entire controller, by using the **mask bits**. There is one bit for each channel and when the mask is set (to logic 1), the DMA requests, both the DREQ (hardware) and the request register (software), for that channel are disabled. The mask bits are set or reset using one of two registers, the single mask bit register or the all mask bits register.

The Mode Register

Whereas the command register controls parameters which affect the entire DMA controller, the mode register controls parameters which only affect individual channels. This enables each channel to be programmed to perform differently. There are four different parameters that can be altered, the mode, the address increment/decrement, the auto-initialisation and the transfer type, see *Figure 3.21*. The channel to be programmed is selected by bits 0 and 1 and the type of transfer by bits 2 and 3. A write operation transfers a byte from I/O to memory and simultaneously activates I/O read and memory write control signals. A read operation transfers a byte from memory to I/O and simultaneously activates memory read and I/O write. The verify transfer is a special function which activates address signals and

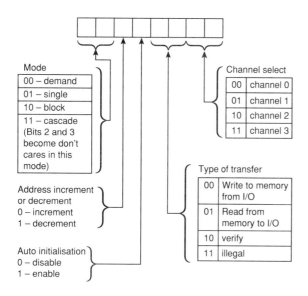

Figure 3.21 The mode register

DMA handshaking but does not actually transfer data, and is used for test purposes to ensure the correct operation of the DMA controller when connected to the microprocessor.

If a channel is auto-initialised the transfer starts automatically by copying the value from the base address and count registers into current address and count registers, at the end of the currently-active channel DMA transfer. The auto-initialised DMA transfer then begins and thereby avoids having to wait until the end of a DMA transfer before programming the start of the next DMA transfer.

So far, the current address register has been assumed to increment by one after every byte transfer. This can be changed by using bit 5 of the mode register to set a channel to decrement the value in the current address register. The current count register is unaffected and always decrements after each transfer.

There are three DMA transfer modes selected by bits 6 and 7: single, block and demand methods. Single is used when one byte at a time is transferred, after which control is returned to the microprocessor, which will execute at least one instruction before the next byte transfer takes place. This mode is used to maintain program execution during the DMA transfer, although both operations are slowed down. Block transfer is the normal method of operation and is used to transfer blocks of data between memory and I/O. In demand mode, the I/O device is unable to transfer data continuously at the same rate as the memory.

For example, if the I/O device is only able to supply 1 kbyte at full speed transfer rates and a 4-kbyte block transfer is requested, then demand mode can be used, so that when the I/O is exhausted, the DMA transfer is temporarily stopped and program execution restarted. When the I/O port is ready to recommence the DMA handshaking signals are used to regain control of the bus.

The fourth mode, cascade, is not a transfer technique, but indicates that additional DMA controllers have been connected. Each additional DMA controller occupies one of the existing channels but provides four more, so that two DMA controllers provide seven channels, three provide 10 channels, and so on. This method of connection is necessary if more than 4 channels are required, as the microprocessor only has one set of DMA-compatible handshaking signals. If the channel is in cascade mode, it cannot be programmed to control a DMA transfer so that bits 2 and 3 of the mode register become 'don't cares'.

Register Commands

The remaining write only command registers, clear high byte flip-flop, mask clear, and master clear, do not program register values but perform a complete function. The clear high byte flip-flop has already been explained. A write to the mask clear register sets all four channel mask bits and therefore enables a request on any of the channels. This is a simple method of enabling all four channels. A write to the master clear register performs a similar operation to the hardware reset, but does not affect any other programmable components. The command, status, request, temporary registers and high byte flip-flop are all cleared ready for programming, and all mask bits are set, disabling any DMA requests that may occur.

The Read Only Command Registers

Of the 8 command registers, there are only two which when read contain valid data and these are the temporary register and the status register.

The Temporary Register

The temporary register contains the value of the last byte transferred and is available to the programmer if required. It can also be used to perform software-controlled transfers. In memory-to-memory DMA transfers, this register acts as the temporary byte storage in between the memory read and the memory write operations.

The Status Register

The status register, see *Figure 3.22*, enables the programmer to obtain two sorts of information about each of the four DMA channels, whether a channel has reached terminal count, that is, if the transfer has been completed and whether there is a request pending, either software- or hardware-generated.

The initialisation and programming of the DMA controller which has a 16-bit address, is extended to 20 bits for the 8086 microprocessor by the use of a programmable input and output (PIO) peripheral, controlling a page register, as illustrated in *Figure 3.23*.

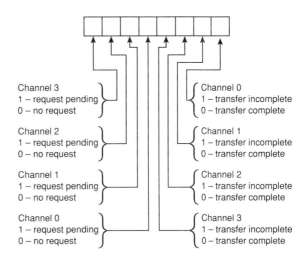

Figure 3.22 The status register

3.14 THE LINK TO THE OPERATING SYSTEM

The link to the operating system is one of the most important and the technique of using interrupts will

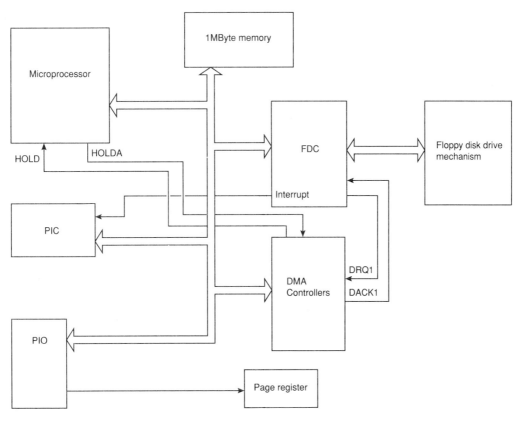

Figure 3.23 FDC, PIC and DMA controllers for fast mass secondary storage

be used, transferring parameters and results via registers and blocks of memory. To be compatible with the IBM PC, similar interrupts and functions will be used, although the actual implementation will be considerably different.

The code given for the microcomputer will only perform a few simple operations, however, these will form the basic building blocks for a complete system.

3.15 FLOPPY DISK OPERATIONS AND SYSTEM SERVICES

The data on a floppy disk is organised into files consisting of a connected list of sectors. A file contains at least one sector, up to the maximum number of sectors on the floppy disk. The file identifier is a string of ASCII alphanumeric characters consisting of the name (8 characters) and the extension (3 characters). The extension is used to indicate the type of contents of the file. For example, assembly language source files might be given the filename extension .SRC. Whereas Pascal files the extension .PAS. A file containing executable program code has the filename extension .EXE. The filename MICRO-COM is used to indicate it is a file for the microcomputer and the extension .EXE to indicate it is executable. This produces a complete file identifier of: MICROCOM.EXE.

The operating system links the filename on the floppy disk and the block of memory used for the DMA transfers using a file handle, see *Figure 3.24*. A file handle is a number which indicates which of the file buffers in memory is to be used for all file transfers to the file on the floppy disk linked with the file handle and is an index into a block of pointers to files on the floppy disk.

A file handle is associated with a filename by opening a file. Opening a file checks that the file exists before allocating one of 20 file handles to it. This is slightly different to the way MS-DOS uses handles. Once allocated the file handle is used, not the file name, to access data on the floppy disk.

As there are only 20 file handles the microcomputer cannot open more than 20 files at any one time. This is usually not a problem. The input and output devices are treated as files as are the keyboard, the display unit, the printer port, the serial port, the mouse, and so on, and these are permanently allocated a file handle. The result of this is to limit the number of floppy disk files that can be open and being accessed, either for reading or writing, to less than 15. For some programs such as word-processors which require many files to be opened

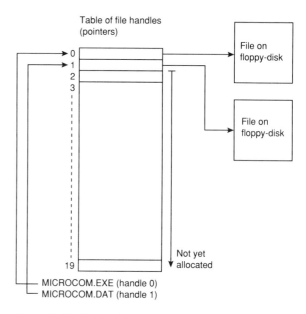

Figure 3.24 File handles

simultaneously, this can be a restriction. Therefore, whenever a file is no longer required the opposite operation of de-allocating a file handle is used to allow other files to be accessed.

Example algorithm

A typical sequence of actions to access a file on the floppy disk consists of:

(1) Opening a file and allocating a handle;
(2) Reading or writing data to a floppy disk file using the allocated file handle;
(3) Closing the file and de-allocating the file handle.

Definitions of Interfaces for File Operation

Open file: interface to operating system

Starting the operation
   INT 021H (interrupt 21 hexadecimal = 32 decimal)
Set
   AH = 03DH
   AL = 00H for read file
       = 01H for write file
   DS : DX points to file name in memory

When the operation completes
If successful:
   Carry flag clear
   AX = file handle

If unsuccessful:
Carry flag set

This operation also sets the file pointer to the first sector of the file on the floppy disc.

Close a file

Starting the operation
INT 021H
Set

AH = 03EH
BX = file handle

When the operation completes

If successful:
Carry flag is clear

If unsuccessful:
Carry flag is set

Read a sector from an open file

Starting the operation
INT 021H
Set

AH = 03FH
BX = file handle
CX = number of bytes in the sector
DS:DX = address of memory for transferring the sector

When the operation completes

If successful:
Carry flag is clear
AX = number of bytes transferred (should be the same as CX)

If unsuccessful:
Carry flag is set

The file pointer is then automatically moved to point to the next sector, so that consecutive reads access consecutive sectors.

Write to an open file

Starting the operation
INT 021H
Set

AH = 040H
BX = file handle
CX = number of bytes in sector
DS:DX = address of memory block containing data to be written

When the operation completes

If successful:
Carry flag is clear

AX = number of bytes written

If unsuccessful:
Carry flag set

Again the file pointer is automatically moved to point to the beginning of the next sector once the write operation has successfully completed, so that consecutive writes access consecutive sectors on the floppy disc.

The interfaces for these four operations are approximately 90% compatible with those used in MS-DOS. However, not all the necessary detail has been included and it would be wise to consult the appropriate MS-DOS manuals before attempting to use these operations on an IBM PC or compatible. The interfaces given have been adapted to execute with the microcomputer being designed.

In the first two operations, two registers, DS and DX, are used to point to the beginning of the file name which is stored in execution memory as data. Segmented addressing is used, with DS containing the segment address and DX the offset. The filename is stored as ASCII characters and the end of it is determined by the NULL character, 00H, allowing filenames to be of variable lengths.

Example

FILE_NAME1 DB 'MICROCOM.EXE', 00H

The quotation marks are used to indicate to the assembler that the ASCII characters are to be converted into their equivalent hexadecimal values. A continuous sequence of characters is known as a **string**, and when the characters are ASCII and terminated by a zero value, the string is called an ASCIIZ string.

The interface for the floppy disk consists of a software-initiated interrupt, INT 021H, with the specific operation required selected by the value in the AH register. The following examples are only four of many possible different actions available in MS-DOS. The additional parameters required by the selected operation are passed in other registers. The open operation has two parameters, one passed in the AL register for whether the file is read only or write only and a memory pointer in DS and DX to point to the ASCIIZ string in memory which contains the name of the file on the floppy disk.

Most operations complete by returning parameters or results. The success or otherwise, is determined by a microprocessor status flag, in these examples the carry flag, or a register. If successful and the selected operation has completed with no errors, the carry flag is cleared and the necessary parameters returned in the selected registers.

For the open operation, the only returned parameter is a file handle contained in the AX register. If unsuccessful, no parameters are returned and the carry flag is set. As the validity of the results is dependent upon whether the operation is successful or unsuccessful this forces the user to include error checking after every operating system function.

Example algorithm and program

The following algorithm and program listing illustrate how a file is opened for reading.

(1) Select the file to be opened;
(2) Open the file;
(3) If no errors, save the file handle.

This then translates into the following program listing.

```
                    ;A simple program to open a file.
                    ;Select a file to be opened.    Step (1)
MOV AH,03DH         ;Select the file open operation.
MOV AL,01H          ;Select a file read function.
PUSH DS             ;Set up the pointer to the filename.
LDS DX,FILENAME
                    ;Open the file.                 Step (2)
INT 021H            ;Perform the operation.
POP DS              ;Restore data segment.
                    ;If no errors, save the
                    ;file handle.                   Step (3)
JNC OK              ;Successful ? Yes, then continue.
CALL OPEN_ERR
                    ;No, then execute error subroutine.
OK : MOV HANDLE1,AX
                    ;Save the file handle.

FILENAME DB 'MICROCOM.EXE',00H
                    ;Filename as an ASCIIZ string.
HANDLE1 DW 00H
                    ;Handle to filename stored here.
```

If the file name and handle had been stored in the default data segment, there would be no need to save DS. However, the above technique allows the file name and handle to be stored anywhere in the 1 Mbyte memory.

The open operation also sets the file pointer associated with the allocated file handle to the first sector of the file. The file pointer is a data variable which is updated automatically by the DOS whenever an open, read or write operation on the file is performed, always pointing to the next element in the file. This avoids the user having to keep track of this parameter and its position in the file. Other types of file operations also control the file pointer

and details can be obtained from the appropriate DOS manual.

The close operation formats the file on the floppy disk to indicate correctly the end of the file and then de-allocates the file name from the handle to make the handle available for another file. The only parameter required by the operation is the file handle, and the only result is whether it was successful or not.

Example program

Example of a close operation. This operation is so simple an algorithm is not required.

```
                    ;Closing a file.
MOV AH,03EH         ;Select the file close operation
MOV BX,HANDLE
                    ;which must already have a handle
                    ;allocated.
INT 021H            ;Perform the file close operation.
JNC OK2             ;Successful ?, Yes, then continue.
CALL CLOSE_ERR
                    ;No, execute the error subroutine.
OK2 :               ;Continue with the program.

HANDLE DW 00H
                    ;Memory location for saving the
                    ;file handle.
```

The remaining two operations, read and write, are similar except that data is transferred from the current sector to the buffer in memory, or from the buffer to the current sector in the file. Three parameters are required for read and write operations which are the file handle, the number of bytes in a sector and a memory pointer to the buffer which will hold the transferred data in executable memory. The buffer must be large enough to hold a complete sector of data, otherwise corruption of memory locations may occur.

The sector to be used is not specified but is the currently valid sector pointed to by the file pointer. This is updated after each read or write to point to the next sector. Therefore this type of file, known as a **sequential file**, can only be read from the beginning to the end and it is not possible to go backwards and forwards. Other types of files, known as **random access files**, are available for non-sequential operations and the full details can be obtained from the appropriate DOS manuals.

Example algorithm and program

The following example program of floppy disk operations uses all four operations to read a file only 2 sectors long from floppy disk and then writes it back to the floppy disk with a different file name.

(1) Open the read file; the file must already exist;
(2) Open the write file; the file must already exist;
(3) Read the first sector;
(4) Write the first sector;
(5) Read the second sector;
(6) Write the second sector;
(7) Close the read file;
(8) Close the write file.

```
                  ;A program to execute read and
                  ;write operations on a floppy disk
                  ;file.
                  ;Open the read file.        Step (1)
MOV AX,03D00H     ;Open the file for reading.
MOV DX, FILE1
INT 021H
JC OK1            ;Successful ? Yes, then continue.
CALL OPEN_ERR
                  ;No, then execute error routine.
OK1 : MOV HANDLE1,AX
                  ;Save the allocated file handle.
                  ;Open the write file.       Step (2)
MOV AX,03D01H     ;Open the file for writing.
MOV DX, FILE2
INT 021H
JC OK2            ;Successful ? Yes, then continue.
CALL OPEN_ERR    ;No, then execute error routine.
OK2 : MOV HANDLE2,AX
                  ;Save the allocated file handle.
                  ;Read the first sector.     Step (3)
MOV AH,3FH        ;Read the first sector.
MOV BX,HANDLE1
MOV CX,512
MOV DX,BUFFER
INT 021H
JC OK_READ1      ;Successful ? Yes, then continue.
CALL READ_ERR   ;No, then execute error routine.
                  ;Write the first sector.    Step (4)
MOV BX,HANDLE2
MOV CX,512
MOV DX,BUFFER
INT 021H
JC OK_WRITE1     ;Successful ? Yes, then continue.
CALL WRITE_ERR
                  ;No, then execute error routine.
                  ;Read the second sector.    Step (5)
OK_WRITE1 :MOV AH,03FH
                  ;Read the second sector.
MOV BX,HANDLE1
MOV CX,512
MOV DX,BUFFER
INT 021H
JC OK_READ2      ;Successful ? Yes, then continue.
CALL READ_ERR ;No, then execute error routine.
                  ;Write the second sector.   Step (6)
OK_READ2 : MOV AH,040H
                  ;Write the second sector
MOV BX,HANDLE2
MOV CX,512
MOV DX,BUFFER
INT 021H
JC OK_WRITE2     ;Successful ? Yes, then continue.
CALL WRITE_ERR
                  ;No, then execute error routine.
```

```
                  ;Close the read file        Step (7)
OK_WRITE2 :MOV AH,03EH
                  ;Close the read file.
MOV BX,HANDLE1
INT 021H
JC OK_CLOSE1     ;Successful ? Yes, then continue.
CALL CLOSE_ERR
                  ;No, then execute error routine.
                  ;Close the write file.      Step (8)
OK_CLOSE1 :MOV AH,03EH
                  ;Close the write file.
MOV BX,HANDLE2
INT 021H
JC OK_CLOSE2     ;Successful ? Yes, then continue.
CALL CLOSE_ERR
                  ;No, then execute error routine.
OK_CLOSE2 :       ;Rest of the program.
FILE1 DB 'MICROCOM.DAT',00H
                  ;Read filename.
FILE2 DB 'OTHERCOM.DAT',00H
                  ;Write filename.
HANDLE1 DW 0000H
                  ;Read file handle store.
HANDLE2 DW 0000H
                  ;Write file handle store.
BUFFER DBS 512    ;A 512 byte buffer used when
                  ;transferring the sector data.
```

3.16 THE PROCESSING UNIT AND LARGE EXECUTION MEMORY

The heart of a microcomputer is the processing unit which executes the user programs and the DOS. Any suitable processing unit is acceptable that incorporates all the necessary system functions, which are:

(1) Fast program execution;
(2) Support for interfaces to operating system (interrupts);
(3) Support for DMA transfers;
(4) Large execution memory.

The 8086 microprocessor is a processing unit capable of supporting the four requirements and has been used for the assembly language examples. It will therefore be used for this case study as well.

The 8086 has a 1 Mbyte executable memory address space and this is divided into two parts to implement the operating system. All microcomputers have some **non-volatile memory** (ROM) to contain the power-on-reset **boot-up program**. This is a program which has to be present immediately the power is applied to the system and therefore cannot be downloaded from a floppy disk. It normally contains the program which can download the rest of the operating system software. This program also initialises the programmable peripherals to a predetermined known state required by the operating system.

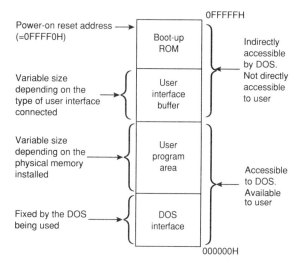

Figure 3.25 8086 memory allocation

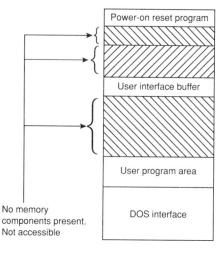

Figure 3.26 Minimum memory system

For the 8086 the boot program has to be contained at the top of the memory space, see *Figure 3.25*. The bottom of memory is used for the interrupt-based interfaces to the operating system and the user interface to the hardware. The resident DOS function programs, once downloaded, are also stored in this area.

The remaining memory is divided into two more sections, the **user interface buffer** which acts as the interface between the input and output devices and the user program area.

The resident DOS program, the interface interrupts and the user interface buffer require a fixed minimum amount of memory to be available in the system, whereas the user program area, which is normally the largest area accounting for over half the available memory space, can be altered depending on user requirements. By only having the minimum memory components in the system the cost is reduced but this does restrict the size of user programs that can be executed. *Figure 3.26* illustrates a system which has the minimum of memory components in all areas.

The operating system has facilities for controlling the allocation of the user memory space to the programs being executed and this is used when adding functions to the DOS operations which have already been loaded.

The Interface to Fast Transfer

The processing unit has no involvement in the fast transfer of data during DMA transfers as it discon-

nects itself from the address, data and control bus when a HOLD request is performed. This releases the memory space and I/O components from microprocessor control and enables the DMA controller to make a direct link, which is much faster.

The Interface to Operating System

The interface to the operating system is via the interrupt structure of the microprocessor and consists of:

(1) Interrupts initiated by the operating system function;
(2) Interrupt vectors to re-direct the call;
(3) Interrupt service subroutines containing code to execute the function.

The lowest 1 kbyte of the 8086 memory contains the interrupt vectors, with the **interrupt service routine code** stored in either the DOS memory area or the power on reset boot up area.

The DOS area contains most of the operating system functions that the user requires and these in turn use the interrupt structure to access more basic hardware-dependent functions maintained in the power-on-reset boot-up program. Using these basic system routines reduces the size of the DOS, freeing memory for user programs and reducing the hardware dependence of the DOS. *Figure 3.27* illustrates how all these programs are linked together using interrupt-based interfaces. For clarity of understanding the return paths are not shown.

A Flexible User Interface

MS-DOS implements a sophisticated **user interface** which controls all of the PC hardware. However, in order to simplify the design of the microcomputer, the only user interface implemented will be the **serial communication link** capable of transferring ASCII characters between the PC and a **Visual Display Unit** (VDU) and keyboard.

The VDU and keyboard, which will henceforth be known as the VDU, receives characters one at a time from the serial communication link and displays them as characters on the screen at the cursor position. The cursor is a flashing line or box indicating where the next character will be displayed. After each character is received and displayed the cursor is automatically moved to the right to the next character position. The screen is comprised of 23 lines with each line consisting of 80 characters. The text displayed is determined by the user program and may or may not be understandable. The keyboard is capable of producing most ASCII characters by single or multiple key presses. These are transferred via the serial communication link to the user program. It is the responsibility of the user program to understand the strings of characters, so that, for example, file names are recognised from a sequence of successive single characters. If the system unit is not expecting any input from the keyboard then any characters transferred are lost.

The VDU is capable of sending and receiving characters simultaneously, but the system unit depends upon the program and programmable serial communication interface being used to achieve a similar effect.

The Interface to the VDU

As with most operations, the interface to the VDU is via an interrupt. The IBM PC uses INT 14H for this purpose and a similar system will be implemented for this microcomputer. This interrupt is used for the serial communications interface and as the VDU is connected to this, the effect is the same as if it is directly controlling the user interface. The interface performs two functions:

(1) Sending a character to the display;
(2) Reading a character from the keyboard,

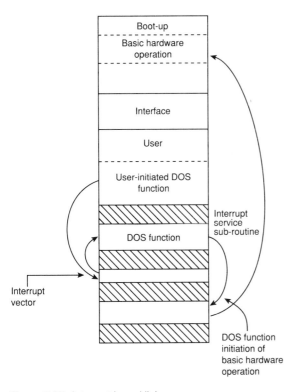

Figure 3.27 Interrupt-based links

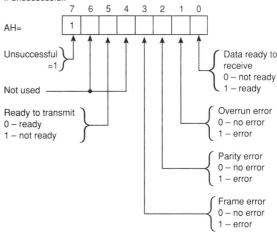

Figure 3.28 Interface to VDU display

and the interfaces for these are illustrated in *Figures 3.28 and 3.29.*

The power-on-reset boot-up program initialises the PSCI for a specific Baud rate and if this is not satisfactory, it is necessary for the user to write a program to re-program it. Adding such a function to the INT 14H would have the advantage of making the initialisation of the PSCI available to all users.

Both the input and output character operations have similar interfaces. The AH register is used to select the operation, input or output, and the AL register contains the ASCII character transferred. If the operation is successful, AH is cleared and AL contains the ASCII character. This applies to both input and output. If unsuccessful, bit 7 of AH is set to a logic 1 with the remaining bits of AH containing status information. The status information applies to the entire communications link and therefore contains information on both the input and output operations. Overrun, parity and frame errors are detectable.

The usual reason for an unsuccessful operation is that the previous character transfer has not completed. For the output operation bit 5 will be a logic 1 when the previous character has not been transmitted and normally the program will wait until this bit is cleared. This is illustrated in the following algorithm and program listing.

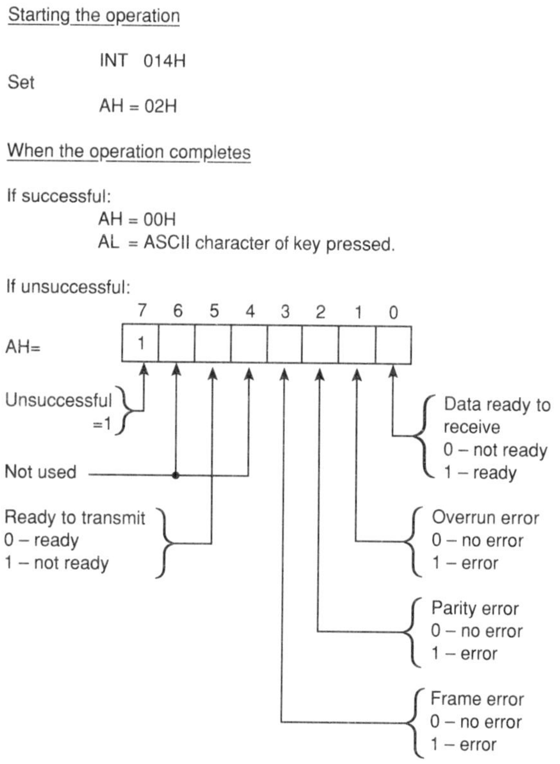

Example algorithm and program

Example of an output operation:

(1) Obtain the character to be transferred;
(2) Initiate the output interface operation;
(3) If successful go to step (6);
(4) If previous character not transferred, repeat from step (2);
(5) Call error handling routine;
(6) Continue with the rest of the program.

```
                    ;Demonstration program for
                    ;using the output interface.
                    ;Obtain the character to be
                    ;transferred.              Step (1)
     MOV AL,'A'      ;The character A is to be
HERE : MOV AH,01H
                    ;output.
                    ;Initiate the output interface
                    ;operation.                Step (2)
     INT 014H
     MOV BL,AL
     AND BL,080H     ;Successful transfer ?
                    ;Yes, go to step (6).      Step (3)
     JZ SUCCESS
     MOV BL,AL       ;No, then test for not
     AND BL,00100000B
                    ;ready.
                    ;If previous character not
                    ;transferred, repeat from
                    ;step (2).                 Step (4)
     JNZ HERE        ;If not ready repeat input.
                    ;If the input interface is
                    ;ready, there must be an
                    ;error. Call error-
                    ;handling routine.         Step (5)
     CALL VDU_ERR    ;Error-handling routine.
                    ;Continue with the rest of the
                    ;program.                  Step (6)
SUCCESS :           ;Rest of program.
```

For the input operation bit 0 of AH indicates when there is no input data. An input operation is unsuccessful when no key has been pressed.

Example algorithm and program

Example of an input operation. This produces almost exactly the same algorithm and program as the output operation except that the output operation is selected for the interface and a different bit is tested for the result.

Starting the operation

Set
INT 014H
AH = 02H

When the operation completes

If successful:
AH = 00H
AL = ASCII character of key pressed.

If unsuccessful:

AH=

Unsuccessful = 1

Not used

Ready to transmit
0 – ready
1 – not ready

Data ready to receive
0 – not ready
1 – ready

Overrun error
0 – no error
1 – error

Parity error
0 – no error
1 – error

Frame error
0 – no error
1 – error

Figure 3.29 Interface to VDU keyboard

(1) Perform an input operation;
(2) If successful go to step (5);
(3) If input not ready, repeat from step (1);
(4) Execute error routine;
(5) Continue with the rest of the program.

```
                    ;Demonstrating the use of the
                    ;input interface.          Step (1)
HERE : MOV AH,02H  ;Perform an input operation.
   INT 014H
   MOV BL,AL        ;Successful ?
   AND BL,080H
                    ;Yes, go to step (5).       Step (2)
   JZ SUCCESS2      ;No, then test for input not
                    ;ready.
                    ;If input not ready, repeat from
                    ;step (1).                   Step (3)
   MOV BL,AL  ;
   AND BL,00000001B
   JNZ HERE         ;If input not ready repeat.
                    ;Execute error routine.      Step (4)
   CALL VDU_ERR     ;Otherwise an error has occurred.
                    ;Continue with the rest of the
                    ;program.                    Step (5)
SUCCESS2 :
```

These two interfaces can be used by user program as the basis for more sophisticated character and string handling routines.

If there is a large number of character string input and output operations it may be useful to add further interfaces to the operating system to perform more complex actions, which could use the two basic functions. MS-DOS does this by having several variations which output an ASCII string of characters to the current display, for example, INT 021H, operation 9.

3.17 THE OPERATING SYSTEM

The majority of the operations are concerned with floppy disks, hence the name DOS, but an operating system implements many more functions. Some of the main ones are listed below:

(1) DOS Boot program;
(2) DOS function selection loop (main DOS loop);
(3) Loading user programs;
(4) Transferring control to user program;
(5) Receiving control back when user program terminates;
(6) Memory allocation;
(7) Floppy disk operations;
(8) System services (input, output, etc.).

The Floppy Disk Operations and System Services

Floppy disk operations and system services have already been covered and the routines which implement the interfaces would need to be implemented.

Memory Allocation

For this particular microcomputer, the memory allocation operations will be avoided by always loading programs at fixed start locations and allocating all memory above this to user programs. This produces a fixed length DOS and a fixed DOS starting point, see *Figure 3.30*. This is not the most flexible method but considerably simplifies the DOS.

Four fixed program start locations are required:

(1) DOS Boot program;
(2) DOS (main);
(3) DOS loop;
(4) User programs.

The DOS Boot Program

The DOS program itself cannot be started directly as it is saved on a floppy disk. Therefore it has to be loaded into memory before it can be executed and this is achieved using a DOS load program. This is a simple program residing on track 0, sector 0 of the floppy disk. This enables the initialisation functions of the FDC to position the head over the correct track. The DOS boot program is loaded by the BIOS

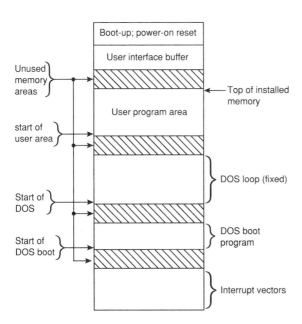

Figure 3.30 Fixed memory allocation

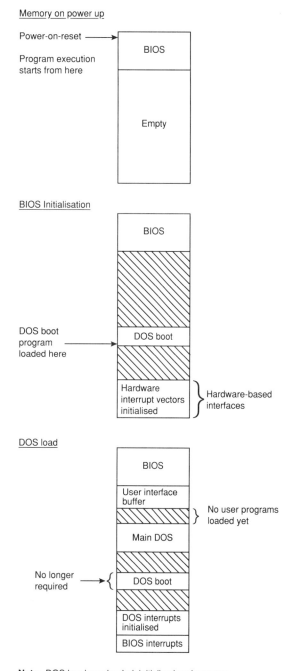

Memory on power up

Power-on-reset

Program execution
starts from here

BIOS Initialisation

DOS boot
program
loaded here

DOS load

No longer
required

Note: DOS has been loaded, initialised and program
control transferred to the DOS main loop.

Figure 3.31 Final BIOS initialisation task

as the last initialisation task and the sequence of operations is illustrated in *Figure 3.31*. The DOS boot program is a fixed length and for this microcomputer it will be assumed to occupy no more than one sector, which is 512 bytes.

The Main DOS Program

The DOS boot program contains information which will load the main DOS program, assumed to be 20 sectors long, into the specified memory area, starting at the fixed address. Once the main DOS is loaded the DOS boot program is no longer required and this memory could be recovered for other uses. This operation will not be implemented in this case study.

The DOS boot program also initialises all the interrupt vectors and all other parameters to the states required by DOS. The hardware will already have been initialised to a known state by the power-on-reset boot-up program resident in ROM.

The DOS is started by transferring program control to the fixed start address within the DOS. DOS initialisations are then performed, after which the main DOS loop is entered. It is possible to change the known initial state of both the hardware and DOS before entering the main DOS loop by adding a configuration file to the boot-up floppy disk. This is a user-generated file containing commands to alter the default configurations. In MS-DOS this file is called CONFIG.SYS. This function has not been implemented for this microcomputer.

Transferring Control back to DOS

As the location of the start of the main DOS loop is at a fixed address, transferring control back to DOS after a user program has completed is simple to achieve. The user simply ensures that the last operation performed is a jump to the start of that location, as illustrated in the program listing in the next example. A more flexible DOS with a relocatable main loop would require a more complex interface to ensure the correct location was known. In MS-DOS, this is provided by interrupt 020H.

Loading a User Program and Transferring Control to it

The two last remaining operating system operations of loading a user program and transferring control to it are closely related and will be considered together.

As all user programs will start at a fixed address it is relatively easy to start loading a user program. However, some additional information is always needed, the most important of which is the length of the program. This information will be contained in the first sector of the user program on the floppy disk and will be loaded and accessed before the rest of the program is loaded. The memory area previously used to hold the DOS boot program which is no longer required, will be used to hold this initial sector, as illustrated in *Figure 3.32*. Once loaded, the number of sectors in the user program is extracted from the initial sector data and is used to load the remaining sectors, sequentially into the user memory area.

Program control is transferred to the first location of the user program memory area and requires the first data elements loaded in the second sector of the file to be executable program code. Data variables are then located at the end rather than at the beginning, or the first instruction is a jump around the data area to the beginning of the user program.

When the user program has completed executing the last instruction must be a jump to the beginning of the main DOS loop.

Example program

The following is the structure required of a typical user program occupying 6 sectors on a floppy disk:

```
SECTOR1 DB 5    ;The number of sectors remaining
                ;in the user program.
        DBS 511 ;The rest of the sector data.
START           ;This is the beginning of the user
                ;program and must be at the
                ;beginning of the second sector.

(5 sectors of user program)

JMP MAIN_DOS_LOOP
                ;The last instruction is a jump
                ;to the main DOS loop.
```

If necessary the last sector is padded out with NULL values to fill a complete sector.

Main DOS Loop

The main DOS loop for this particular microprocessor is only able to select one function, the loading and execution of user-generated programs. The sequence of actions the main DOS loop executes to achieve this is illustrated in the following algorithm.

Example algorithm

(1) Display the DOS prompt on VDU display;
(2) Wait until a key is pressed;
(3) If the key is not "L" for load, repeat from (1);
(4) Get the file name from the user via keyboard;

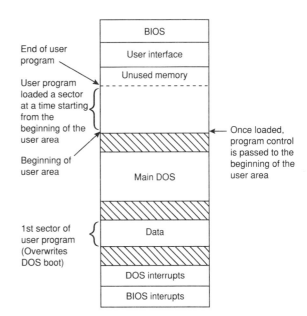

Figure 3.32 Loading a user program

(5) Open the file and if any errors repeat from (1);
(6) Load the first sector into the DOS boot area;
(7) Get the number of sectors in the rest of the user program;
(8) Load all the sectors from floppy disk sequentially into the user memory area;
(9) Close the user file and if any errors repeat from (1);
(10) Transfer control to the beginning of the user program memory area;
(11) User program executes;
(12) On completion of the user program, repeat from step (1).

3.18 REAL-TIME CLOCK

A feature of the disk operating system that is not immediately obvious is the requirement for a real-time clock which is used to indicate the time the files on the floppy disk were last altered. This operation can be made available to the user through the operating system as one of the operations of the DOS main loop. In this case study, the time could be displayed upon the VDU screen whenever the key T is pressed on the VDU keyboard. The interface to the time operation is as follows.

Interface to the Time Function

This uses INT 021H to indicate it is a DOS function. The function to get the system time is selected by

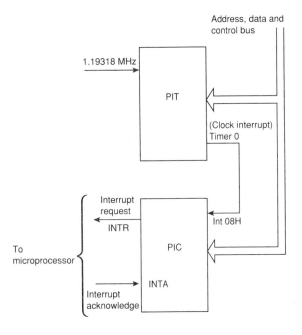

Figure 3.33 Real-time clock

putting 02CH into the AH register before initiating the interface.

When the interrupt returns the following registers contain the time as simple binary numbers.

CH Hours, 0 to 23,
CL Minutes, 0 to 59,
DH Seconds, 0 to 59.

This can be used to obtain and then display the time on the VDU screen as illustrated in the following algorithm and program listing.

Example algorithm

(1) Get the system time;
(2) Display time message on VDU;
(3) Display the time on the VDU;
(4) Return to the main DOS loop.

The implementation of the algorithm is left as an exercise for the reader.

As this is a real-time clock, an interrupt should be used, generated by a fixed frequency source, as illustrated in *Figure 3.33*. It is easier to obtain stable high frequency oscillators and a basic frequency signal of 1.19318 MHz which is IBM PC-compatible, is used as the input to a timer in a **Programmable Interval Timer** (PIT) where it is reduced to the required interrupt frequency. The PIT performs the reduction in frequency and a **Programmable**

Interrupt Controller (PIC) generates the correct interrupt handshaking signals and re-direction of the interrupt vector.

The **Non-Maskable Interrupt** (NMI) could have been used to avoid the need for a PIC but it is usual to use the NMI for urgent system interrupts such as memory errors. Therefore a PIC is necessary and this has the advantage of providing several other interrupt signals from devices such as the FDC and DMA controller for fast data transfers and the serial communication link for interrupt-driven communications.

No operating system functions and user programs must interfere with the clock interrupt, otherwise the time will not be accurately maintained.

3.19 THE COMPLETE DESIGN

All the major requirements of the microcomputer have been considered and block diagram designs presented. When gathered together into a complete block diagram design as shown in *Figure 3.34*, all the functions required of a microcontroller consisting of mass secondary storage, processing unit and execution memory and user interface are incorporated, including the real-time clock.

Most of the design in this case study is compatible with the IBM PC as is most of the software. However, the design is not a completely compatible solution and it would be necessary to consult the appropriate manuals in order to write programs that would execute on an IBM PC.

Summary

The design of a microcomputer was considered. The full design procedure was not followed as this would have required lengthy documentation. Instead, various important points were considered and typical design solutions for both hardware and software considered. Where possible, the solution is compatible with the IBM PC to illustrate how a standard design of a microcomputer is arrived at. The interfaces and structure of a simplified operating system are considered in relation to the microcomputer design and some simple techniques implemented. Not all of the software is included.

The concept of functional-block top-down design is satisfactory with the solutions produced being flexible and robust. Some reduction in software and hardware is possible although this would lead to a reduction in flexibility which may be important for the future expansion of the product.

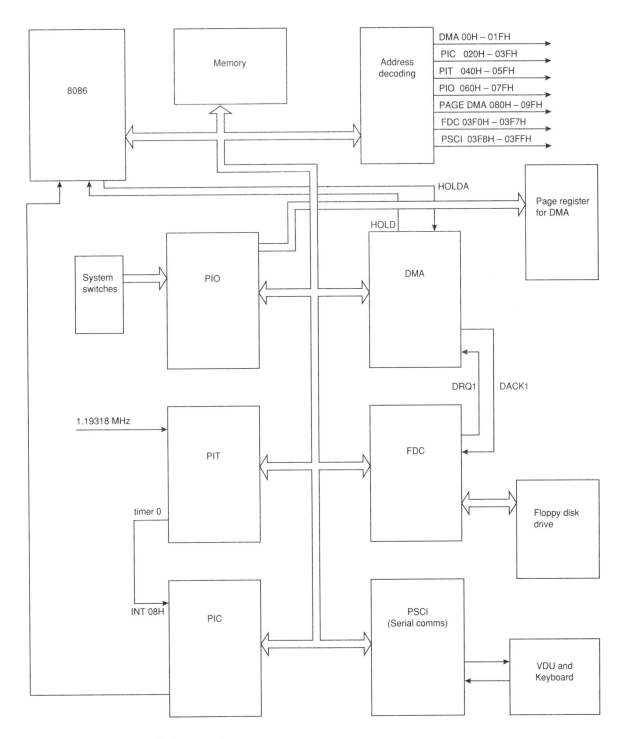

Figure 3.34 Basic personal microcomputer

FOUR

State of the art

4.1 INTRODUCTION

The 8086 microprocessor is an example of a device that can be used to produce microcomputers that are either simple or complex and sophisticated. Simple microcomputers are used to execute a small range of programs, sometimes only one. As the programs become larger in order to implement more complex and sophisticated products such as desk-top publishing, the microcomputers become more complex and sophisticated in order to execute them in real-time. If a 50 kbyte program takes 0.5 seconds to execute the user does not perceive any delay in the response. However, if a 500 kbyte program takes 5.0 seconds to execute the user definitely notices the delay. Therefore designers of microcomputers are continually improving the systems so that larger programs will execute in the user's real-time.

A variety of techniques are used to improve the performance of microcomputers and this chapter will consider some of the important ones. Some of the techniques such as bus systems, are designed to allow a user to upgrade the microcomputer so that a user executing small programs could have a cheap basic system, while a user who wishes to execute desk-top publishing packages could enhance the basic system with additional hardware, to provide better facilities such as graphics and to execute programs faster. Others such as co-processors are specifically designed to make the programs execute faster.

A third option is to use different microprocessor architectures such as concurrent processors or **Reduced Instruction Set Computers** (RISC) specifically to execute programs as fast as possible. These are discussed in the next chapter.

4.2 BUS INTERCONNECTIONS

In order to be able to add extra hardware to a microcomputer there must be a suitable interface.

This section will consider the hardware part of an interface that can be used to add extra hardware modules to a microcomputer.

The signals which constitute the system hardware interface are known as the bus. A bus is a group of connections between different components in the system, which carry information from the master device to the slave device(s). The information consists of data, control signals and arbitration signals, with most of the signals being connected in parallel to all of the components. The bus signals can be uni-directional, such as the address lines which originate from the microprocessor, or bi-directional such as the data bus to allow two-way transfers.

Bus Functions

There are three main categories of bus signals which are data transfer, data handshaking and arbitration, see *Figure 4.1*. The function of these signals is to transfer data and control information between the microprocessor and the modules via the hardware part of the interface.

Data transfer. The data transfer signals comprise the majority of the signals within a microprocessor system and consist of the address signals, data signals and some command signals, such as read, write and status.

The aim of this group is to carry or transfer information from one module to another. A module could be a **Central Processing Unit** (CPU), a **memory module** or an **I/O module**. The result of the transfer produces a change in the receiving module, either in the data or the module status, or it will produce some sort of response.

Data handshaking. Handshaking is a method of ensuring that the transmission and reception of the data is confirmed and basically indicates when each transaction begins and ends.

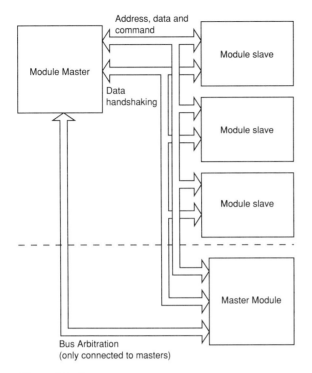

Figure 4.1 Bus systems

Arbitration signals. A master is a device or component capable of issuing commands to the rest of the system and an example of a master is a microprocessor. A device or component which is only capable of responding to requests or commands that are passed to it, usually from a master, is called a slave and most memory and I/O components are slave devices.

If a system contains more than one master, then some method of deciding which master can use the system bus interface at any moment in time, is necessary. It is not desirable for two or more masters to attempt to transfer data to or from the same module at the same time.

There are two aspects to the processor arbitration, access and priority. Access ensures that all masters can access the resource they require at some time in the future after the initial request is made. This prevents a master from continually using a resource as this would prevent all the other masters from using it.

Priority is similar to access but deals with the situation when two or more masters are waiting to access a resource. The priority of the masters is used to decide the order in which they will be allowed to access the system bus interface. Access

only ensures that all masters, even those with a low priority, eventually obtain the resource they request.

Data transfer signals. For the 8086 microprocessor, the address and data signals are:

AD_0–AD_1 (16 bits of multiplexed data and address)

A_{16}–A_{19} (4 high order bits of the memory address)

The important control signals are:

$\overline{RD}$ Read (active low); transfers data from a module to the master

$\overline{WR}$ Write (active low); transfers data from the master to the slave

$\overline{BHE}$ Bus High Enable (active low)

S0–S3 Status signals

$DT\overline{R}$ Data transmit or receive, used to select the direction of the bi-directional data buffers

$\overline{DEN}$ Data transceiver enable (active low), used to enable the bi-directional data buffers.

These are illustrated in *Figure 4.2.*

Note: the bar above a signal name is used to indicate that the signal is active low, that is, it is active when it is a logic zero.

The data handshaking signals. There are three main methods of handshaking called **protocols** that are implemented in microprocessors: synchronous, asynchronous, and semi-synchronous.

The synchronous bus handshake. The synchronous protocols use a clock signal to indicate the beginning and end of the transfer and the

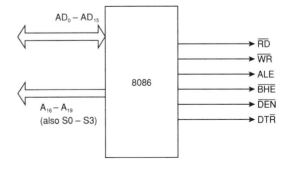

Figure 4.2 8086 address and data signals

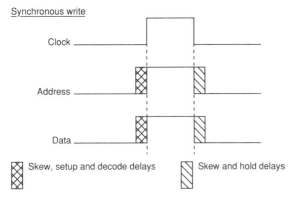

Synchronous write

Clock

Address

Data

⊠ Skew, setup and decode delays   ⊠ Skew and hold delays

Figure 4.3 A synchronous handshake

asynchronous protocols use two handshaking lines that are not controlled by clocks.

An example of a synchronous handshake is shown in *Figure 4.3* which consists of three different sets of signals, the clock (which is the handshaking signal), the address and the data signals. The diagram shows when the signals are active, rather than particular logic values. There are two transfers of interest, a read and a write and these have different timings.

Write Transfer

The timing diagram of *Figure 4.3*, shows a write transfer taking place. As the transfer will start as soon as the clock signal goes active, that is, the rising edge of the signal, then the transfer should begin. As the transfer is from the master (the microprocessor) to the slave (the memory) then the address and data are already known. The transfer starts as soon as the clock signal becomes active as indicated by the rising edge in *Figure 4.3*, when the transfers commence.

To ensure that the transfer begins at the rising edge of the clock signal the values on the address and data signals should already be present at the slave. This allows for any internal delays inside the slave so that the transfer can begin immediately. This time is indicated by the shaded area at the beginning of the address and data signals.

In addition to allowing for the internal delay of the slave, three other major delays are allowed for: setup, skew and decode. The setup delay is required for the slave component to be ready for the transfer. The setup delay is the minimum time a control signal has to be present on the inputs to the slave before the clock becomes active to ensure the correct logic state is recognised when the transfer begins. Some logic inputs require an amount of time to recognise

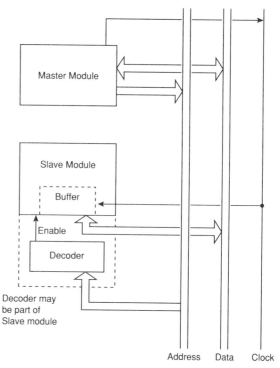

Master Module

Slave Module

Buffer

Enable

Decoder

Decoder may be part of Slave module

Address   Data   Clock

Figure 4.4 Master slave system

the state of an input signal and the output cannot begin until after they have been recognised.

The skew and decode delays are required to overcome problems introduced by the system design. *Figure 4.4* illustrates a typical master slave system, indicating that the slave is physically separated from the master. This separation means that the signals take a finite time to travel from the master to the slave. This will not be a problem if all the signals travel along the same path as they would all arrive at the same time. However, on most implementations, different signals travel along different paths, having different lengths, therefore arriving at different times. The difference in arrival time is called **skew** and is illustrated in *Figure 4.5* where the two address signals, A_0 and A_1 start together, but because the path lengths are different they arrive displaced. The difference between the first and last to arrive in a batch of signals is important and is called the skew delay and has to be allowed for in the timing calculations. This value can be altered by changing the physical layout of the components on the PCB.

To select a location within the slave some form of decoding is used, which has a small number of inputs and a larger number of outputs. At any one time, only one of the outputs will be active and this will be connected to the location involved in the transfer. To ensure that the transfer is completed during the clock period, the selected location must be activated in time. The delay introduced by the decoder has to be allowed for, before the clock signal becomes active.

The address and data signals are designed to arrive at the slave before the clock signal within a period of time greater than the sum of the setup, skew and decode delays.

Each slave could have a different setup, skew and decode delay and this would make designing a system difficult if each individual slave/bus path were calculated. Instead, manufacturers ensure that all the different slave components have setup delays within a certain fixed maximum. The designer must then maintain the skew and decode delays below fixed maximum values throughout the system. The system master is then created to operate within the timing constraints imposed. This can make it difficult to connect different types of masters and slaves from different manufacturers as they are usually designed with different setup times.

The transfer then takes place while the clock is active. When the clock signal becomes inactive, illustrated by the falling edge in *Figure 4.3*, the address and data signals must be maintained at their active states for a short delay afterwards. This is necessary to ensure that the correct values are used by the slave as, if they were changed immediately, some of the slave logic inputs may still be active and recognise the changes. This is similar to the setup delay, but is called the **hold delay** and is required

to ensure that the slave logic buffers have been deactivated before the input signals are deactivated. In addition, a further skew delay has to be allowed to maintain all the signals during the hold time of the slave. Within a system, the master would maintain the signals active after the inactive clock for a maximum hold value which a slave buffer's hold and skew delay must be within, to ensure a correctly functioning system.

Read Transfer

During the read operation the slave transfers the selected data to the master. The data is not immediately present on the data signals when the clock signal becomes active because the slave has to fetch the data value from its internal location and then transfer it to the output buffers. At this point it appears on the data signals, as illustrated in *Figure 4.6*. The fetching process takes a finite time, so that the data appears some time after the activated clock signal. The address signal must have been present before the activated clock signal, to ensure that the internal fetch in the slave can start immediately the clock is activated and an allowance for setup, skew and decode delays is made.

The transfer is completed in a similar manner to the write operation, so that when the clock becomes inactive the data and address are maintained for a further hold period. For the address signals, this is the hold and skew delay of the slave. However, because the data is transferring to the master it is the hold and skew of the master that is allowed for. Usually, the master buffer hold delay is shorter than the slave hold delay, as the master is a more important component and is designed for a faster operation. If this is not the case, the longer of the two values is used in calculations to ensure that both the master and slave transfer correctly. The skew delay

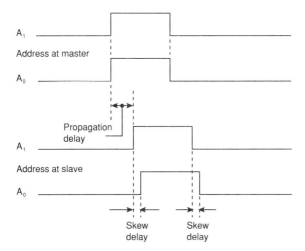

Figure 4.5 Illustration of propagation and skew delay

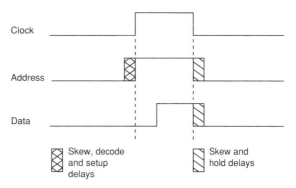

Figure 4.6 Synchronous Read

required is the same, as the skew does not change if the direction the signals travel along the wires is changed.

As the skew delay could be different for each master-slave combination, the maximum skew for the system is calculated and used in all the calculations. Alternatively, a maximum value is specified and all master-slave combinations are then designed to have a skew less than that value.

Round Trip Propagation Delay

A final delay of interest is the round trip propagation delay. This is the time taken by the clock signal travelling from the master to the slave plus the time for the subsequent change of the data to travel from the slave to the master. This delay is only of interest during the read operation when data is being transferred from the slave to the master, as in a write operation the master places the data onto the data bus before the signals are active.

The round trip propagation delay must be exceeded to ensure the signals have their correct values at the end of the transfer, which is denoted by the clock becoming inactive. This delay occurs at the same time as the hold delay of the master buffer and can be overlapped with it. As the two delays are overlapped, only the larger of the hold or round trip propagation delays needs to be used in the calculations.

Other Delays. There are some other minor delays which can usually be ignored except for larger systems operating at high bus transfer rates. For example, in a practical system there is a non-zero delay between transfers to allow time for the master to complete internal re-initialisation. Also, the slave will have a non-zero access time.

These delays have been allowed for by specifying the master clock mark/space ratio to be 1 : 1. The delays are all added together to form the space delay of the clock pulse but so far the width, or mark, has not been specified. Therefore, by allowing an equivalent mark width as space width, the internal re-initialisation and space access times are allowed for. If it is known that the mark/space ratio of the clock is not 1 : 1, but say 1 : 2 as for the 8086, then it is easy to make the appropriate adjustments.

Summary of bus speed limitations. The effect of these delays is to place a minimum limit on the bus transfer time, so that a bus transfer, either read or write, cannot take place in less time than the minimum. This limits the maximum transfer rates, called

the **bus bandwidth** , that the bus can operate at. A typical value for a 16-bit microprocessor would be between 1 and 3 MHz.

Advantages of the synchronous handshake. The synchronous bus handshake has two significant advantages. The first is that it is a simple system requiring only one signal, the master clock signal, to coordinate all the bus transfers. Secondly, it is the fastest of the three types of handshaking as the delays that have to be allowed for have been minimised. Therefore the bandwidth of synchronous systems is higher assuming that all other factors are equal.

Disadvantages of the synchronous handshake. It must also be recognised that the synchronous bus handshake has a serious disadvantage. Because of the necessity of performing the complete data transfer within the specified bus cycle period, then any slaves or masters with delay times greater than those specified cannot be connected immediately to the system.

If slow modules are to be connected to the system, the master clock frequency has to be reduced, in order to increase the bus cycle time. This results in a reduction in bandwidth for the complete system and not just when the slow module is being accessed.

Example

The bus cycle time can be calculated using the following equation (Stone's equation for calculating the bus cycle time, *Microcomputer Interfacing*, Addison Wesley, 1983). An example calculation is given below for the system shown in *Figure 4.7*.

$$T_{transfer} \geq T_{setup} + T_{decode} + 2T_{skew} + (T_{hold}T_{RT\text{-}PROP})_{max}$$

This is a simple system, having a single master and a single slave. The master clock signal has two inverters in its path, each of which introduces a propagation delay of 10 ns and a physical path length of 20 cm.

The decoder in the address lines introduces a decode delay of 25 ns in the top part of the address signals and 40 ns in the bottom part of the address signals, with the address signals physical path lengths all being 40 cm.

The bi-directional data signal connections have no delays introduced other than that caused by the physical length of the path, which is 35 cm.

The maximum setup delay of any component is 15 ns and the maximum hold delay is 20 ns.

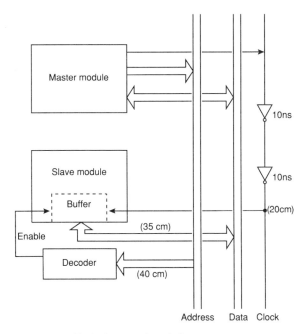

Figure 4.7 Typical system bus timing

Any lengths not shown can be considered to be negligible, and the speed at which signals travel along the physical signal paths has been assumed to be 10 cm/ns. This is a little slow but allows a margin of error which will include all methods of product construction.

Some of the delays required by the equation, such as setup, decode and hold, can easily be deduced. For the remainder, some simple calculations are performed.

The round trip propagation delay is the time taken for the master clock to travel to the slave plus the time taken for the response from the slave to reach the master.

The time taken for the clock signal to travel from the master to the slave is the two inverter propagation delays plus the time taken to travel 20 cm, which is:

$$\text{Clock delay} = \text{prop del} + \text{prop del} + \text{dist/vel}$$
$$= 10 + 10 + (20/10) \text{ ns}$$
$$= 22 \text{ ns}$$

The time required for the response to reach the master is the time a change on the data signals takes to travel 35 cm along the data bus from the slave to the master. Assuming that signals travel at the same speed in either direction on the data bus, this becomes:

$$\text{Response time} = \text{distance/velocity}$$
$$= 35/10 \text{ ns}$$
$$= 3.5 \text{ ns}$$

Therefore the round time propagation delay, RT-PROP, is:

$$\text{RT-PROP} = \text{clock delay} + \text{response delay}$$
$$= 22 + 3.5 \text{ ns}$$
$$= 25.5 \text{ ns}$$

This is greater than the hold delay, so that the function

$$\text{MAX (RT-PROP, HOLD)}$$

returns the RT-PROP values of 25.5 ns as its result.

The skew delay is the maximum difference between any of the address and data signals. The data signals travel the fastest, having only 35 cm to travel with no other delays and as already calculated this takes 3.5 ns.

The longest time taken for any signal is that for the address lines, which travel 40 cm and therefore takes 4.0 ns. The decoder delay is not included in the skew calculation as it was included in the decoder delay. All of the other signals have delays somewhere between these two so the maximum skew delay is:

$$\text{SKEW} = \text{slowest signal} - \text{fastest signal}$$
$$(\text{address} - \text{data})$$
$$= 4.0 - 3.5 \text{ ns}$$
$$= 0.5 \text{ ns}$$

The skew delay is small in this example as a simplified connection scheme is used. Therefore, the resulting bus cycle time, BUS, can be calculated from the following equation:

$$\text{BUS} > \text{Setup} + \text{Decode} + 2 \times \text{Skew} + \text{RT-PROP}$$
$$> 15 + 40 + 2 \times 0.5 + 25.5 \text{ ns} = 81.5 \text{ ns}$$

Assuming an even mark/space ratio master clock signal, then the maximum bus bandwidth, BANDWIDTH, is:

$$\text{BANDWIDTH} < 1/(2 \times \text{BUS})$$
$$< 1/0.163 \text{ MHz} = 6.1 \text{ MHz}$$

Asynchronous Handshake

If the access times of the slave modules vary widely, the asynchronous bus handshake can be used and enables all the modules to be connected together without having to use a low clock frequency as

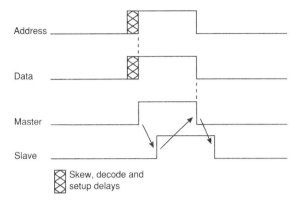

Figure 4.8 Asynchronous write

would be the case for the synchronous bus hand-shake. The full title of this type of bus is the 'fully interlocked asynchronous bus'. Each data transfer is tailored to the speed of the modules involved, usually the slave as most master modules operate at high speeds.

Figure 4.8 illustrates a typical read operation for this type of bus, where instead of a single master clock signal there are two signals, one called master and the other slave. Obviously, the master signal originates from the master module and the slave signal from the slave module. As this is a write, the master module places the address and data values onto the signal lines a short period before the hand-shaking signals are activated. This allows time for the skew, hold and setup delays which are the same as those for the synchronous handshake. The master module then activates the master signal to indicate to the slave module that the address and data are correctly placed. Some time later, equivalent to the access time of the slave module buffer, the slave activates the slave signal to indicate to the master that the data has been correctly received.

Now that the data transfer has been completed, the bus handshake has to be completed in order to be ready for the next transfer. The handshaking is completed by the master signal being taken inactive to confirm to the slave module that it has under-stood that the transfer was completed successfully. The slave then deactivates the slave signal and is ready for the next bus transfer. There is no need to allow a hold and skew delay at the end of the address and data signals as the slave will not activate the slave signal until after the data has been correctly transferred to its internal buffer and the input buffer disabled. This prevents any corruption of the trans-ferred data.

For a read operation the same procedure is followed as illustrated in *Figure 4.9*, except that the data is not placed onto the data signals at the same time as the address. This is because for a read operation it is the slave which places the data onto the data bus signals and until the address has been correctly received it is not able to identify the correct data. When the address has stabilised, the master signal is activated to indicate to the slave that the required data can be placed onto the data sig-nals. A short delay is required to allow for skew on the data signal paths before the slave activates the slave signal. The active slave signal indicates to the master that the correct data is present on its input buffer and can be correctly transferred into the buffer. Following this the master signal becomes inactive after allowing for setup delays. To complete the handshake the slave deactivates the slave signal, indicating that it has observed that the master has correctly received the data. The bus is now ready to initiate further data transfers.

Asynchronous bus bandwidth. It is only possible to find the maximum bus transfer rate and hence the maximum bus bandwidth for individual master-slave combinations, as each different slave may have a different set of delay times. It is also possible for the same slave to execute the handshake at different speeds in successive data transfers due to internal variations. However, some calculations can be performed which show that the asynchronous hand-shake must always take longer than the synchronous handshake, even if the slave is as fast as one used in a synchronous bus system.

Asynchronous bus handshake (minimum timing). The following delays have to be allowed for in the

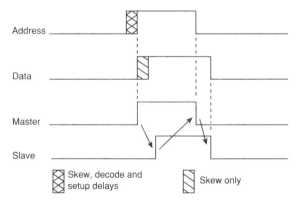

Figure 4.9 Asynchronous read

asynchronous bus handshake and these enable the bus timing equation to be constructed.

(1) The skew and setup times of the address to the slave and the address decode delays are all present, as with the synchronous handshake.

(2) Also the skew and hold delays associated with the return of data from the slave to the master have to be allowed for.

(3) In addition, unlike the synchronous bus which only requires one round trip propagation, the asynchronous handshake has to allow for two round trip propagation delays to enable the two-signal bus handshake to operate correctly. The first round trip indicates that the transfer can begin, and the second indicates that the transfer has completed.

When all these factors are combined into the equation for calculating the minimum bus transfer time, the following equation is created (see Stone):

$$T_{transfer} \geq T_{setup} + T_{decode} + 2T_{skew} + 2T_{RT\text{-}PROP}$$

The delays indicated are the same as for the synchronous handshake, except that there are two round trip propagation delays. This result means that the asynchronous handshake will always take longer and therefore has a lower bus bandwidth than the synchronous bus transfers.

Advantages of the asynchronous bus handshake. The advantage of the asynchronous bus handshake is that it enables slave modules with varying access times and other associated delays to be incorporated into the same system, but without having to reduce the bus transfer rate to that required by the slowest slave. Each master-slave combination within the system is individually controlled by the two handshaking signals.

Disadvantages of the asynchronous bus handshake. The addition of the second handshaking signal has the disadvantage of increasing the complexity of the system, which increases the cost of the system. More importantly, the second handshaking signal introduces the need to allow for a second round trip propagation delay so that even if fast slave modules were used, the bus transfer rate would always be less than that possible if a synchronous bus handshake were used.

The Semi-synchronous Handshake

The synchronous handshake has the advantage of having the highest bus bandwidth but the disadvantage of not being able to access slow slave modules. The asynchronous handshake has the advantage of being able to access fast and slow slave modules in the same system, but the disadvantage of a lower bandwidth to accomplish this. The semi-synchronous handshake is an attempt to combine the advantages of both types of handshaking, of fast bus transfers and wide differences in slave access times.

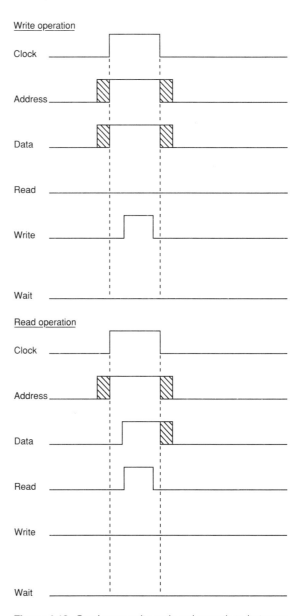

Figure 4.10 Semi-sync. write and read operations between a master and a fast slave

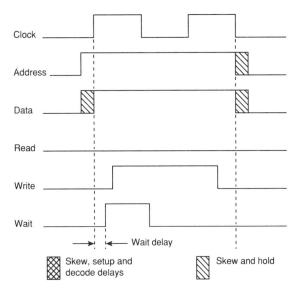

Figure 4.11 captions within image:
— Wait delay
Skew, setup and decode delays   Skew and hold

Figure 4.11 Semi-synchronous extended Write

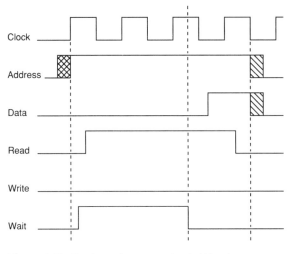

Figure 4.12 Semi-synchronous extended Read

There are two signals which control the data transfer, as with the asynchronous handshake, but they are not fully-interlocked. The master clock signal is essentially the same as the clock signal bus handshake in synchronous systems, whereas the wait signal, which originates from the slave, is used to indicate that a slow slave is being accessed. When the wait signal is inactive, the bus operates as a synchronous bus and *Figure 4.10* illustrates a write and read operation between the master and a fast slave. As can be seen, the transfer is controlled by the master clock signals and is a synchronous data transfer. This allows fast slave modules to transfer data at synchronous speeds.

When the wait signal is activated to indicate that a slow slave module is being accessed, the bus cycle is extended as illustrated in *Figures 4.11 and 4.12*. The bus transfer is extended by complete clock cycles, provided the wait signal is active within a certain period from the beginning of the data transfer. Complete clock cycles are added to the data transfer for as long as the wait signal is active and this allows slaves with varying access times to be connected to the system without incurring a speed penalty when using the fast slave modules.

The wait signal has to have a propagation delay which allows the module furthest away from the master module to activate the wait signal within the period allowed at the beginning of a data transfer for it to be recognised. This places a restriction on the physical length of the bus signals in the system and therefore restricts the number of slave modules that can be added.

Advantages of the semi-synchronous bus handshake. The semi-synchronous bus handshake combines advantages of the high speed of the synchronous bus handshaking with the versatility of asynchronous handshaking. This allows slave modules with widely-varying access times to be connected together in the same system but does not restrict the maximum bus transfer rate.

Disadvantages of the semi-synchronous bus handshake. The disadvantage of the semi-synchronous bus handshake is that the physical bus length is restricted to ensure that the wait signal can always arrive at the master, within the specified period from the beginning of the data transfer commencing. This restricts the number of slave modules that can be connected.

The IBM PC bus uses a semi-synchronous bus handshake to obtain the advantages and the number of modules, or I/O cards, is restricted as a consequence of this.

Arbitration Protocols

If a microcomputer system contains more than one master module a method of deciding which master has control of the bus system is necessary and this is called arbitration. Arbitration is necessary because there is usually only one bus system consisting of address, data and control signals, common to all modules, whether master or slave. As a master must have sole use of the address and data signal

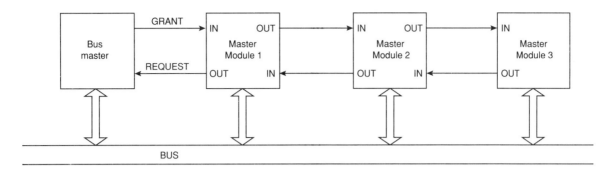

Figure 4.13 Daisy Chain Arbitration

paths while it is performing data transfers, arbitration is used to enable the transfer of the control from the master using the bus system to the next master requesting use of the bus system.

Arbitration performs two actions. The first is to decide on the priority of the master modules in the system with the higher priority masters being able to obtain quicker access. The second action involves the actual transfer of control from one master to the next. At all times the bus system will be under the control of a master, or in the process of transferring control.

Daisy Chain Arbitration

The daisy chain arbitration protocol has a structure similar to that shown in *Figure 4.13*, with the arbitration signals being 'daisy chained'. The two important signals are called grant and request. Request is a signal line which the master modules activate in order to gain access to the bus and grant is used to indicate when a module can begin to access the bus. The bus master contains the arbitration control logic which has the function of deciding when a transfer of bus control can be made, to which module and the transfer of control itself. The bus master only controls when a transfer of bus control can be made, while the physical order of the master modules decides the priority and the master modules themselves conduct the transfer of bus control from one master to the next.

The request signal is connected into a module and then out of the module again to be connected to the input of the next module, until the request is transferred through to the bus master. The bus master then makes a grant which will be transferred from the bus master to the other master modules one after the other. The result of this process is that the master modules nearer to the bus master obtain a

grant before the modules further away and therefore have a higher priority.

The bus master can be an ordinary master module which has been designated to be the bus master to control the operation of the request and grant signals. The bus master has the exclusive right to use the bus and to transfer control so that it has the highest priority. However, the bus master is usually programmed to respond to a request from the other master modules as quickly as possible by activating the grant signal to ensure that all modules can gain control of the bus within a relatively short period of time. Normally a master module, including the bus master, will only perform one data transfer via the bus after a request has been made, before passing on the control to the next requesting master module.

An example of the arbitration signals connected to a master module is shown in *Figure 4.14*. The request and grant functions are implemented by using four signals. These are request-in, request-out, grant-in and grant-out. The request-in signal which comes from a module on the (lower priority) right-hand side

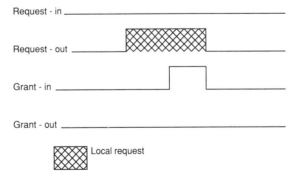

Figure 4.14 Arbitration signals of a master module making a local request

is inactive, indicating that there are no lower priority modules which wish to use the bus system. The request-out, is activated because this particular master module wants to make a data transfer via the bus system. Therefore it must obtain control of the bus system and has activated the request-out signal. This will be called a **local request**.

The grant-in becomes active some time after the request is made due to the time required for the bus master to finish using the bus, and for the request to be processed and a grant made. The grant-in signal is received by this requesting master module but is not passed on by activating grant-out as there is a local request pending.

Figure 4.15 illustrates the signals when a request is made by a lower priority master module using request-in. This is passed out to request-out after a small propagation delay caused by the internal logic circuit of the master module. Some time later the grant-in signal becomes active and as there is no local request pending the grant-out is activated after a short internal propagation delay.

The example in *Figure 4.16* shows that a lower priority request is made after a local request. When the grant-in is received the local module makes use of it first. However, when the local module has completed a data transfer via the bus system, the request-out remains high because of the lower priority request-in. This results in the grant-in remaining high so that it can be passed onto the lower priority module.

If a lower priority request-in has been received, passed on and a request-out obtained and then a local request is made, which has a higher priority, the local module will have to wait until the lower priority request-in is deactivated as bus transfer in progress cannot be interrupted. After the lower

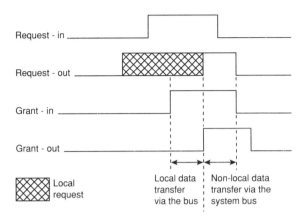

Figure 4.16 A local request made before a non-local request

priority request-in becomes inactive, the request-out will remain active as there is a local request pending and the master module will be able to make use of the still active grant-in.

The transfer of bus control is made reliable by specifying that for a module to be free to seize control of the grant-in signal, the request-out must be made active, the request-in inactive and the grant-in signal becomes active after the request-out was made. This effectively prevents the higher priority module from interrupting the bus transfer of a lower priority module.

Usually one data transfer using the system is permitted to take place if there are any other requests pending to ensure that any lower priority modules eventually gain control of the bus system. If no other modules are requesting use of the bus then one module is able to make continuous use of it. It still has to make each request separately, allowing all signals to become inactive in between each data transfer otherwise higher priority modules are prevented from gaining control of the bus. If continuous data transfers were allowed a lower priority module, once it had gained control of the bus, would remain in control until the continuous sequence was completed and there would be no method the higher priority modules could use to stop this.

Because the daisy chaining of the arbitration signals implements the priority of the master modules, the modules should be inserted into the bus connection system with that in mind.

A point of interest is that the arbitration signals are not connected in parallel to all master modules, as the other bus signals are. As a backplane connection system would be used for a multiple module system, this means the additional modules have to

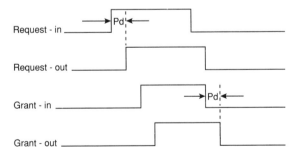

Pd – Propagation delay through the module

Figure 4.15 Arbitration signals of a master module with no requests pending

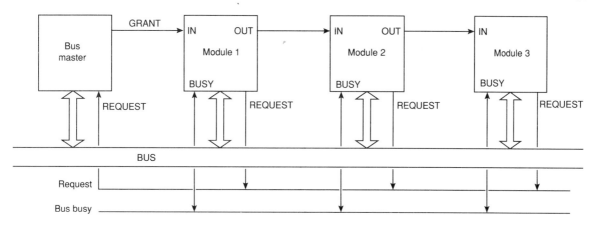

Figure 4.17 The safe daisy chain protocol

The Safe Daisy Chain Arbitration Protocol

In an ideal environment, the two-wire daisy chain protocol would be satisfactory. However in a real system the presence of noise on the arbitration signals means that the two wire system can fail if a local request is pending. For a local request to be pending, request-in, request-out, grant-in and grant-out must be active, so that a lower priority master module has control of the bus system. A noise spike on the grant-in signal would be recognised by the local master module as permission to start a data transfer. This would be started part way through the data transfer of the master module, which already has control of the bus system causing a serious bus error to occur.

To overcome this problem the safe daisy chain arbitration protocol can be used consisting of three signals. This is the method adopted by most system designers and is illustrated in *Figure 4.17*. The grant signal remains the same and is daisy chained to all the master modules. However, the other two signals, request and bus busy, are connected in parallel to all the master modules instead of being daisy chained. The request signal is an output from the master modules all connected in parallel and must therefore be wire-OR connections. The bus busy signal is bi-directional, being controlled by the modules themselves and is used to indicate that data transfers are being made.

The safe daisy chain protocol works in the following way. When a master module requires access to the bus system, it activates the request signal but does not take control until the bus busy signal is inactive *and* it detects the rising edge of the grant signal. It is not necessary for the module to check the state of the request signal before activating it, as it is designed to be activated simultaneously by several master modules without causing any damage. Once a master module has gained control of the bus system by having a request outstanding, an inactive bus busy signal and a detected rising edge on grant, the bus busy signal is activated by that master module. This prevents all other master modules from mistaking noise signals superimposed on the grant signal as valid grant signal rising edges.

The bus master activates the grant signal whenever a request signal is detected *and* there is an inactive bus busy signal. This will only occur when there are no modules currently using the bus.

4.3 INTRODUCTION TO MULTIPROGRAMMING

Any program or part of a program, such as a subroutine, which executes some task or action which is independent of other tasks is known as a process. When several processes are executed one after another, that is in series, this is known as **uniprogramming**. *Figure 4.18* shows three processes, A, B and C operating in a uniprogramming environment, with A executing first, then B and finally C. If it is possible to execute two or more processes simultaneously: this is known as **multiprocessing**. To achieve this on a single microprocessor requires the code for each process to be present in memory and then to be executed in a time-multiplexed fashion to produce a multiprogramming environment. [Note: only one instruction from one process can be executing at any one time.]

be inserted in sequence, starting as near to the bus master as possible to ensure that all the modules have continuous daisy chain connections.

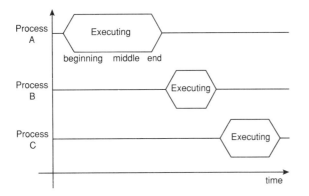

Figure 4.18 Uniprogramming

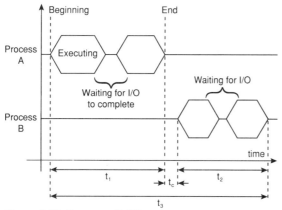

Figure 4.19 Process with I/O

In a multiprogramming environment the processes involved cannot require the complete and undivided use of the CPU but must be able to stop executing to allow another process to start or continue. The switching back and forth between processes is achieved using interrupts and on an ordinary system, multiprogramming can be used to increase system throughput significantly by overlapping I/O and CPU performance.

For example, in figure 4.19 two processes, A and B are illustrated which both contain I/O operations and take a total time to execute of:

$$t_3 = t_1 + t_2 + t_c$$

where t_c is the time taken to change from executing process A to executing process B and is usually much smaller than the process execution times and can normally be ignored. By now executing these two processes in a multiprocessing environment as illustrated in *Figure 4.20*, where a switch to the other process is made whenever an I/O operation is

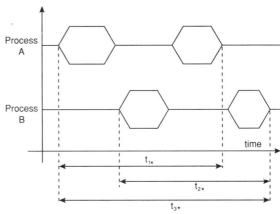

Figure 4.20 Uniprogramming with I/O overlap

required. The total time required to execute both processes is now:

$$t_{3*} = t_{1*} + t_{2*} + t_c$$

where $t_{3*} < t_3$

However, it should be noted that the time taken to complete executing each individual process is longer, so that: $t_{1*} > t_1$ and $t_{2*} > t_2$

If the processes do not contain any I/O operations it is still possible to execute them in a multiprocessing environment by using interrupts, as illustrated in *Figure 4.21*. This shows three processes, A, B and C which execute for a small period of time, called a **time-slice**, before stopping and then allowing any other processes to execute. This technique does not reduce the total execution time for the three processes, as the context switching time now becomes significant:

$$t_A + t_B + t_C = t_{A(uni)} + t_{B(uni)} + t_{C(uni)} + Nt_c$$

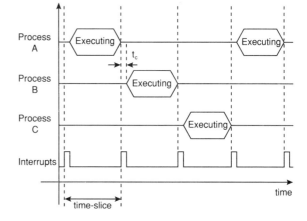

Figure 4.21 Multiprogramming

where t_A, t_B and t_C are the times to complete executing the process in a multiprocessing environment;

$t_{A(uni)}$, $t_{B(uni)}$ and $t_{C(uni)}$ are the times required for the processes to execute in a uniprogramming environment;

t_c is the context switching time;

N is the number of switches made between processes.

The value of N can be found from:

$$N = (t_A + t_B + t_C)/(\text{time-slice})$$

so that the smaller the time-slice, the larger the number of context switches and hence the longer it takes to execute any individual process. The effects of this can often be seen on a main frame computer which has several hundred users connected. It is normal to give each user consecutively a time slice of the CPU execution, and the system is said to be **time-shared**. During busy periods when everyone is accessing the CPU, the response time increases considerably and in some instances virtually renders the system unusable.

Process Management

To enable a multiprocessing system to operate, the various states of each process being executed must be managed. There are only three main states (although some commercial systems do further subdivide), see *Figure 4.22*.

(1) *Running:* The process is being executed by the CPU. This continues until the process completes or the end of the allowed time slice occurs, whichever is the sooner.

(2) *Blocked:* Execution cannot be continued because it is waiting for an event (input, output, or until a specified time) to occur.

(3) *Ready:* Execution of the process can continue at the next available time-slice. This state is entered when the end of the time-slice, or input or output operation is required.

To ensure that a process moves from Running to Ready at the end of the time-slice, a real-time clock is required to generate the interrupts, which initiate the change of states. The real-time clock has to be implemented in hardware so that it is not under software control. This prevents any individual process, either deliberately or accidentally, altering the time-slice period to receive an unfair share of the available CPU resources.

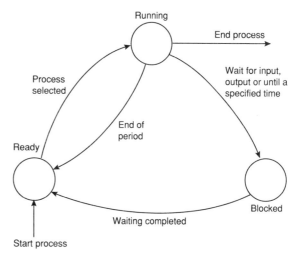

Figure 4.22 The states of a multi-processing system

The Ready Queue

The ready queue is used to indicate which of the available processes is to be transferred to the 'Running' state at the next time slot. The simplest system implements a first-in/first-out queue, which gives equal priority to all processes, and always selects the process which has been in the queue the longest, so that processes are added to the bottom of the queue and taken from the top.

Structure of a General Ready Queue

Figure 4.23 illustrates the structure of a general ready queue, and consists of two pointers, the process table and the process control blocks. The first element pointer indicates which process is to be executed next (i.e. the top of the queue) and the last element pointer indicates the last process added. The last element pointer is required to make it easier to add further processes to the bottom of the queue. Each process then points to the next process in the queue using the **Forward Queue Pointer** (FQP) so that a linked list of processes is produced. In this example the Process Identification is the same as the position in the process table. The actual Ready Queue consists of processes P1, P4, P5 and P2, to be executed in that order (in a linked pointer format).

The remaining process table entries are either running, blocked or unused. The process with the number 0 is used to indicate the end of the queue and therefore is not used as a pointer to a process control block. The process control block is the area in memory where the temporary data associated

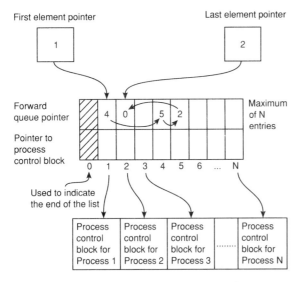

Figure 4.23 The structure of a General Ready Queue

with each process is maintained whenever it is not executing.

When the CPU switches from one process to the next, it is necessary to:

(1) Save the status of the process in the control block;
(2) Update the process control block;
(3) Get the number of the next process;
(4) Update first and last element pointers and put the process on the bottom of the queue if further time-slots are required;
(5) Change the state of the "new" process to running, and restore its status and temporary variables.

To add a new process to the queue:

(a) Its process number is stored in the forward queue pointer (FQP) of the last-element, and into the last-element pointer;
(b) Clear its FQP to indicate the last element;
(c) Adjust its process control block as necessary.

If the processes only have a short life-time, for example, they are only executed once, then the complexity of the general ready queue is unnecessary, and the simplified form illustrated in *Figure 4.24* can be used. (This is similar to the structure used in the transputer.) There are still first and last element pointers but these point directly to memory locations containing the process control blocks and not to the process table. As each process is started it is added to the bottom of the list and given a number related to its position in the list. As each process

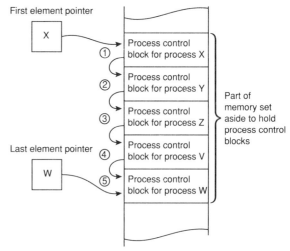

Figure 4.24 Simplified Ready Queue

control block is the same length it is easy to find a particular process from its list number.

Assigning Priority

So far, we have considered all the processes to have the same priority, but it is normal for a multi-programming environment to have various priority levels, to give higher priority modules or processes more of the available time-slots. To achieve this, the first and last element pointers are replaced by a prioritised ready queue, which consists of a table of first and last element pointers at different priority levels, see *Figure 4.25*. *Figure 4.26* illustrates an example of a ready queue using the priority table outlined in *Figure 4.25*. Each priority level is complete in itself and gives the following priorities:

> Priority 0 None
> Priority 1 $2 \rightarrow 4 \rightarrow 6 \rightarrow 1$
> Priority 2 $5 \rightarrow 8$
> Priority 3 None

To select the next process, the priority table is searched for a non-zero first element pointer starting with the highest priority level and then executes that process having deleted it from the ready queue.

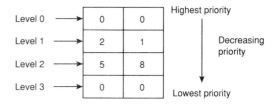

Figure 4.25 Prioritised Ready Queues

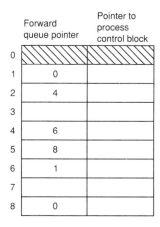

Figure 4.26 Ready queue

It is now much more complicated when a time-slot ends. If the process is put straight back into the last element pointer of the same priority, it would be continuously executing time-slots (after other processes with the same priority) thereby excluding other processes from executing. The remaining lower priority levels will never be executed until all higher priority processes have completely executed. Alternatively, after having a high priority a process could be assigned a lower priority which would be increased or decreased as the remainder of the processes were executed to produce a dynamic priority level.

4.4 COPROCESSORS

Microprocessors are used to perform the manipulation of data such as re-arranging it, simple arithmetic, logic operations and so on. The majority of these manipulations are simple and can be implemented directly with a single microprocessor instruction. These manipulations include simple integer arithmetic addition, subtraction, multiplication and division.

However, there are some requirements, particularly those involved in scientific work such as physics and engineering, which require a more sophisticated mathematics capability with a higher resolution than is possible with integer arithmetic. This higher resolution is obtained by using scientific notation which expresses numbers as a mantissa multiplied by the selected base raised to some power. The common bases used are 10, as these numbers are most readily understood by users and 2, as this is the base most easily implemented in computers. An example of a number expressed in base 10 is given below with some specific examples. It is usual to alter the power of the base until the number is between −1.0 and +1.0.

$$\text{Scientific Notation} = \text{mantissa} \times 10^{\text{characteristic}}$$

Examples are:

$$0.3 \times 10^2$$
$$0.165\ 472\ 98 \times 10^{-15}$$

Once **scientific numbers**, also known as **floating-point numbers**, can be manipulated a range of other mathematical functions can be implemented such as sine, cosine, tangent and so on, which can be difficult to implement using ordinary microprocessor integer number instructions.

The ability to manipulate scientific numbers directly can be added to the standard microprocessor but this creates a logically more complex device requiring many more logic gates. This in turn leads to greater design and production costs, resulting in a more expensive final component.

Many applications do not require the ability to manipulate floating point numbers so the cheaper, less complex devices are preferred. For those applications which do require these extra abilities, a solution would be to design two microprocessors, one simple and one complex. This is not a preferred solution as it leads to difficulties in different programming languages, deciding which microprocessor to use and when and so on. The alternative is to have a standard simple microprocessor with the additional complex functions contained in an add-on hardware component, as illustrated in *Figure 4.27*.

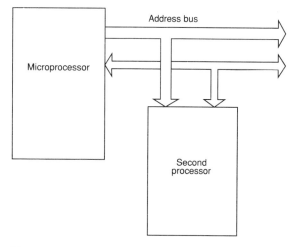

Figure 4.27 Coprocessor

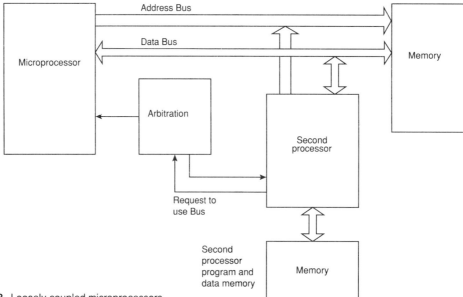

Figure 4.28 Loosely coupled microprocessors

This device can then be included if required or just left out.

There are two main techniques for adding a second processing unit to a computer system; the loosely coupled and the closely coupled techniques. Most types of microprocessor can be loosely coupled through the use of arbitration, enabling general-purpose microprocessor add-ons to be produced. This has the advantage of producing components suitable for a much larger market which reduces the component costs. The arbitration process is slow compared with the speed of execution of programs so that if there is a large amount of communication between the two processing units, time is wasted. The additional arbitration logic required is not excessive as most computer systems already implement this technique to control ordinary bus requests, see *Figure 4.28*. The alternative approach of using a closely coupled second processing unit requires specific devices of which the coprocessor is the most efficient, see *Figure 4.29*. Generally, the tighter the coupling the faster the arbitration process so that less time is wasted communicating between the two components.

The coprocessor will only operate correctly with the microprocessor it was designed for as special techniques and signals are used to connect the two together and produce the high speed arbitration. This results in an increase in the speed of execution of the coprocessor functions with the extra advantage that the coprocessor can be treated as a part of the main microprocessor. The coprocessor's programmer's model is added to the microprocessor programmer's model, see *Figure 4.30*, rather than being treated as a separate programmable component. The assembly language is extended to include a superset of instructions which can execute on the coprocessor, see *Figure 4.31*, but which do not perform any actions if executed by the main processor.

Some types of microprocessors may be connected to more than one type of coprocessor so that a

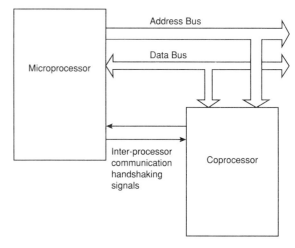

Figure 4.29 Tightly coupled second processor (coprocessor)

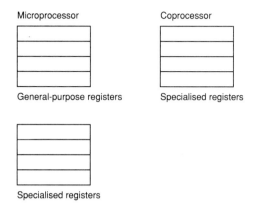

General-purpose registers   Specialised registers

Specialised registers

Figure 4.30 Extended programmers model

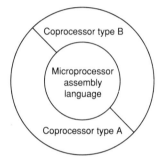

Figure 4.31 Extended assembly language instruction set

mathematics coprocessor and an I/O coprocessor could be added, with each having its own non-overlapping extensions to the assembly language.

A consequence of the tight coupling of the coprocessor and the main processor is that the co-processor cannot have its own separate program and data memory areas as is possible in loosely coupled systems. Therefore the microprocessor has to fetch all the instructions, including those for the coprocessor. The coprocessor then continuously monitors the address and data busses until a coprocessor instruction is identified. This is then copied by the coprocessor from the bus and executed. The coprocessor ignores all other instructions and the main processor ignores all coprocessor instructions.

The separation of instructions is achieved in the 8086 by preceding coprocessor instructions with the ESC (for escape) instruction. This indicates that the following instruction is for the coprocessor, with the main processor treating it as a no-operation (NOP), see *Figure 4.32*.

As coprocessor instructions tend to be more

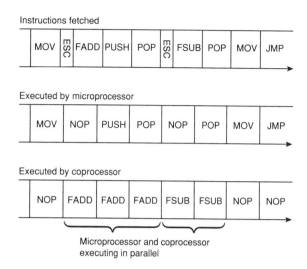

Figure 4.32 Coprocessor instruction fetching

complex than microprocessor instructions, the micro-processor will probably have fetched and executed several more of its own instructions before the co-processor has finished the first. If these contain further coprocessor instructions, the microprocessor is forced to wait until the coprocessor is ready to proceed.

The intercommunication between the micro-processor and the coprocessor is performed by special signals, QS0, QS1, $\overline{RQ}$/GTO, TEST/BUSY, used to ensure that the transfer of data and results is correctly achieved. *Figure 4.33* illustrates the major signals used by the 8086 and the 8087 for these purposes.

The tight coupling between the microprocessor and the coprocessor provides the highest speed of execution of the programs and in addition some

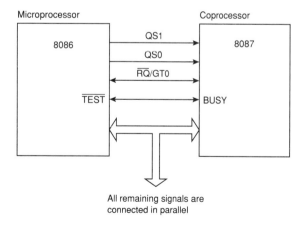

Figure 4.33 8086 and 8087 interprocessor connection

small degree of parallelism in the programs. Because the coprocessor can only be used with one particular type of microprocessor, this restricts the potential market for the component and leads to the coprocessor cost being high. For the 8086 microprocessor, the 8087 mathematics coprocessor is approximately 10 times the cost of the 8086 component. This high cost can restrict the potential market as the coprocessor may then represent 50% or more of the total system component costs. By leaving the coprocessor out, an 8086-based system can be made cheaper. The drawback is that the performance is much reduced for programs requiring floating point mathematics capability.

The IBM PC is an example of this. The mathematics coprocessor is not present in the standard system and most users do not really notice a lack in performance as they do not perform many floating point number calculations. However, some programs such as **Computer Aided Drawing** (CAD) software packages, recommend that the mathematics coprocessor be added in order to obtain a satisfactory speed of operation. Some CAD packages will not execute on a system unless a mathematics processor is present as otherwise the speed of operation is too slow for it to be useful.

Mathematics Coprocessor

Although it is possible to design coprocessors for almost any specialised function, the most common commercially-available device is the mathematics coprocessor. This is due to the many programs for the scientific and research environments which perform complex calculations using floating-point numbers. This produces sufficient demand for the microprocessor producers to invest in the development of a coprocessor. In addition, there is a standard method of representing and manipulating floating-point numbers rather than several different techniques. Therefore the coprocessor only has to implement a single unchanging technique which all users are aware of and which does not require much explanation.

The Number System

As described previously, floating-point numbers are represented in the scientific format and comprise three parts: the sign, the mantissa and the characteristic. In order to simplify their use on microprocessors, some alterations are made to the scientific representation.

Normalisation. One of the alterations made is to ensure that the mantissa is always between two fixed limits which is achieved by altering the characteristic and this is called normalisation.

Example

For decimal numbers the two limits used for normalisation are: 0.1 and 1.0 or − 0.1 and −1.0 where the sign of the number has no effect on the process. Any number is then adjusted to fit within these limits.

$$25.6 \quad \text{becomes} \quad 0.256 \times 10^2$$
$$-5036.519 \quad \text{becomes} \quad -0.503\,651\,9 \times 10^3$$
$$0.000\,812 \quad \text{becomes} \quad 0.812 \times 10^{-3}$$

Rather than represent the characteristic as a power of 10, the notation E, is used to indicate an **Exponent**, which is an alternative name for a characteristic.

$$0.256 \times 10^2 \quad \text{becomes} \quad 0.256E2$$
$$0.812 \times 10^{-3} \quad \text{becomes} \quad 0.812E-3.$$

The characteristic has a positive or negative sign to indicate numbers greater than 1.0 (a positive exponent) and less than 0.1 (a negative exponent).

Computer systems allocate a fixed number of bits to the mantissa and exponent, which limits the number of significant digits that can be represented and allocate a limit to the positive or negative value of the exponent. For the 8087 long-real format, which is equivalent to the IEEE standard for binary representations for real numbers, the mantissa is limited to 53 bits which allows a maximum of 15 significant digits and the exponent is limited to 11 bits giving a possible range from: $E - 2047$, exponent , $E2048$.

However, only a section of this possible range is used for reasons which will be explained later and the allowed exponent range is: $E - 308$, exponent , $E309$.

Numbers that are smaller or larger than this range cannot be represented.

Biased exponent. To simplify operations as much as possible a biased exponent is used. This requires a fixed positive number to be added to the exponent of all numbers which is sufficiently large to ensure that all exponents are stored as positive integers. This removes the need to consider exponent signs when manipulating numbers.

For the long-real format of the 8087 coprocessor this number is 308, which forces all exponents to be positive values.

For example:

$$0.563E{-}27 \text{ becomes } 0.563E\,(-\,27 + 308)$$
$$= 0.563E281$$
$$0.8721E5 \quad \text{becomes } 0.8721E\,(5 + 308)$$
$$= 0.8721E313.$$

The exponent for long-real uses 11 bits allowing numbers from 0 to 2047 to be represented. Therefore the halfway point is 1023 which allows the maximum variation in the exponent, positive or negative about this value. Because this number is representing powers of 2 rather than powers of 10 then when it is converted to represent powers of 10 this becomes 308. Therefore all exponents must lie within the range: E − 308 , exponent , E308, otherwise the number is too small or too large to be represented. Readers are directed to the IEEE standard if they wish to find out more about this.

Combining normalised biased exponent numbers. When arithmetically combining two numbers that are represented in scientific notation, the three parts of the number, the sign, mantissa and exponent, are individually combined in specific ways. Although the numbers are stored in a normalised biased exponent scientific notation, they cannot always be combined in that format.

Multiplication

When multiplying two numbers together, the three parts which constitute the numbers can be combined independently and do not require any pre-processing. However, some post-processing of the mantissa and the exponent may be required to maintain normalisation.

The sign combination. As the signs can only be positive or negative there are only four possible combinations as indicated in Table 4.1 where the sign of the result is also shown.

Table 4.1 Sign Combination during multiplication

Sign	Operation	Sign	Result
positive	×	positive	positive
positive	×	negative	negative
negative	×	positive	negative
negative	×	negative	positive

The mantissa combination. The two mantissas are multiplied together and the result may need to be normalised to remove any leading zeros and maintain the mantissa in the range 0.1 to 1.0.

Example

Assuming that the following two mantissas are to be combined :

$$M1 = 0.5630$$
$$M2 = 0.8721$$

Then the result is :

$$M1 \times M2 = 0.5630 \times 0.8721$$
$$= 0.490\,992\,30$$

This result does not require normalisation. Note that the result will usually have more significant digits than the individual mantissas. The number of significant digits in the result can be found by summing the significant digits in the two mantissas. In this example, each mantissa has four significant digits so the result has eight significant digits. The trailing zeros are considered to be significant.

In order to maintain the accuracy it must be possible to allow the result to contain more significant digits than the two mantissas and in the 8087 mathematics coprocessor this is achieved by performing all operations in 80-bit representations, rather than the 64 bits the numbers are stored in. The conversions from 64 bits to 80 bits and from 80 bits to 64 bits are performed automatically when transferring between the microprocessor and the coprocessor. The 80-bit format allows intermediate results to be maintained at a higher accuracy, so that rounding errors are only introduced when the final result is saved in memory, being converted from the 80-bit to 64-bit format.

Example

The following example would require normalisation as a post-processing operation.

Assuming that:

$$M1 = 0.132$$
$$M2 = 0.563$$

then the result is:

$$M1 \times M2 = 0.132 \times 0.563$$
$$= 0.074\,316$$

This would then be normalised to remove the leading zero to:

$$0.74316E{-}1$$

The non-zero value of the exponent produced must now be added to the result of combining the original two exponents, in order to maintain normalisation.

The exponent combination. Normally, for multiplication of scientific numbers, the two exponents are added together. However, for biased exponents this would cause an overflow of the available bits, caused by the result containing the equivalent of two biasing constants. To prevent this, the biasing constants are subtracted from the exponents before they are added. The two exponents are then added and finally the bias constant is added to the result. The result of this is that multiplication of two numbers may require both pre-processing and post-processing operations.

Example

Assuming that the following two characterisitics (exponents) are to be combined:

$$C1 = E281$$
$$C2 = E313$$

then the result is:

$$C1 + C2 = E(281-308) + E(313 - 308)$$
$$= E - 27 + E5$$
$$= E-22$$

Then
$$= E(-22 + 308)$$
$$= E286$$

Example

Now that the techniques for combining the signs, mantissas and exponents of two scientific numbers have been outlined, this example indicates the combination of two such numbers where for:

	Value1	= +0.563E281
Then	S1	= positive
	M1	= 0.563
	C1	= E281

and for:

	Value2	= +0.8721E313
Then	S1	= positive
	M1	= 0.8721
	C1	= E313

If value1 and value2 are now multiplied together, the result is

$$Result = (S1 \times S2)(A \times B)E((C1 - 308) + (C2 - 308) + 308)$$
$$= +0.4909923E286$$

The order in which value1 and value2 are combined is not important as multiplication is commutative.

$$value1 \times value2 = value2 \times value1$$
$$= +0.4909923E286$$

Division

When two numbers are being divided a similar set of operations is performed on the signs, mantissas and exponents. However, there is an additional consideration as division is not commutative and the order of the numbers is important, so that:

$$value1/value2 \ ? \ value2/value1$$

except for the special case when value1 = value2 and the result is 1.0.

The sign combination. Table 4.2 indicates how the signs are combined for division and is the same as the combination of signs for the multiplication operation. Only the mantissa and exponent are combined in a different way.

Table 4.2 Sign Combination during division

Sign	Operation	Sign	Result
positive	divide	positive	positive
positive	divide	negative	negative
negative	divide	positive	negative
negative	divide	negative	positive

The mantissas combination. The two mantissas are divided without any alteration. If necessary the result is normalised and an adjustment made to the exponent in the same way as for multiplication.

Example

Assuming that the two mantissas are to be combined:

$$M1 = 0.563$$
$$M2 = 0.8721$$

Then the results are:

$$M1 / M2 = 0.563 / 0.8721 = 0.645 568 168.$$

Alternatively:

$$M2 / M1 = 0.8721 / 0.563 = 1.549 023 091$$

The second result would need to be normalised to:

$$Result = 0.1549023091E1$$

The result of combining the original two exponents

must now be altered by adding the value of this local exponent to complete the normalisation.

The number of significant digits in the result is not directly related to the significant digits in the mantissas. Due to this, it is inevitable that some rounding errors will occur in the result. These are reduced by the use of the extended 80-bit format but it should be remembered that the possibility of rounding errors always exists.

The exponents combination. For division the exponent of the second number is subtracted from the exponent of the first and if the order of division is changed then the exponent calculation is also changed. The bias constant does not have to be subtracted from the exponents before the subtraction is performed as there will not be an overflow or underflow anywhere within the range of exponents allowed. Therefore, for division no exponent pre-processing is required. However, post-processing of the result exponent is necessary as the normalisation has been removed automatically.

Example

C1 = 281 (exponent of first number)

C2 = 313 (exponent of second number)

If the first number is divided by the second number then the result of the exponent combination is:

$$C1 - C2 = 281 - 313 = -32.$$

The resulting exponent is unbiased, as the subtraction removes the biasing, therefore post-processing is required to add the bias constant and maintain the exponent in the correct format. The correctly-biased exponent is:

$$Result = 308 + (-32) = 276$$

If the order of division is reversed, the exponent combination will be as follows:

$$C2 - C1 = 313 - 281 = 32$$

The post-processing then adds the bias constant to produce:

$$Result = 308 + 32 = 340$$

Example

This example demonstrates the complete operation, where for:

$$Value1 = +0.563E281$$

Then

$$S1 = positive$$
$$M1 = 0.563$$
$$C1 = E281$$

and:

$$Value2 = +0.8721E313$$

Then

$$S2 = positive$$
$$M2 = 0.8721$$
$$C2 = E313$$

Then the result is:

$$value1/value2 = (S1/S2)(M1/M2)E((C1 - C2) + 308)$$
$$= +0.645568168E276$$

If the order of the division is changed then the following result is obtained:

$$value2/value1 = (S2/S1)(M2/M1)E((C2 - C1) + 308)$$
$$= +1.549023091E340$$

This result requires normalisation as the mantissa is greater than 1.0, so that the final answer is:

$$value2/value1 = +0.1549023091E341$$

Adding and Subtracting

When multiplying or dividing numbers it is not necessary to adjust the values before combining them, however, normalisation may be required afterwards. For addition or subtraction, the exponents of both numbers have to be the same before the operation can be performed and this is achieved by pre-processing which increases the smaller exponent until it is the same as the larger exponent. This results in the mantissa of the adjusted number becoming less than 0.1 and the number is no longer normalised. Removing normalisation effectively places a limit on the magnitude of numbers which can be combined. The 8087 mathematics coprocessor is able to manipulate the equivalent of 15 significant numbers so that if the exponents of the two numbers differ by more than 15, the smaller number effectively becomes zero. This is because shifting the decimal point to the left introduces leading zeros. For the long format, after 15 shifts the entire mantissa is zero, and all the significant digits have been lost. This would then be an error that was introduced into the calculation, but because of the lack of significance of the mantissa, it is not a serious problem. For very accurate calculations it may be necessary to use an alternative format in order to obtain an increased accuracy.

Example

This example indicates how two scientific numbers are adjusted before being combined as:

$$value1 = + 0.3156E310$$

where

    S1 = positive
    M1 = 0.3156
    C1 = E310

and:

$$value2 = +0.7169E313$$

where:

    S2 = positive
    M2 = 0.7169
    C2 = E313

The smaller exponent is M1 and it is increased by the difference between the original two exponents. In this example:

Increase = $|(C1 - C2)|$ (the absolute value of the difference)

         = 3

Therefore the mantissa M1, is adjusted by this amount and value1 becomes:

$$value1 = +0.0003156E313$$

Once the two exponents have been adjusted to be the same, no further operations on them are performed.

The signs combination. Table 4.3 indicates how the signs are combined to produce the sign of the result and it is a complex process which is also dependent upon the magnitude of the two mantissas.

Table 4.3 Addition and subtraction sign combination (zero is taken to be positive)

Sign of A	Operation	Sign of B	Result
positive	+	positive	positive
positive	+	negative	if A > = B then positive else negative
negative	+	positive	if A < = B then positive else negative
negative	+	negative	negative
positive	−	positive	if A > = B then positive else negative
positive	−	negative	positive
negative	−	positive	negative
negative	−	negative	if A < = B then positive else negative

The mantissas combination. Once the exponents have been adjusted to be the same, the two mantissas are combined together, bearing in mind the value of the signs and the operation, addition or subtraction. The result may, or may not, require normalising afterwards but the bias constant does not have to be added or subtracted, as the result automatically has a biased exponent.

Example

Where for:

$$value1 = +0.3156E310$$

Then:

    S1 = positive
    M1 = 0.3156
    C1 = E310

and for:

$$value2 = +0.7169E1028$$

Then

    S2 = positive
    M2 = 0.7169
    C2 = E313

$$Result = value1 + value2$$

The exponent of the smaller value has to be adjusted, as the mantissa must always be less than one, until the two exponents are the same, so that value1 becomes:

$$value1 = +0.0003156E313$$

and the result is:

$$value1 + value2 = (S1 + S2)(M1 + M2)E313$$
$$= +0.7172156E313$$

This result does not require normalising as the mantissa is less than 1.0 and greater than 0.1.

Example

For:

$$value1 = +0.3156E310$$

then:

    S1 = positive
    M1 = 0.3156
    C1 = E310

and for:

$$value2 = 0.7169E313$$

Then

S2 = positive
M2 = 0.7169
C2 = E313

Result = value1 − value2

As the value1 exponent is smaller than that of value2, it has to be adjusted by the difference, as in the previous example, so that value1 becomes:

value1 = +0.0003156E313

where:

S1 = positive
M1 = 0.000 315 6
C1 = E313

As the two exponents are now the same, the mantissas are combined as described in Table 4.3. Both the signs are positive and as the subtraction operation is being performed, then the mantissa of value2 is subtracted from the mantissa of value1. As M1 , M2 the result is negative.

$$\begin{aligned} \text{Result} &= \text{value1} - \text{value2} \\ &= (S1 - S2)(M1 - M2)E313 \\ &= -0.7165844E313 \end{aligned}$$

which does not require normalisation.

Example

For: Value1 = 0.10E311

Then

S1 = positive
M1 = 0.10
C1 = E311

and for: value2 = 0.10E314

Then

S2 = positive
M2 = 0.10
C2 = E314

Result = value2 − value1.

Value2 has the smaller exponent so it is increased by the difference, $|(C1 - C2)|$, which is 4, the mantissa altered so that value1 becomes:

value1 = +0.000010E314

where:

S1 = positive

M1 = 0.000 010
C1 = E314

As both S1 and S2 are positive and the operation to be performed is a subtraction, then the mantissas will be subtracted as indicated in Table 4.3: M2 − M1 and the result will be positive as: M2 . M1.

$$\begin{aligned} \text{Result} &= 0.10E311 - 0.000010E314 \\ &= +0.09999E314, \end{aligned}$$

The mantissa is less than 0.1 so the result requires normalisation. This is achieved by reducing the exponent until the correspondingly-altered mantissa is within the range 0.1 to 1.0. The final result is therefore:

Result = +0.9999E313.

Stack-orientated Arithmetic Operations

In order to be as general-purpose as possible, the mathematics coprocessor uses a stack-orientated approach for its operations which is more flexible than using special-purpose registers. All the numbers are passed to the coprocessor stack followed by the selected arithmetic operation which operates on the top two values on the stack. This method of arithmetic computation is used by most **High Level Language** (HLL) compilers, as it is general-purpose, machine-independent and capable of supporting the required arithmetic functions.

Although this model is ideally suited to the microprocessor and coprocessor, it is not the natural method for European mathematics, which usually identifies one of the values, followed by the operation required, followed by the second value, with the result on the right, as below:

value1 operation value2 equals result

e.g.   4 + 2 = 6

The stack-orientated approach requires the values to be pushed onto the stack and the operator selected. The result obtained is then left as the top of the stack and can be popped off, see below:

```
push (value1)
push (value2)
operator
pop (result)
```

which becomes

```
push (4)
```

```
push (2)
+
pop (6)
```

Putting a value onto the coprocessor stack, is called a **Floating-point LoaD**, FLD, and removing a value from the stack is called a **Floating-point STore**, FST.

In stack-based operations only the **Top Of Stack**, TOS, and the **Next On the Stack**, NOS, are of real interest, as illustrated in *Figure 4.34*. The selected operator uses TOS and NOS as the two values, replacing TOS with the result.

As most computer memory is organised as words, 4 words of computer memory are required to store each 64-bit number. However the real number stack maintained internally by the coprocessor is at least the width of the representation of numbers used. The 8087 has a stack where each element on the stack is 80 bits long. The stack is 80 bits wide so that a more accurate representation of intermediate results is possible, so that rounding errors are minimised. The extra 16 bits are available to enable additional significant figures to be temporarily maintained as illustrated in the following simple example.

Example

Assume that all numbers can only be represented by two significant digits at all stages. Then the calculation:

$$\text{Result} = (\text{Numb\_A}/\text{Numb\_B}) \times \text{Numb\_C}$$

where:

$$\text{Numb\_A} = 5.5$$
$$\text{Numb\_B} = 2.0$$
$$\text{Numb\_C} = 7.0$$

becomes:

$$\text{Result} = (5.5/2.0) \times 7.0 = (2.75) \times 7.0$$

which after rounding becomes:

$$\text{Result} = (2.8) \times 7.0 = 19.6$$

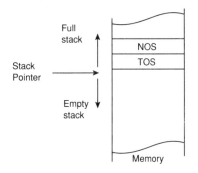

Figure 4.34 Stack operations

which after further rounding to two significant figures becomes:

$$\text{Result} = 20$$

If the intermediate results are maintained at a higher accuracy of 3 significant figures, then the result would become:

$$\text{Result} = (5.50/2.00) \times 7.00$$
$$= (2.75) \times 7.00 = 19.250$$

which after rounding to three significant figures, becomes 19.3.

If this is now rounded to two significant figures the final result becomes 19.

This is the most accurate answer possible with two significant figures and demonstrates how maintaining intermediate results at a higher accuracy results in a more accurate final result.

In the previous example it should be noted that the numbers were converted from two significant figures to three significant figures before the calculation began and the result converted back from three to two significant figures at the end of the calculation. For the 8087 coprocessor these conversions are performed automatically when transferring between the computer memory and the 8087 internal stack and this is illustrated in the following example.

Example

A typical sequence of operations which might be required is shown below:

$$\text{Numb\_A} = 6.0$$
$$\text{Numb\_B} = 4.0$$
$$\text{Numb\_C} = 11.0$$

The result required is:

$$\text{Result} = \text{Numb\_A} + \text{Numb\_B} + \text{Numb\_C}.$$

The sequence of coprocessors instructions required to perform this would be:

$$\text{Numb\_C,Numb\_B,Numb\_A,+,+} = \text{result}.$$

and a sequence of program code to implement this would be:

```
FLD Numb_C ;push Numb_C Numb_B and Numb_A onto
           ;the internal 80-bit wide stack,
           ;automatically converting from 64
           ;bits to 80 bits
FLD Numb_B
FLD Numb_A
FADD       ;adds Numb_A and Numb_B, replacing
           ;Numb_B with the result, and
           ;decrements TOS
```

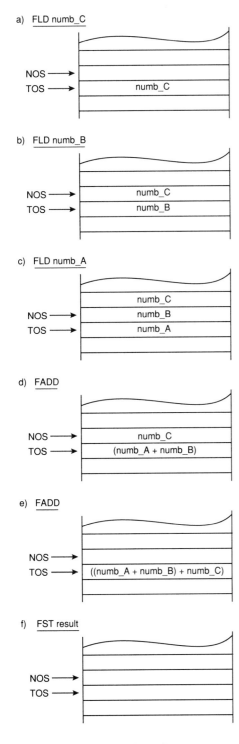

a) FLD numb_C

NOS →
TOS → numb_C

b) FLD numb_B

NOS → numb_C
TOS → numb_B

c) FLD numb_A

numb_C
NOS → numb_B
TOS → numb_A

d) FADD

NOS → numb_C
TOS → (numb_A + numb_B)

e) FADD

NOS →
TOS → ((numb_A + numb_B) + numb_C)

f) FST result

NOS →
TOS →

Figure 4.35 Arithmetic Operations

FADD   ;adds (Numb_A + Numb_B) to Numb_C,
              ;replacing Numb_C with
              ;(Numb_A + Numb_B + Numb_C) and
              ;decrementing TOS
FST result   ;save (Numb_A + Numb_B + Numb_C)
              ;from TOS into memory called
              ;result. Automatically converts
              ;from 80 bits to 64 bits

The state of the stack after every instruction is shown in *Figure 4.35*. First the values Numb_A, Numb_B and Numb_C are pushed onto the stack, with Numb_B being NOS and Numb_A being TOS. The add operation is then performed on NOS and TOS, that is, Numb_A + Numb_B, and the result placed into NOS, which is then made into the TOS, see *Figure 4.35(d)*. A second add operation is performed which adds NOS and TOS, that is, adds Numb_C to (Numb_A + Numb_B) to form (Numb_A + Numb_B + Numb_C). This is placed into NOS, NOS is made into TOS, see *Figure 4.35(e)*. Finally, the result is transferred from the TOS into memory, see *Figure 4.35(f)*.

A similar sequence of actions can be performed for every other possible combination of values and operations. The only restriction is that there is a limit on the number of elements that can be stored on the floating point stack. This limits the number of values which can be placed on the stack at any one time during the calculation of equations. However, by careful selection of the values stored and the sequence of operations performed, this limitation is not a serious problem.

Example

Implement the following equation as a sequence of floating-point stack operations:

$$\text{Result} = ((\text{Numb\_A} + \text{Numb\_B})/\text{Numb\_C} + \text{Numb\_D}) \times \text{Numb\_E}$$

FLD Numb_E   ;push Numb_E, Numb_D, Numb_C,
              ;Numb_B and Numb_A onto the stack
FLD Numb_D
FLD Numb_C
LD Numb_A
FADD   ;adds Numb_A and Numb_B together,
              ;replaces NOS, converts NOS to TOS,
FDIV   ;divides (Numb_A + Numb_B) by
              ;Numb_C, replaces NOS, converts
              ;NOS to TOS.
FADD   ;adds Numb_D to (Numb_A + Numb_B)
              ;/Numb_C, replaces NOS, converts
              ;NOS to TOS.
FMUL   ;multiplies ((Numb_A + Numb_B)
              ;/Numb_C (+ Numb_D) by Numb_E,
              ;replaces NOS, converts NOS to
              ;TOS.
FST result   ;Transfer the result into memory.

Programmer's Model of the 8087 Mathematics Coprocessor

The 8087 mathematics coprocessor implements the long-real normalised biased exponent format for number representation and uses the stack-oriented model for arithmetic computation. It has the programmer's model as illustrated in *Figure 4.36* which, it should be remembered, is effectively added to the programmer's model for the 8086 microprocessor.

The 8087 mathematics coprocessor model consists of a control word, status word and an 8-element, 80-bit wide, floating-point stack. The stack is 80 bits wide as an extended long-real format, called temporary-real, is used to represent all real numbers when they are being manipulated by the 8087. This enables the intermediate results to be maintained with a much greater accuracy, so that rounding to the specified bit length, 64 bits for long-real, is as accurate as possible.

The real formats are automatically converted into the temporary-real format when loaded onto the stack and automatically converted back into the required format when removed from the stack. This process is invisible to the programmer and user and can effectively be forgotten.

There are only 8 elements in the floating-point stack as most arithmetic operations can be performed in this short stack. For complex equations it may be necessary for the program to break up the equation into smaller equations which can be

handled. It is the programmer's responsibility to ensure that the stack does not overflow, by too many values being pushed onto it, or underflow, by too many values being popped from it.

Control word. The 8087 is a sophisticated device capable of supporting several different models of arithmetic computation, all described within the IEEE specification, with the control word used to select the required arrangement. *Figure 4.37* illustrates how the bits of the control word are allocated and the four major functions they control:

(1) The model of infinity used;
(2) The rounding technique used;
(3) The precision used;
(4) The interrupt available.

The Model of Infinity

It may not seem particularly important to discuss infinity when the number values are limited anyway, but for some specialised types of arithmetic manipulation it is important to be able to specify some of

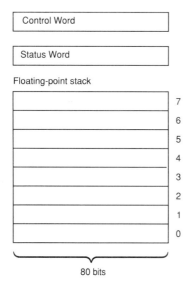

Figure 4.36 Simplified Programmers Model of the 8087 Mathematics Coprocessor

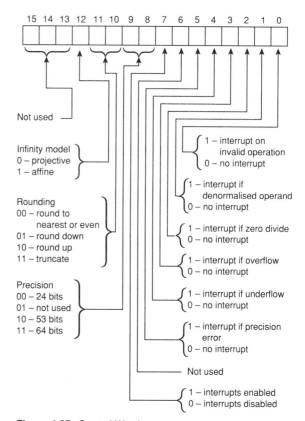

Figure 4.37 Control Word

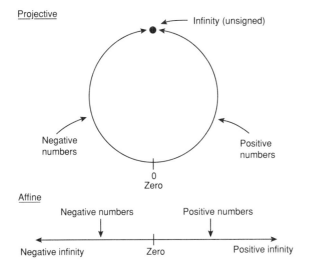

Figure 4.38 Models of infinity

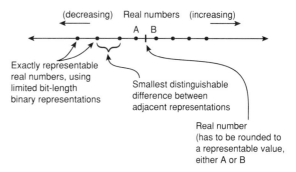

Figure 4.39 Rounding real numbers

the mantissas of infinity. For the purposes of the mathematics coprocessor, infinity can be considered to be the number which is too large to be represented by the real format being used within the coprocessor. *Figure 4.38* illustrates the two different models available, projective and affine.

The projective model represents infinity as a number having no sign which can be approached by either a large positive number or a large negative number. In the projective model the sign becomes irrelevant. This is the recommended model.

The affine model treats negative infinity as being different from positive infinity so that although the number is too large to represent its sign is still important.

Rounding Techniques

Any limited bit-length binary representation of real numbers is inherently inaccurate as the number must be rounded to a representable value. *Figure 4.39* illustrates this concept and shows values separated by the minimum distinguishable difference between values. If a real number lies between two of the representable values which will usually be the situation then a decision has to be made as to which of the two adjacent representable values should be used.

The rounding technique which introduces the minimum error is rounding to the nearest representable value. The maximum rounding error of any number is then plus or minus half the smallest distinguishable difference between adjacent representable values. This assumes that the representable values

are separated by equal amounts. That is, the scale is linear. This is the normal representation but other non-linear representations are possible for specialised purposes.

For 15 significant decimal digits this amounts to: ± 0.5 in 10^{15} or as a percentage error, it becomes:

$$\pm\ 0.5/10^{15} \times 100\% = \pm\ 0.5 \times 10^{-13}\ \%$$

which is very small. However, for some scientific applications which require a much greater accuracy an alternative format is used, perhaps with 20 or 30 significant digits. Such representations are not defined by the IEEE standard.

If the real number lies exactly halfway between two representable values then an arbitrary decision has to be made to either round up or down, the error being the same in either case. The 8087 solves this problem by rounding to the nearest adjacent even values representation.

An alternative rounding technique is to always round down to the adjacent representable value which produces a maximum error for 15 significant decimal digits of $+1.0$ in 10^{15} which as a percentage error is:

$$+1.0/10^{15} \times 100\% = +1.0 \times 10^{-13}\ \%$$

which is twice the error when rounding to the nearest representation.

Similarly, rounding up to the nearest highest representable value which is just greater than the real number, produces a maximum error for 15 significant decimal digits of:

$$-1.0/10^{15} \times 100\% = -1.0 \times 10^{-13}\ \%$$

which again is twice the maximum error of rounding to the nearest representation.

To convert from real numbers to integers a chop rounding technique is used, which is for numbers with an exponent greater than 1. It operates by deleting the part of the number from the decimal point to the right of the number.

Precision

The precision control bits select the format of numbers being manipulated. Alternative formats are the short-real which uses 32 bits to represent the number of which 24 are used for the mantissa and the temporary-real which uses an 80-bit representation, of which 63 bits are used for the mantissa. However, whatever the format specified by the precision bits, all numbers are automatically converted into the 80-bit temporary real format when loaded onto the coprocessor stack. This obtains the maximum possible accuracy at all times, with the results being automatically converted back to the specified format when transferred from the coprocessor stack to computer memory.

Interrupts

Coprocessor interrupts, of which there are six, are generated if an error is detected by the coprocessor during floating point operations. These are controlled by the remaining section of the control word which is divided into two parts, the global interrupt enable, bit 7, and the individual interrupt enables.

For any interrupt to be activated the global interrupt bit has to be set (bit 7 = 1) and the individual error bit also enabled (bit n = 1). Then if an error is detected a hardware signal is generated which interrupts the master microprocessor to initiate a floating-point error interrupt handling service subroutine. A programmable interrupt controller (PIC) is used to redirect the interrupt vector, as illustrated in *Figure 4.40*. Depending upon the particular application, some or all of the possible floating point error situations may be ignored or disabled.

Most of the errors listed in *Figure 4.37* are self-explanatory, except for the underflow and overflow errors. Overflow occurs when the characteristic of a number is larger than that permitted, that is, the number is too large, as illustrated in *Figure 4.41*. With underflow the number is too small and the characteristic is less than that permitted. These errors are easy to detect with biased characteristics.

Although there is a region where numbers are too small to represent and cause an underflow error, the value of zero is treated as a special case and is considered to occur in the middle of the non-representable number range.

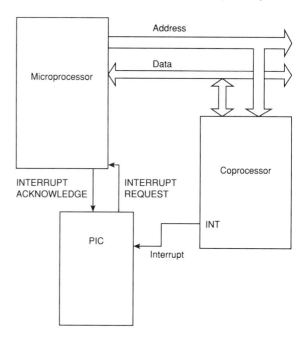

Figure 4.40 Adding a PIC to a Coprocessor

Underflow and overflow errors are usually caused by intermediate values being outside of the allowable range, even though the final result may be representable. This problem can sometimes be avoided by changing the order of calculations.

Example

$$ValueA = 0.1E - 308,$$
$$ValueB = 0.2E10,$$
$$ValueC = 0.3E308.$$

The possible calculation is:

$$Result = (ValueA/ValueB) \times ValueC.$$

One possible order of calculation would be to solve inside the brackets first, which would produce:

$$(ValueA/ValueB) = 0.1E308/0.2E10 = 0.5E - 318$$

and cause an overflow error as the maximum allowed characteristic value is 308. However, if the equation was re-arranged to:

$$Result = (ValueA \times ValueC)/ValueB$$

Then the intermediate result becomes :

$$(ValueA \times ValueC) = 0.1E - 308 \times 0.3E308 = 0.3E - 1$$

and the final result becomes:

$$0.3E - 1/ValueB = 0.3E - 1/0.2E10 = 0.15E - 10$$

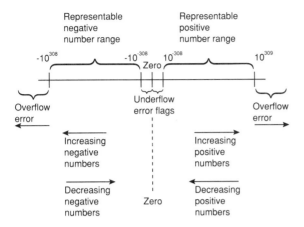

Figure 4.41 Representable number range

All of the values, intermediate and final, are now valid representable numbers.

Status Word. The status word in the 8087 programmer's model is used to enable the microprocessor to monitor various parts of the coprocessor operation and has four main functions as illustrated in *Figure 4.42*; busy, top of stack, condition codes and interrupt indicators.

Busy. This bit can be monitored by the microprocessor to determine whether the coprocessor is executing an instruction or if it is idle. This is used to detect when an executing instruction has completed so that the results can be obtained by the microprocessor. There is also a hardware version of this signal which can be used to synchronise the transfer of results automatically.

Top of Stack. The top of stack indicates which of the 8 possible coprocessor stack locations is to be treated as the top of stack (TOS) for the next coprocessor instruction.

Condition Codes. The condition codes can be monitored by the microprocessor to determine status information about the coprocessor. If more information about these is required the appropriate data manuals should be consulted.

Interrupt Indicators

The remaining bits are used to indicate when an error has been detected and an interrupt request generated. These bits are similar to those in the

control word which enable or disable the hardware signal associated with the interrupts, but are used by software to check whether an error has occurred, rather than allowing an interrupt to be generated. Bit 7 indicates that an error has been detected and an interrupt request made and bits 0 to 5 identify which particular error was detected and requested an interrupt.

The status word always correctly indicates when and what error has occurred as the bits are set before determining if a hardware interrupt signal is to be generated. This allows the status word to be

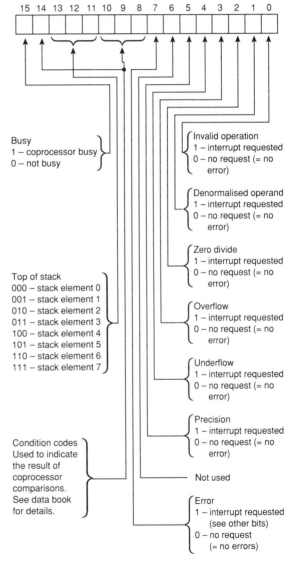

Figure 4.42 Status word layout

used in two different ways, polled and interrupt-driven. If the interrupts are disabled and no hardware signals are made available, the status word can still be used to check for errors. To identify when an error has occurred, the status word has to be checked after every operation. This technique avoids the need for a PIC. Alternatively, if the interrupts are enabled it is only necessary for the floating-point interrupt service routine to check the status word to determine which error has occurred. This avoids the need to check the status word for errors after every instruction and is therefore quicker, but it does require a PIC to be present in the system.

FIVE

Advanced microprocessor techniques

5.1 CURRENT TRENDS

To understand why the current generation of microprocessors has been produced it is necessary to consider what the main requirements have been recently.

More Memory

The initial 16-bit microprocessors, such as the 8086, had what was considered to be a large physically-addressable memory space when first designed. This was because the majority of early 8086 programs were derived from those implemented on 8-bit microprocessors which had already filled the available memory, see *Figure 5.1*. So the 16-bit microprocessor with a much larger memory was able to implement these programs easily, see *Figure 5.2*, and have plenty of additional unused memory space.

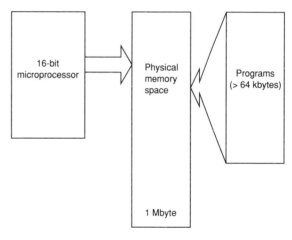

Figure 5.2 16-bit Microprocessors, memory and small programs

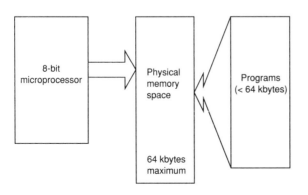

Figure 5.1 8-bit Microprocessors, memory and programs

However, programmers soon took advantage of the increased memory available to write larger programs which were more sophisticated and did more things. The result was the same as for the 8-bit microprocessors, in that the physical limitation on the size of the microprocessor memory space restricted the writing of new and larger programs, see *Figure 5.3*.

Therefore, what was required was a larger physical memory space which could be achieved by designing microprocessors with larger physically-addressable memory spaces. However, it is probable that eventually a similar situation will occur with

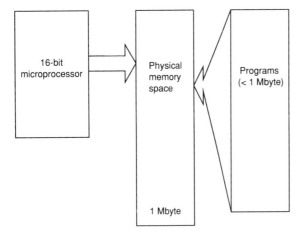

Figure 5.3 16-bit Microprocessors, memory and large programs

programs being larger than the maximum physically-addressable memory space, particularly for multi-user systems which ideally require a large memory space for each user with a resulting very large memory space required for the system.

Another factor which becomes important as physical memory increases is the cost of the memory components. Although the cost per memory location is decreasing with time, the amount of memory required is increasing at a faster rate and at several Megabytes for a minimum system, the system memory cost becomes important, see *Figure 5.4*.

System memory cost = memory required

× cost per memory location.

Even though the microprocessor could be

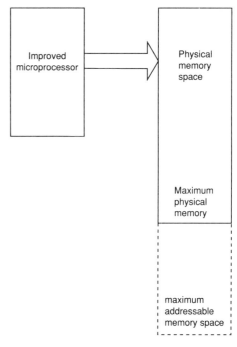

Figure 5.5 Incompletely implemented system memory

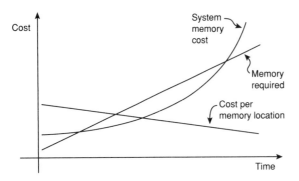

Figure 5.4 Increasing system memory costs

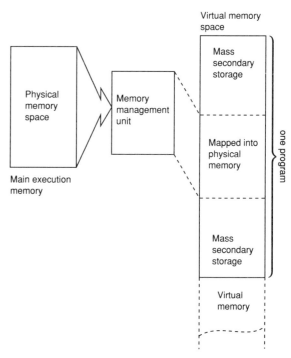

Figure 5.6 Virtual memory

designed with an increased addressable memory space, the cost of the system memory would restrict the amount of physical memory actually implemented, see *Figure 5.5*, which in turn would still restrict the size of programs that could be implemented.

Memory Management Unit (MMU)

The aim therefore, is to make the physical memory space appear to be much larger than it actually is. This is called **virtual memory** and requires the presence of a memory management unit (MMU) in the system, as illustrated in *Figure 5.6*.

As far as the programmer is concerned this effectively allows an almost unlimited virtual memory space to be implemented. The MMU maps or translates virtual addresses in the program into physical addresses for the memory components. This is made easier if the program has been written using relative addressing rather than absolute addressing. With relative addressing the physical address of the instructions does not matter provided that the virtual memory mapping is linear, as illustrated in *Figure 5.7*. In the virtual memory at address X is an instruction to access the location that is +2 locations further on. When this is mapped on to the physical memory, the instruction is now at address Y rather than X, but because the instruction was relative, that is, access +2 locations further on, the program does

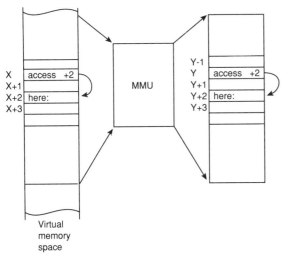

Figure 5.7 Relative addressing with linear mapping

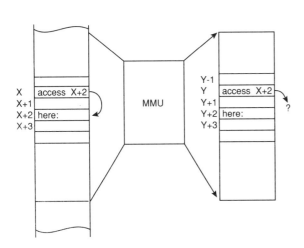

Figure 5.8 Absolute addressing

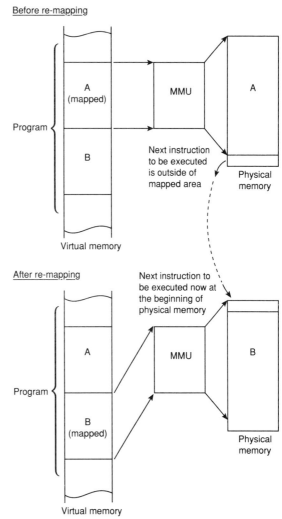

Figure 5.9 Re-mapping

not need to be changed when mapped by the MMU.

If the same program is implemented using absolute addressing, as illustrated in *Figure 5.8*, the program in virtual memory is almost identical except that the instruction at location X is to access the absolute location at (X + 2). When this program is mapped onto physical memory, the instruction is placed at physical memory address Y, but the instructions will still try to access location (X + 2), which may not be a valid address and will almost certainly not be the correct address.

Multiple Virtual Memory Blocks

Although any program being executed will usually have all the instructions placed consecutively in memory so that remapping of physical memory only occurs infrequently, see *Figure 5.9*, the program may access several data areas scattered throughout the virtual memory space, see *Figure 5.10*. These cannot all be mapped into physical memory if only one virtual memory block is used. Therefore, the MMU is able to map different blocks of physical memory to various parts of the virtual memory address space, see *Figure 5.11*. This allows additional flexibility so that part of DATA2 can be placed above DATA1 in physical memory, whereas in virtual memory they were ordered DATA1 followed by DATA2.

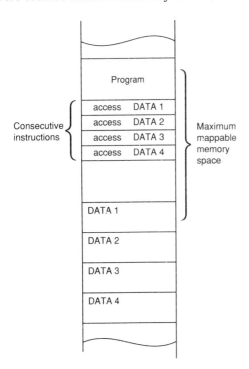

Figure 5.10 Typical virtual memory program

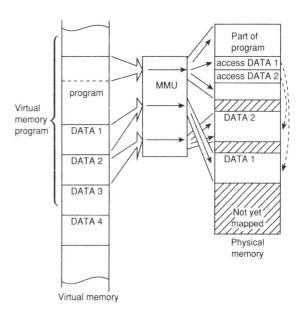

Figure 5.11 Multiple segment mapping by MMU

The MMU has to be more sophisticated now as direct relative addressing cannot be used. Instead, relative addressing from the beginning of the mapped areas is used and the MMU has to translate the relative virtual address into a relative address that can be used in physical memory.

For the 80286, which is an improved version of the 8086, segments are used to hold programs and data, accessed via offsets from the beginning of the segment. The MMU translates the segment adress from virtual into physical memory space whereas the offset remains the same relative address in both. Only the address of the beginning of the block changes.

Swapping Segments

Figure 5.6 showed that the part of the program not mapped to physical memory was maintained in secondary mass storage, such as a hard disk unit or a floppy disk unit. Whenever a remapping of a segment is required the new segment is fetched from secondary mass storage. This requires two types of operation; to make enough room in physical memory for the new segment and to fetch the next correct segment, illustrated in *Figure 5.12*. The making of sufficient space in physical memory and identifying the next segment to be fetched are activities undertaken by the operating system.

The operating system is able to determine how much physical memory space is available by inter-

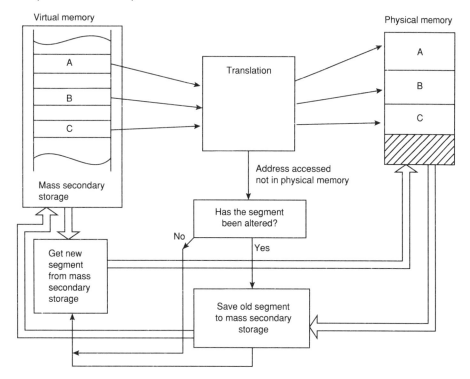

Figure 5.12 A virtual memory system

rogating the MMU. If there is insufficient space for the new segment the operating system re-arranges the existing segments to maximise the free physical memory space, see *Figure 5.13*. If the free physical memory space is still insufficient for the new segment, the operating system has to delete one of the other segments. The decision as to which segment to delete is a complex one and various techniques are available.

To make room for the new segment, the old segment can obviously be overwritten with the new one. However, before this can be done a check has to be made to determine if the segment has been altered while in physical memory. If a change has been made by writing to the segment, the MMU detects this and sets the 'changed' flag. Then when the segment is to be replaced, the operating system checks the 'changed' flag. If a change has been made, the segment must first be saved to the virtual memory program stored on secondary mass storage, to ensure that the virtual memory program state is always correct. Once the segment has been changed the new segment can be transferred from virtual memory (secondary mass storage) into physical memory.

To help decide which segment should be deleted

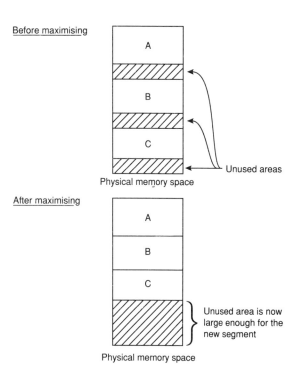

Figure 5.13 Maximising memory space

there is an additional flag for each segment which indicates whether the segment has been read or written since it was mapped. This is in addition to the 'changed' flag which only indicates whether a write operation has been performed on that segment.

One technique of obtaining free memory would be to remove the smallest segment that would create sufficient room which has not been accessed at all since it was mapped in. This indicates a low usage of that segment and removing it would cause the minimum disruption to the program as a whole. If that fails, then the smallest segment that would create sufficient room for the new one is removed, even if it has been accessed.

The complete simple algorithm is shown below:

(1) If there is sufficient free physical memory, then load the new segment, or –
(2) Delete any segments that have not been accessed and if sufficient, load new segment, or –
(3) Delete segments that have not been changed and load new segment, or –
(4) Save a segment that has been 'changed' to

secondary mass storage, delete it and then load new segment.

The decision is more complex than this decision algorithm would seem to indicate, because if the deleted segment was then immediately required again, an alternative segment would have to be removed to put the deleted segment back. This can lead to many hard disk accesses, each of which may take considerable time relative to instruction execution time and results in a poor system performance.

In order to maintain a high speed of instruction execution, even when programs have to be mapped, the MMU performs the translation of segment addresses as quickly as possible, so that there is no change in performance from using the MMU and not using the MMU. This requires many of the virtual memory tests to be under the control of the MMU. The MMU then detects accesses to segments that are not mapped to physical memory and alerts the operating system, via an interrupt that some action is required. A typical virtual memory computer

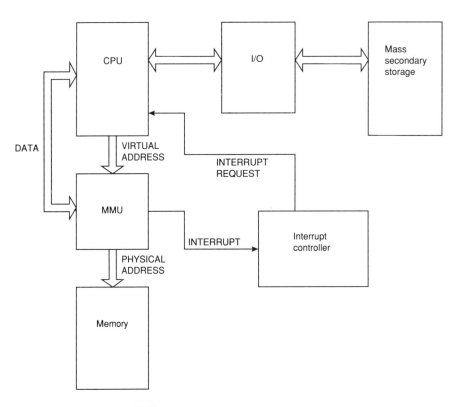

Figure 5.14 Typical system containing a MMU

system is illustrated in *Figure 5.14* and consists of an MMU between the microprocessor and memory which creates an interrupt signal when an illegal access is made. The interrupt controller then redirects it to alert the operating system which has control of the secondary mass storage. The operating system then makes the decision as to which segment, if any, should be deleted, whether it should be saved to disk or just overwritten. Then it decides which segment of the program should be transferred from secondary mass storage to the physical execution memory.

Prioritised Access

One aspect of memory management that has not really been considered until now is prioritised access, which enables a priority to be given to each segment of a virtual memory program. Then each time an access is made to a segment, the priority of the calling program segment is compared with the segment being accessed. If it is the same or higher, then the access is made, otherwise an error situation is reported to the operating system.

This is illustrated in *Figure 5.15*, where segment A of priority 3 has an access request to segment C. Segment C is priority level 2 which is lower than that of segment A so the access is allowed. Alternatively, segment B of priority 1 has an access request to segment C. Segment C has a higher priority of 2 and therefore the request is denied and an interrupt to the operating system is generated to indicate that an error situation has occurred.

A segment is able to make accesses anywhere within its own segment and it is only for inter-segment accesses that the priority is checked.

The priority checking has to be implemented by the hardware of the MMU so that it cannot be altered by a user program. This prevents a user from accessing the operating system and altering the priority settings in order to access higher privileged segments. This is a necessary requirement for multi-user systems to prevent a user from accessing other users' programs, data and the operating system software. This helps to prevent "hacking" which can be considered to be the unauthorised accessing of data and programs of one user by another user.

A typical MMU would implement four levels of priority which are generally arranged as shown in *Figure 5.16*. The kernel of the operating system containing all the basic software functions required has the highest priority. This can then be considered to be surrounded by layers of software, each with a lower priority containing less and less sensitive soft-

ware. These layers might be BIOS and file handling which are system services, or application services such as libraries of program code and finally, with the lowest priority, applications themselves. User programs reside in the applications priority level which is the lowest, where there are further techniques implemented to prevent access between users.

The result of this priority ordering is that user programs cannot access any applications services, systems services or kernel. This would be too restrictive and techniques are implemented which enable a low priority segment to access a higher priority service. These techniques tend to specify special points which have additional software error checking to prevent unauthorised usage, at which low priority segments may access higher priority segments to perform limited higher priority functions. Note that the operating system kernel can access any segment, anywhere in memory, as all segments will have an equal or lesser priority. This is necessary for the operating system to perform its functions. It is very important therefore to prevent users from changing their privilege levels to the highest level, as this would give them access to everything in virtual memory.

Faster Processing

As well as having an increased memory space, both physical and virtual, it is required to execute program instructions at a faster rate. This is necessary because the programs have become much larger and have many more instructions to execute. Therefore, in order to obtain complete program execution in a time acceptable to the user, the instructions have to

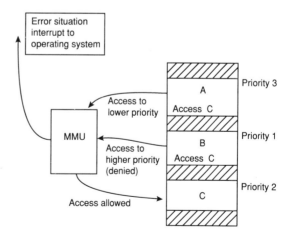

Figure 5.15 Prioritised access

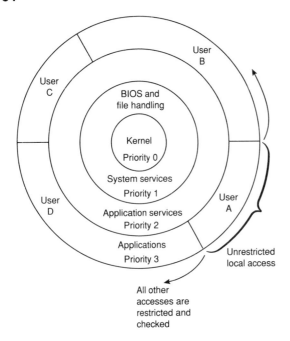

Figure 5.16 Privilege levels for a typical virtual memory system

be executed at a faster rate. In the next section it is discussed how RISC architectures could be used to obtain this speed of execution. Sometimes it is necessary to obtain speed improvements in CISC architectures and there are methods of achieving this.

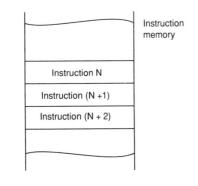

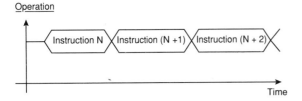

Figure 5.17 Non-pipelined instruction execution

Increased clock speed. The throughput of instructions is affected by the clock speed. Increase the clock speed and the rate at which instructions are executed is immediately increased. Table 5.1 gives some indication of how the increasing system clock frequency increases the MIPS for each generation of microprocessor. Each new generation of microprocessor also adds a further increase in the MIPS by improved architecture (compare 8 MHz 8086 and 8 MHz 80286) as well as increased system clock frequencies. This results in an almost 9-fold increase in MIPS from the 5 MHz 8086 to the 25 MHz 80386, as well as an increase from 16 bits to 32 bits in the size of the data values that can be directly handled.

Table 5.1 Increasing system clock frequency

Microprocessor	*System clock*	*MIPS (approximate)*	*Data bus width*
8086	5 MHz	0.7	
	8 MHz	1.1	16
	10 MHz	1.4	
80286	8 MHz	2.0	
	10 MHz	2.5	16
	16 MHz	4.0	
80386	16 MHz	4.0	
	20 MHz	5.0	32
	25 MHz	6.2	

Note: The IBM PC uses a 5 MHz 8088 (similar to 5 MHz 8086) whilst the IBM PC/AT uses 8 MHz 80286, hence the 3-fold increase in speed of program execution

Improvements in Internal Architecture

The basic internal architecture of a microprocessor is a simple one which allows only one instruction to be executed at any one time. Each instruction has to be completed before the next one can be started and the instructions are contained sequentially in program memory and are executed one after another, see *Figure 5.17*.

As discussed in RISC architectures, improvements in speed can be obtained by simplifying the execution of instructions by fixing the instruction length and only having a few basic instructions. However, the same basic technique of executing an instruction still applies which can be separated into three basic actions (see *Figure 5.18*):

(1) Instruction fetching;
(2) Instruction decoding;
(3) Instruction execution.

Instruction overlap. The techniques discussed so far have concentrated on reducing the time taken by the individual actions, so that the clock speed can be increased in order to reduce the total instruction

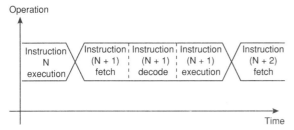

Figure 5.18 Instruction actions

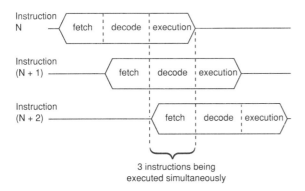

3 instructions being
executed simultaneously

Figure 5.19 Overlapping instructions

execution time. An alternative technique is to organise the internal architecture of the microprocessor so that several instructions are in the process of executing at any one time. This is called instruction overlap and the simplest technique is to overlap the three parts of an instruction, fetch, decode and execute, using three successive instructions as illustrated in *Figure 5.19*.

This enables a maximum of three instructions to be executing simultaneously and has the effect of tripling the instruction execution rate without having to increase the clock speed. In addition, there is still only one instruction fetch unit, one instruction decode unit and one instruction execute unit as with non-overlapping instruction microprocessors, so programming these overlapping instruction microprocessors is just the same. The drawbacks are that the internal control of the three units is more complicated which will limit the clock speed and more transistors are required to implement the overlapping so other functions may not be possible, as the maximum number of transistors available for the entire microprocessor is limited. Another problem is that it takes three instructions before the full overlapping process is operating properly and this becomes important if a program contains a lot of

branches, jumps or subroutines, as each of these causes the overlapping to be ineffective. For example, in *Figure 5.19*, if instruction N was a branch to some other part of the program, then by the time it was executed, the two immediately following instructions would have already been fetched and would have to be discarded. The overlapping must then begin to build up again. The result of this is a significant loss of performance if the program has a high proportion of branches. This indicates how changes in the architecture of the microprocessor have an effect on the way in which programs are written.

Memory Caches

One of the problems of increasing the clock speed of a microprocessor to make it execute programs faster is that the memory components used must also operate at a proportionally higher rate. Faster memory components cost more and for systems requiring large amounts of memory, the cost becomes prohibitive. Slower, cheaper memory components have to be used and the high speed operation of the microprocessor becomes unusable. One technique to avoid this problem is to use a memory cache.

A memory cache is a block of high speed (and expensive) memory components connected between the microprocessor and the main, slower, memory system, as illustrated in *Figure 5.20*. The contents of a selected block of memory components are copied from the main memory system into the cache memory block by the cache controller. Then whenever the microprocessor accesses memory, the access is made via the memory cache. If the contents of the memory location are contained within the cache a high speed access can be made.

If a read is made no further action is taken, but if a write is made then a process known as a buffered write or a delayed write is made. The new value is initially written to a location in the cache at high speed with the microprocessor quickly moving on to the next instruction. The cache controller detects that a

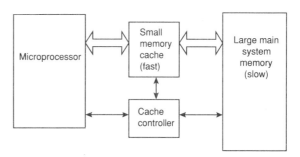

Figure 5.20 Memory cache

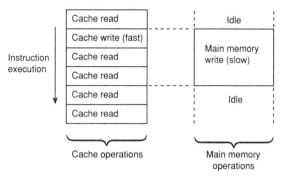

Figure 5.21 Memory cache operation

write to cache has been made and initiates a second write to copy the contents of the newly-written cache memory location into the correct location in the slower main memory system. This is independent of the microprocessor and achieves two things: first the contents of main memory always contain the correct values, even when a cache is being used and second, the slow speed of the main memory system does not slow down the execution speed of the microprocessor. This is illustrated in *Figure 5.21*.

There are several drawbacks to using a cache; reading a location which is not in cache memory and writing a location which is not in cache memory and the resulting complexity of the cache controller.

Usually, if a write is made to a non-cache memory location, the microprocessor is slowed down and the write made directly to the main, slow memory system as illustrated in *Figure 5.22*. Obviously, this is undesirable and the aim is to ensure that all locations written to are maintained in the cache. A similar situation may occur if two successive writes are made to the cache as the cache controller will still be copying the first write into main memory when the second write to cache occurs. Depending on how sophisticated the cache controller is, the microprocessor may be forced to idle until the cache controller catches up.

If a read is made which is not in cache memory the operation of the cache memory is suspended while a transfer is made from main memory into cache memory. In order to try and reduce the number of such transfers, the cache controller will copy a small block of memory locations from main to cache memory, usually about 16 bytes, called a line. The size of the line is based on the observation that successive accesses to memory are usually made to closely-grouped memory addresses and by copying a small block, future accesses will probably already be present in the cache. The cache controller first has

to decide which line within the cache can be discarded to make room for the new values, achieved by using a **Least Recently Used algorithm** (LRU) to identify which line was used the least since the last cache update.

The aim is to obtain the highest rate of successful accesses to the cache as possible, which is called the hit rate as this leads to the fastest execution speeds. Parameters which have to be optimised are:

(1) *Cache size:* the larger the better, except this increases the cost;
(2) *Line size:* the larger the better, except this increases idle time as updates to the cache take longer;
(3) *Cache controller:* the more flexible the better, except that more transistors are required to implement the cache functions, slowing down the cache controller and making it more expensive.

Two caches can be implemented to obtain further increases in speed; one for instructions which would normally be a read only memory not requiring write through and a second cache for data memory, requiring both a read and write ability. This effectively requires two cache controllers for optimum performance which is expensive. Alternatively the cache is split into two, one part for instructions and one part for data.

Built-in Debugging Facilities

As microprocessors become more sophisticated it becomes more difficult to locate faults and errors in the software and hardware. One method of making this easier is to include error detection and debugging facilities into the microprocessor itself, rather than relying on expensive test instruments.

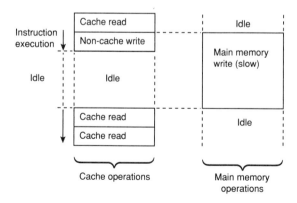

Figure 5.22 Write to a non-cached memory location

One useful feature is **self test** where, if a set of special signals is applied to a microprocessor, usually immediately after a reset operation, the microprocessor executes a series of internal tests designed to identify any faults in the various parts of the microprocessor. Typically, 50% of the total microprocessor component can be tested in this way and this increases the reliability of systems made with such microprocessors.

When testing software it is useful to be able to stop program execution of selected points and view the internal state of the microprocessor, its registers and memory contents. This can be achieved using **in-circuit emulators** to emulate the operation of the microprocessor under test. These devices are expensive and can be difficult to utilise correctly. An alternative approach is to include **debugging registers** within the microprocessor itself.

Debugging registers are a simplified form of address detection hardware, which detect when specified registers or memory locations are accessed and then cause program execution to be transferred to a special program for viewing the internal state of the microprocessor. This avoids the need for expensive and complex emulators. The debug registers are set up with the memory locations of interest, by the special viewing program. Control is then transferred to the program under test, which executes until one of the specified locations is accessed. At that point control is transferred back to the special viewing program and the contents of registers and memory locations are analysed to determine where the faults may exist.

Higher Levels of Functional Integration

As technology advances it becomes possible to increase the number of transistors that can be fitted on to one piece of silicon. This process can be used to integrate several components of a computer system into one single component and examples of this are the integration of a memory management unit, a cache controller, an arithmetic coprocessor and the microprocessor itself into a single component. Such a component is the 80486 which integrates the 80387 arithmetic coprocessor, the 80306 microprocessor, a memory management unit, a cache controller and cache memory.

Reducing the number of components has several advantages:

(1) A reduced PCB size, from three or four components down to only one;
(2) increased speed of operation as one of the limiting factors is the length of connections between components, whereas integrated components have shorter path lengths and can therefore execute faster;
(3) Increased reliability as the number of soldered connections on an integrated component is significantly lower than for the discrete components and reliability is directly proportional to the number of connections;
(4) Reduced power consumption as less signal pin drive circuits are required, which indirectly allows the main power supply to be reduced. An example of this is the power supply for IBM Personal Computers, which was 63.5 Watts in the original PC. This peaked at 180 or 220 Watts for the standard AT and it has now been reduced to approximately 80–90 Watts for the highly-integrated versions of the AT now available.

Disadvantages are the increased difficulty in producing the large areas of defect-free semiconductors used to create the integrated components, which leads to higher component costs. However, this is usually more than compensated for by the reduction in other costs, as listed under the advantages.

Table 5.2 Trends in transistors per integrated component

	1970	1975	1980	1985	1990	1995	2000
Transistors per mm²	100	200	800	2500	7000	20,000	50,000
Size of silicon per component (mm²)	120	180	220	340	500	700	1000
Total transistors per component (1000's)	12	36	176	850	3500	14,000	50,000

Table 5.2 indicates how the dual advantages of increasing the number of transistors per square millimetre of semiconductor and increasing the size of the piece of semi-conductor per component leads to large increases in the number of transistors per component. The increase is approximately $\times 1.4$ per year in the number of transistors per component and leads to a prediction that by the year 2000, components will contain 50 million transistors. Compared with the 1.5 million used in the 80486 it becomes obvious that significant improvements in microprocessor performance are possible.

Parallel Processing

Existing microprocessors are being limited in their speed of operation by the time taken for individual transistors to switch on and off. Few improvements are predicted in this area unless a significant breakthrough is achieved. However, as demonstrated previously, the number of transistors available is set to increase steadily and therefore improvements in the rate at which instructions can be executed can be achieved by considering different architectures, rather than relying on making transistors switch more quickly.

Most of these changes in architecture result in several operations being performed simultaneously and these types of architecture are known by the general term of **parallel processing**. These architectures can be separated into two main types:

(1) Internal parallelism;
(2) External parallelism.

Internal parallelism contains the parallelism within a single component and several examples of this type have already been discussed, such as instruction overlap, sometimes called pipelining and integrating several components into one.

One new type of internal parallelism is superscalars which have a very wide instruction size of 128 bits or more compared with the 80386 which has a 32-bit instruction width. This is used to contain several different instructions which, if they were 32 bits, would allow four instructions to be contained within one very wide instruction. The microprocessor then has several processing units, which can be similar or different, such as arithmetic coprocessor, integer unit, graphics unit and so on. This enables many times more instructions to be executed without having to increase the clock speed. The main disadvantage of such superscalars is the difficulty in actually writing programs for them as most programming techniques are not inherently parallel even on the small scale required. In addition, there is the problem created by having bus widths of 128 bits or more.

External parallelism is when two or usually more identical microprocessors are connected together into a single computer system. The disadvantages are much the same as for superscalars except that the programming is even more difficult as thousands of microprocessors can be connected together in 'parallel'. The bus width problem is usually solved by reducing the number of direct connections between microprocessors, rather than increasing them.

The transputer, discussed in the next section, is the most widely used external parallel processing microprocessor and this has reduced the interconnection bus between microprocessors to only two signals, has integrated an arithmetic coprocessor and a memory component into a single component and uses a RISC-based architecture. There is also a special programming language called Occam specifically designed for writing parallel processing programs, although this has not proved to be particularly popular and a major proportion of the programming of those devices is performed using special parallel versions of standard programming languages such as C and Fortran.

5.2 THE TRANSPUTER AND OCCAM

The complex underlying mathematical concepts of the transputer will not be described, only some of the practical consequences. Instead the aim is to give a 'feel' and 'understanding' of how to use the transputer and the exciting possibilities this device opens up. The mathematical basis of the transputer is so well designed that it becomes invisible to the user, thereby avoiding the necessity of delving into the inner workings of the transputer to obtain the desired results. Occam is the native language of the transputer and will be explained in suitable detail, in order that the concept of communicating sequential processes, parallelism and concurrence may be understood. The transputer can be programmed directly in the high level language Occam, without having to resort to assembly language input and output interfaces at any stage.

One of the major advantages of the transputer is the ability to simply add more transputers together in order to obtain increased processing capability. A sequence of examples will be used to illustrate primitive processes, such as assignments, input and output functions, constructs i.e. parallel and sequential processes, declarations, channel assignments and syntax, etc.

Introduction to Block-structured Programming

A block-structured language is one in which the internal parts of the program can be separated into distinct sections, or blocks, which perform a specific operation, see *Figure 5.23*. Each block is self-contained which means that all the information and instructions required to perform the operation are contained within the block, or will be passed to the block. The block is therefore defined by its internal operation specification and the interface with the rest of the program. This means that a block can be replaced with a completely different block, provided that the internal operation specification and program interface remain the same. Blocks can also be

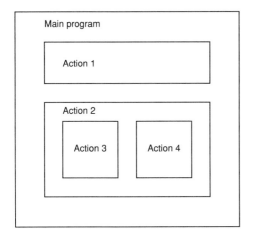

Figure 5.23 Block-structured programming

nested in order that complex operations can be constructed of simpler ones without involving the remainder of the program. Anything inside a block is 'invisible' to any outer blocks, but is visible to any 'inner' blocks.

Good programming techniques. The input and output of data to and from each block is always made via a single 'user-defined interface', see *Figure 5.24*. This is a user-defined interface as the program language does not define it for the user. This allows flexibility. The variables in each block are then invisible to other blocks and data can only be input and output through the user-defined interface. This enables boundary conditions to be applied to the data passed and test conditions to be imposed upon the data.

The Occam-to-computer Interface

The transfer of information and data between the Occam program and the hardware of the computer, for example, the floppy disks, keyboard, monitor, etc., is made through a standard interface, using Occam links, see *Figure 5.25*. If required, other user-defined link names can be included if information is to be saved after the program has terminated, for example, on a floppy disk.

Block-structured Programming using Occam

Only a few statements will be considered which are important for block-structured programming.

There is no statement terminator as such but the end of the statement is indicated by the end of the line of text. Spaces and spacing have great syntactical significance in Occam. Upper and lower case characters can be used but Occam reserved words must be in capital letters otherwise they are treated as variable names. Variable names can be upper case or lower case provided that they do not include a reserved word in upper case.

User-defined Blocks. The main Occam program consists of user-defined blocks, which can be nested if required, that are called procedures. A procedure has a similar structure to the main program block except that the name PROC is used to identify the block and the interface is user-defined. The user-defined interface is then between that particular block and the rest of the program rather than between the program and the hardware.

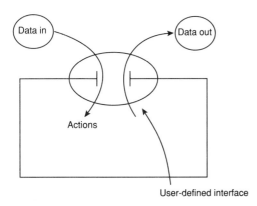

Figure 5.24 User-defined interface

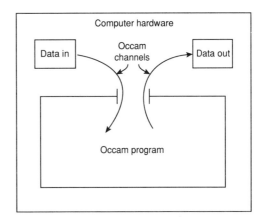

Figure 5.25 Interfacing to the computer

Example

PROC proc_name(user_defined_interface)

   – – { rest of procedure statements}

A program then consists of one or more user-defined procedures and a main block of statements. The user-defined interfaces require some data variables to operate on, which are defined at the beginning of the program.

Note: anything which appears after two consecutive minus symbols, – – , is treated as a comment and not as an Occam statement. This has been reinforced by using curly brackets { } to enclose the comments. Only the text on the right of the same line as the two minus signs is treated as a comment. Comments do not extend to following lines.

Example

```
                    – – {all this line is treated as a comment}
x  : = y + z      – – {only text after – – is comment}
                    – – {this line is treated as a comment
but this line is not and would produce an error when
compiled}
```

Example

```
Program quadratic(input,output)
    – – {variable definition}
PROC user_name1(user_defined_interface1)
    – – {rest of procedure statements}
PROC user_name2(user_defined_interface2)
    – – {rest of procedure statements}
    – – {main block}
    – – {user-defined variables, statements and}
    – – {procedures}
```

Blocks can be nested within one another to almost any level. The procedure statement is one method of creating a block and the indentation structure is another.

The procedure block has essentially the same structure as the main program and can consist of user-defined variables and user-defined procedures, with a main loop or block, delimited by indentation. This contains a user-defined combination of data variables and user-defined procedures.

Example

```
PROC example1(user_defined_interface) =
    – – {user-defined variable definitions}
PROC internal1(user_defined_interface2) =
    – – {procedure internal statements}
    – – {rest of procedure example1 statements}
    – – {main loop}
    – – {user-defined procedures, variables and}
    – – {statements}
```

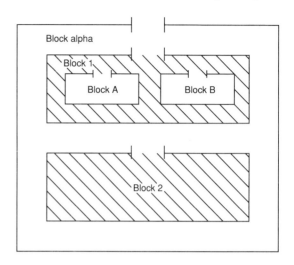

Figure 5.26 Nesting blocks

Notes. Internally-defined procedures are optional. If they are defined they can only be used within the procedure within which they were defined. They cannot be used in any other block or the main loop, because the block structure renders the internal operation of any block invisible to all other external blocks.

An example is given in *Figure 5.26*, where blocks A and B can only be used by block1 as they are invisible to block2 and block Alpha. Similarly, only block1 and block2 can be accessed by block Alpha.

If block1 is used by block Alpha this will indirectly access blocks A and B. Otherwise blocks A and B cannot be accessed. In addition, only procedures defined previously in the program listing can be accessed, so that block2 could not access block1 or block Alpha.

Data Variables

To perform useful actions, a program must have some input data values, perform some actions on these and output some data values to produce the result, as indicated in *Figure 5.27*.

The format in which the data is maintained is called the type of the data and the most useful Occam types are:

INT   All positive and negative whole numbers.
REAL64 All positive and negative scientific numbers.
BYTE   Numbers $0 \rightarrow 255$.

The remaining types are given later.

Example

```
INT username1
- - {main loop or PROC which uses username1}
```

Occam allows almost any combination and length of characters to be used in user-defined names. This allows 'names' or 'labels' which convey meaning to be used.

Example

```
INT numberoforanges:
```

The type specification is separated from the user-defined name by a space and the complete specification is terminated by a colon.

Procedure Blocks

After the optional definition of variables, the block of the procedure may contain any valid Occam statements. Some of the commonly-used ones are:

```
(1) IF
      <condition true>
      <action>
(2) IF
      <condition1 is true>
      <action1>
      <condition2 is true>
      <action2>
(3) WHILE <condition true>
      <action>
```

Each of the <action> statements may be constructed of a separate block containing more Occam statements.

Example

```
PROC add (INT number1,
            INT number2,
            INT result) =
BYTE ch
writeln ('Shall I begin')
- - {writeln would be a user-defined}
- - {output procedure}
readln(ch) - - {readln would be a user-defined}
- - {input procedure}
    IF
      ch = 'y'
        SEQ
          number_1 = number_1 * number_1
          number_2 = number_2 * number_2
          result = number_1 + number_2
    IF
      ch <> 'y'
        result = number_1 + number_2:
```

Points of interest. The two symbols, := can be read as meaning 'becomes equal to', so that A := B + C is read as 'A becomes equal to B plus C'.

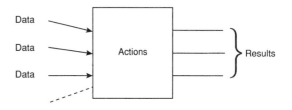

Figure 5.27 Data variables

The four arithmetic operations are:

```
+ addition,
- subtraction,
* multiplication,
/ division.
```

The IF statement requires the condition to be true before the next statement can be executed. Therefore the equality (ch = 'y') is used to obtain such a result. If the variable, ch, contains the letter 'y' then the first equality will be true, otherwise it will be false, in which case the second equality is tested, found to be true and the second statement is initiated.

Finally, the colon terminates the PROC definition.

5.3 THE OCCAM LANGUAGE

The transputer and its programming language Occam were developed together in order that programs can be written without knowing what hardware is available.

Occam is a multi-programming environment where one or more processes can be executing simultaneously, on one or more transputers. This means that several different programs could be executing simultaneously, or different parts of the same program, or one part of the program could be operating on several different sets of data, simultaneously. The software could then be executing on a single transputer or a network of transputers as this makes little difference to the operation of the program.

An example is shown in *Figure 5.28,* which shows a single transputer executing three different independent processes, P,Q and R, simultaneously. The lines with arrows indicate a communication link between processes. The communication links can be implemented either as software when memory locations are used, or hardware. As far as Occam is concerned, hardware and software are practically the same and there are only processes and communication links.

If it is necessary to speed up the operation of a

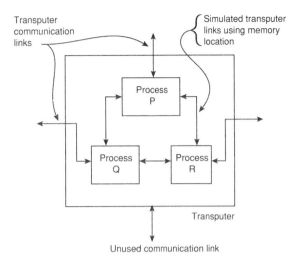

Figure 5.28 Concurrent processes

convert the data transmitted on a link into a **parallel format** suitable for:

(1) An I/O port;
(2) A memory address;
(3) Some other function.

New adapters are being designed all the time. The transputer can also be optimised for specific hardware tasks such as graphic controllers, disk controllers, etc.

Although Occam was designed to be used with the

transputer-based system, further transputers can be added to achieve this, as illustrated in *Figure 5.29*. Each of the processes of the previous example have been allocated to a separate transputer and an increase in speed of execution is possible. Simply adding more transputers does not necessarily lead to an increase in the speed of execution of the processes, as the increase in the rate at which the program is executed is limited by the rate at which data can be transferred between transputers. As the number of transputers executing a program is increased, the rate at which data is transferred throughout the system tends to decrease. This is due to the increased length of communication paths within the system, whereas the individual transputer-to-transputer communication links still operate at the same rate, independently of how many transputers are added. The result is that increasing the number of transputers in a system increases the amount of computing resource that is available but at the same time, makes it more difficult to actually utilise.

There is no need to allocate complete processes to each transputer as only part of a process may be allocated, as shown in *Figure 5.30*. Process R has been divided between two of the transputers and the remaining two processes allocated to the remaining transputer. This is only possible if process R can be conveniently divided in this way.

The protocol used for the serial communications links is not RS232C but a special high speed one that was specifically developed for the transputer. In addition, there are peripheral adapters which will

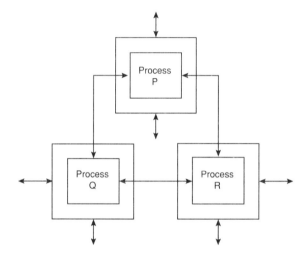

Figure 5.29 Processes on separate transputers

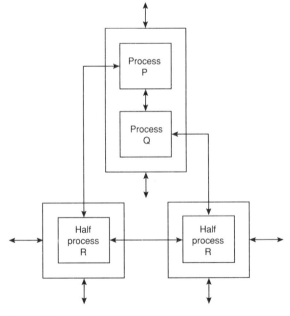

Figure 5.30 An alternative allocation strategy

transputer to take advantage of the multi-processing capabilities of the transputer, it is possible to program the transputer in its own assembler language or any other High Level Language (HLL) for which a compiler has been developed. If parallel processing of programs written in other languages is required, then an Occam 'Harness' must be used to link the separate modules together. The preferred language for programming the transputer is Occam.

Programming

The basic unit of each program is the process. Each process is effectively independent of all other processes (as required for parallel programming), but is able to communicate with other processes via a communication link. This link can be implemented either as hardware or software, as already mentioned. The internal operation of the process is hidden from the user and is completely specified by the messages exchanged with other processes. This is similar to the way block-structured HLLs operate, see the chapter on the introduction to Pascal.

Similarly, each process may be a combination of several communicating sub-processes, where none, some, or all of the processes are implemented in hardware.

Changes to the transputer do not affect the communication link, so that different versions of the transputer and upgrades can be performed without having to change the program or any other hardware.

Occam Model

The following is a more detailed overview of the language than that given in the section on block-structured programming. In Occam, processes are connected to form concurrent systems with the processes themselves being finite. Finite means that the processes have a specific beginning, a middle and a guaranteed end. Processes cannot contain any infinite loops which will execute for ever. This is necessary to ensure that the time-slicing operates correctly. However, it is possible to write programs which use processes to create infinite loops.

Example

```
WHILE TRUE
  process1
```

Each action in the process, or set of parallel processes, can be a set of **sequential processes** or a set of parallel processes. As processes may consist of several other processes, the amount of concurrence may vary from moment to moment.

Concurrence can be considered to be the ability to have several unrelated processes executing simultaneously. On a single transputer this is not possible although the use of time-slicing makes it 'appear' to happen. Only if two or more transputers are connected together and executing the same program can true concurrence be said to be occurring.

Each Occam process can be reduced to three primitives:

(1) *Assignment:* computes a value and sets a variable equal to it;
(2) *Input:* inputs values into a process (which have been output from a different process);
(3) *Output:* outputs values from a process (which then form the input to a different process).

A channel is a one-way link between two processes, with one process outputting data to the channel and the other process inputting data from the channel. If bi-directional communication is required then two channels must be used.

Language Constructs

Assignment. This assigns the value in result to answer:

```
answer := result
( := means 'becomes equal to', as in Pascal)
```

Input. Inputs data from channel comm1 into the variable called 'message', where the data type arriving on the channel must match the data type of the variable:

```
comm1 ? message
```

Output. Outputs data from the variable called 'reply' to channel comm2. The channel automatically conforms to the data type of the variable:

```
comm2 ! reply
```

Sequential. The SEQ is the reserved word used to indicate that sequential processes are to be used (one after the other). Each process identifier is placed on a separate line and must be indented two spaces. There is no statement terminator like the semi-colon in Pascal, instead the two space indentation forms that function. This example will execute the process called Process1, then Process2 and finally Process3:

```
SEQ
  Process1
  Process2
  Process3
```

Example

This simple example inputs a value from channel comm1, increments it, and then outputs it to channel comm2:

```
SEQ
   comm1 ? visitors
   visitors := visitors + 1
   comm2 ! visitors
```

Parallel. The processes called action1, action2 and action3 start executing simultaneously. The complete parallel construct terminates when all of the processes have terminated and effectively has an execution time equal to the slowest process:

```
PAR
   action1
   action2
   action3
```

Example

Inputs a value from channel comm1 into 'visitors' and, at the same time, outputs a value from 'reply to' channel comm2:

```
PAR
   comm1 ? visitors
   comm2 ! reply
```

Note: On a single transputer, a channel is implemented between the processes via memory which simulates the functions of a serial link.

Conditional constructs. There can be any number of processes in the list following the IF but only one of them, Process1 . . . ProcessN, will be executed. The process executed will be the first one reading, which has a 'true' condition starting at the top of the list and working downwards. This construct is similar to the CASE statement in Pascal.

```
IF
   <condition1>
      Process1
   <condition2>
      Process2
   . . .
```

The processes to be executed are indented a further two spaces making a total of four, to indicate that they are sub-processes.

The end of the sub-process statement is indicated when the next condition is found as this will only be indented by two spaces.

Example

This process will increase 'coffee' only if 'visitors' = 0, otherwise the SKIP process is executed. SKIP is a built-in function which does nothing. Its use here serves no useful purpose but is used for illustration.

```
IF
   visitors = 0
      coffee := coffee + 1
   visitors <> 0
      SKIP
```

Alternative Construct. Only one of the processes, Process1, Process2 . . . ProcessN, is executed, and that is the first one which has an input from a channel ready. This is similar to the IF statement except that the program will wait at this point until one of the input channels receives some data:

```
ALT
   input1
      Process1
   input2
      Process2
   input3
      Process3
   . . .
```

Example

This program either receives a data input from a channel called 'count' and puts it into signal following which the variable 'counter' is incremented, or inputs from channel 'total' into 'signal', after which the counter value is output and then reset to zero, as the process executed if the channel called 'total' has an input first is a sequential construct:

```
ALT
   count ? signal
      counter := counter + 1
   total ? signal
      SEQ
         out ! counter
         counter := 0
```

Repetition. The actions defined by Process1 will be repeated while the condition is true and can be used to make infinite loops by creating a condition which is always true:

```
WHILE <condition>
   Process1
```

Example

This will decrement X in units of 5 until the remainder is less than 5:

```
WHILE (X – 5) > 0
   X := X – 5
```

Sequential Replication. This repeats Process1, n times:

```
SEQ i = 0 FOR n
  Process1
```

and is equivalent to:

```
WHILE i < n
  SEQ
    Process1
    i := i + 1
```

This is a new type of construct, peculiar to Occam, as it is based upon the capability of executing the same process several times, one after the other. The data used can be different each time, or it is possible to use the output data from one execution of the process as the input data for the next time the process is executed. This enables the same actions to be performed iteratively on a set of data.

Parallel Replication. This is slightly different to the previous construct, in that instead of executing the same process sequentially with pipelined data, n similar copies of Process are constructed using data indexed by i. These are then executed in parallel and this sort of construct is particularly useful when performing operations such as matrix multiplication:

```
= 0 FOR n
  Process(i)
```

Data Types

The Occam programmer has the capability of using different types of variables, such as integers and real numbers:

CHAN : communication channel
TIMER : real time clock, required for concurrent processes.
BOOL : Boolean
BYTE : 8-bit numbers, 0–255
INT : The most efficient implementation of integer numbers, which may be different among different transputer versions
INT16 : signed integers 16 bits long
INT32 : signed integers 32 bits long
INT64 : signed integers 64 bits long
REAL32 : 32-bit floating-point numbers conforming to IEEE P754 draft 10.0 standard, for the computer implementation of real numbers
REAL64 : same as REAL32 except that 64 bits are used

Declarations. As with Pascal, each variable used within a program has to be declared and have a type assigned to it. The method of definition used in Occam is to give the type first, followed by the variable name separated by a space and terminated with a colon.

Example

This declares X as an integer for use in the process called Process1:

```
INT X :
Process1
```

Arrays

Only one-dimensional arrays have been implemented in Occam 1, but there is an updated version of the Occam language, Occam 2, which has multi-dimensional arrays, as well as many other additional useful constructs.

```
coordinates[N] INT :
```

This will define an array of N integers called coordinates.

Named Processes

Occam is a block-structured language, as already discussed, with the ability to give a name to a complete process so that it can be used elsewhere in the program.

```
PROC square(INT n, INT sqr) =
  sqr := n * n :
```

This defines a process called 'square', which has two parameters, n and sqr, which have both been defined as integers. In this instance, n is used as an input variable, and sqr as the output variable. In fact they can both be used as inputs and outputs, as this definition is similar to the VAR definition of parameters in Pascal procedure. Multiple parameters for a PROC are separated by a comma with the definition of the PROC being terminated by the colon at the end of the last statement. The PROC is then used in the same way as Pascal procedures are used by simply including the name of the process, without the reserved word PROC or the rest of the definition, but including the names of the variables being used to pass parameters, e.g.

```
square(x,result)
```

which results in the variable 'result' becoming equal to the square of the contents of the variable x.

In addition, Occam contains all the arithmetic operators and Boolean operators available in Pascal

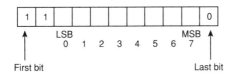

Figure 5.31 Transmission protocol

Figure 5.32 Acknowledgement

and other High Level Languages. Bit operations, shift operations and hexadecimal numbers can also be used directly within the language if required.

Timer

Because Occam is a concurrent language, each transputer has a built-in **real-time clock** in order to produce the time-slices required by multi-processing systems. The clock is called real-time, not because it gives the time of day, but because the frequency of the clock cannot be altered. The value of the timer is available to all of the processes being executed by the transputer. This allows it to be used to synchronise independent processes, but it is also organised in such a way that each process can maintain an independent timer if required.

The timer is an Occam process and is effectively an integer variable containing a number representing the time. It can only communicate via an Occam channel.

5.4 TRANSPUTER HARDWARE

Communication Links

Each communication link provides two Occam channels and any channel can transmit or receive at any time, as they are independent of every other process except the controlling one.

The transputer uses dedicated point to point serial communication links for several reasons:

(1) There is no contention when requesting the use of a communication link between two separate transputers, or even between two processes executing on the same transputer;

(2) There is no capacitive load penalty as is the case for multiple connections to a signal,

therefore the rate of data transfer can be high, typically 10 MHz;

(3) Adding further transputers does not saturate an individual communication link, but rather increases the bandwidth of the system as a whole, although utilising the extra bandwidth can be difficult.

The format for the transmission, which is asynchronous, is shown in *Figure 5.31*. A subsequent byte will not be transmitted until the acknowledge after the previous byte, see *Figure 5.32*, is received back at the transmitter. This ensures correct synchronisation between processes independent of the type of transputer at each end of the link.

There are two main methods of interfacing a transputer to external I/O components and mechanisms using either a special peripheral control transputer which communicates via a link and contains on-board parallel I/O, as illustrated in *Figure 5.33*, or alternatively, link adapters can be used, as shown in *Figure 5.34*, which, when connected to a serial link of a transputer, convert the serial data into parallel data. The parallel data can then be used in the same way as parallel data from any microprocessor-based system, which may be in a microprocessor-compatible format, or as a simple parallel I/O format.

Memory-mapped Peripherals

As with some other microprocessors, such as the 8086, I/O components can be placed into the memory

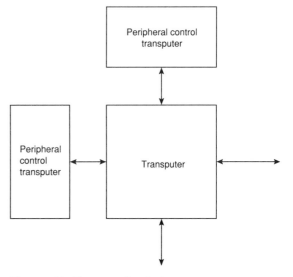

Figure 5.33 Transputer interfacing

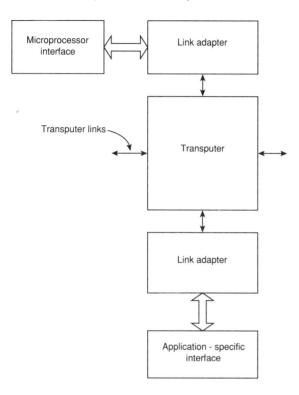

Figure 5.34 Link adapters

of the transputer and then treated as RAM locations. This is illustrated in *Figure 5.35* and can be used to simplify the system so that special transputers or link adapters are not required. However, the I/O components must be capable of performing a read or write operation in the same time as the transputer performs a memory read or write, typically 250 ns or less. Newer versions of the transputer operating at internal frequencies of 20 MHz or more, have memory access times of less than 125 ns and it can be difficult to obtain I/O components capable of responding correctly within this short time period.

Bootstrapping

As with most other microprocessors, the transputer can be made to boot up from ROM, that is, start executing the program stored at a specific point in memory, usually maintained in ROM. In addition, the transputer can be made to boot up from a serial link, when the boot program is taken to be the first message received on any one of the links. Only the first link to receive a message will have that message treated as the boot program. If the first message received is not the boot program the transputer will not execute correctly.

The selection of booting from ROM or a link is determined by the logic state on one of the transputer pins, whenever a reset, a power-on or a software-initiated reset is performed. The facility of selecting the source of the boot program has been included so that the transputer can be operated without any external memory which requires some method of transferring a program into the transputer internal RAM. In networks of transputers, booting from a link can be used to pass the boot program from transputer to transputer until they have all received the bootstrap program. The bootstrap program is normally a more sophisticated program loader which allows the main program to be loaded and then executed.

The flexibility of being able to create a program and then deciding how many transputers will be used to execute it and also how the program will be distributed between the transputers is very useful. It allows programs to be created, compiled, executed and tested on relatively inexpensive development systems containing only a single transputer, where the majority of faults can be identified and rectified. Then when ready, the program can be transferred via a serial link onto a network of transputers with the knowledge that further problems will probably

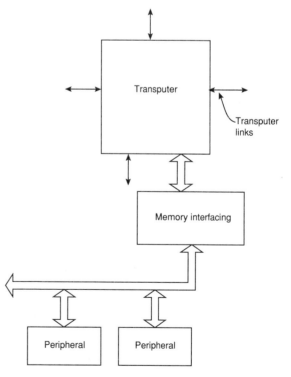

Figure 5.35 Memory-mapped peripherals

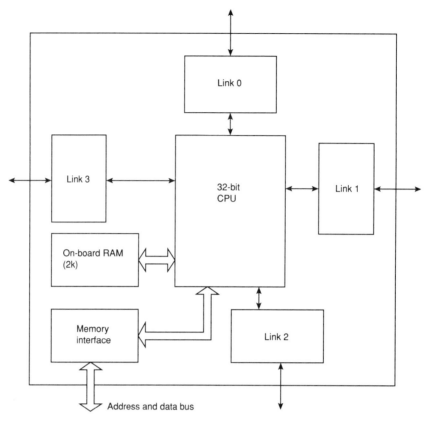

Figure 5.36 Internal transputer architecture

only be associated with the distribution of the program on multiple transputers.

This avoids the need to use expensive in-circuit emulators for the development of transputer-based systems and, in fact, no transputer emulator systems exist because of this facility. It also avoids the need to create complex systems of multiple microprocessors, with arbitration and system memory.

The Internal Transputer Architecture

The internal architecture of the T414 transputer is shown in *Figure 5.36* and consists of a 32-bit Central Processing Unit (CPU), four serial transputer communication links, which make four Occam output channels and four input channels, 2 k × 32 bits of on-board high speed Read/Write Memory (RWM) and a memory interface which implements a 32-bit address and data bus. Other members of the transputer family of components have variations on this which alter the number of links, the amount of on-board high speed RWM and the inclusion of an

integrated floating-point arithmetic unit. These alterations produce variations on the basic programmer's model outlined below.

The Programmer's Model

Normally the programmer will use Occam to program the transputer. However, if assembly language programming is required, the programmer's model as illustrated in *Figure 5.37* is used. There are only six registers, three of which, A, B and C form a push-down stack-starting with A. This means that if a value is transferred to the registers, it is always transferred to A. The previous contents of A are transferred to B and those in B transferred to C. Logical and arithmetic operations always take place using the values on this stack, for example, ADD will add the values in A and B and leave the result in A, with the previous contents of A being lost.

When a value is transferred from registers, it is always taken from A, with the contents of B being transferred to A and C to B. It is the programmer's

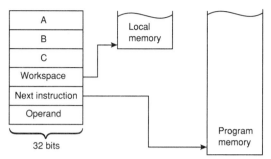

Figure 5.37 The assembly language programmers model of the transputer

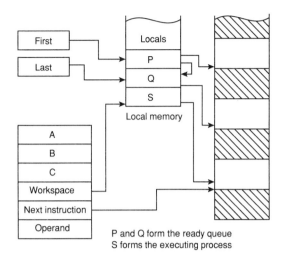

P and Q form the ready queue
S forms the executing process

Only one level of priority is shown

Figure 5.38 Scheduler

responsibility to ensure that the push-down stack does not overflow. This checking is performed automatically by the Occam compiler.

The workspace register is the base pointer to an area of memory used as a local workspace with the A register forming a 32-bit offset pointer from the base address contained in the workspace register. This memory does not have to be the internal RWM.

The instruction pointer points to the 32-bit memory location containing the next instruction. This is not quite the same as pointing to the next instruction, as the instructions vary in length from one byte to many bytes. Data, including instructions, is always fetched from memory, as 32-bit words so that a 32-bit word could contain up to four instructions. An internal queue of pre-fetched instructions is used to maintain an accurate pointer to the next instruction to be executed.

The final register is not user-accessible and is used to extend the instruction length up to 32 bits long. The normal instruction length is 8 bits which through a simple system of prefixes can be extended to two, three or four bytes long. This method has been implemented to simplify instruction fetches, which in turn allows the rate of instruction fetches to be increased, thereby increasing the throughput of the CPU. In addition, it allows the basic set of assembler-language instructions to have new instructions added, as required by the new versions of the transputer, but without altering the basic instruction format.

The transputer has 16 basic instruction types which have been implemented as a RISC-type core architecture. The use of prefixes to extend the instruction length enables several hundred variations on the 16 basic instructions to be produced.

The Scheduler

A microcoded scheduler is contained within the processor which implements the time-slicing technique used by the transputer, using part of the local memory as illustrated in *Figure 5.38*. Two priorities of linked processes are implemented, using first and last element pointers and the simplified ready queue as explained earlier. *Figure 5.38* shows three processes in the queue, of which two, P and Q, form the ready queue and R, the executing queue.

Time-slicing is used, but a process is not removed from the executing state if it is on the high priority list, until it has completed. This requires all high priority processes to be guaranteed to complete within a short time, otherwise the transputer will lock up. On the low priority list, processes get two time-slices of approximately one millisecond length after which time the process is stopped at the next descheduling point and placed back onto the ready queue. A descheduling point is one of the following operations:

> Input message
> Output message
> Output byte
> Output word
> Timer alt wait
> Timer input
> Stop on error
> Alt wait
> Jump
> Loop end
> End process
> Stop process

5.5 REDUCED INSTRUCTION SET COMPUTERS (RISC)

There are two main approaches to the design of microprocessors, the complex instruction set architecture and the reduced instruction set architecture, each of which has its own significant advantages.

Complex Instruction Set Computers (CISC)

The complex instruction set aims to provide the microprocessor with an instruction, or a variant of an instruction, which provides every type of operation that may be required. Examples of this are:

(1) Register-to-register moves;
(2) Logical operations;
(3) Arithmetic operations;

and so on. In addition, sophisticated and complex methods of physical address creation by program instructions are incorporated, so that High Level Language programs can be compiled into compact machine code programs. The aim is to produce a powerful compact set of instructions so that the program can be implemented using the minimum number of instructions. This results in short programs which saves program memory space and also achieves a high execution rate, see *Figure 5.39*. The instructions may vary in length from one to six or more bytes.

A crude measure of the processing capability of a microprocessor is the maximum number of instructions that can be executed in a second. This is usually measured in Million Instructions Per Second, or **MIPS**. The 8086 has a value between 0.5 MIPS and 3 MIPS depending upon the instruction sequence used in the measurement. A more realistic assessment of a particular microprocessor performance

can be obtained when it is incorporated into a complete system. This is because other factors, such as memory access times, can degrade the microprocessor and hence system performance, from the ideal. The main reason for a reduction in system performance is the use of slow memory. This increases the time taken for memory accesses which results in the instruction fetches taking longer and any accesses to data stored in memory taking longer. Due to the increased access time the system MIPS rate is reduced. Memory components with longer access times are used as they have a reduced cost and this is an important factor in modern computer systems which require very large execution memory spaces.

New computer systems need to be capable of providing almost limitless memory space with a short access time. The cost of short access time memory components is significant, so that the cheaper but slower memory components are attractive to designers. To enable the slower memory components to be used without a performance penalty, microprocessor architectures have become more sophisticated and use **memory management techniques**. The main memory management technique consists of a small block of memory, called a **cache**, with a short access time which is used in conjunction with a larger block of cheaper, slower access time memory, to achieve between 90% and 99% of the performance of a system containing short access time memory only.

With this type of memory management the performance is then dependent on the system architecture and a low MIPS microprocessor may enable a system to be designed with a larger MIPS rating than one using a higher MIPS microprocessor. An example of this is that an 8086 with an 8087 mathematics coprocessor can, in certain circumstances, produce a higher MIPS system than an 80286 with a 80287 mathematics coprocessor. In isolation the 80286 microprocessor is rated at 3 times the MIPS of the 8086 microprocessor.

These factors complicate the comparison of RISC and CISC architectures and in order to simplify this comparison, only the microprocessors themselves will be considered and not complete systems.

Increasing the MIPS Value

The MIPS value can be increased for any microprocessor by increasing the basic clock frequency which reduces the time required by each instruction to execute, see *Figure 5.40*. However, there are limits on increasing the MIPS value this way, one of which

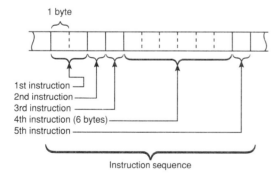

Figure 5.39 Variable length instructions

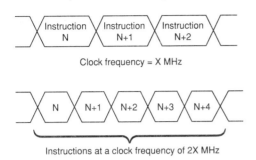

Clock frequency = X MHz

Instructions at a clock frequency of 2X MHz

Figure 5.40 Increasing the clock rate

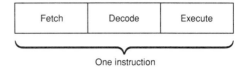

One instruction

Figure 5.41 The Instruction Cycle

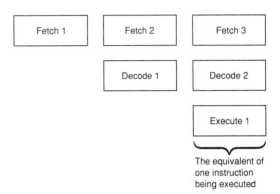

The equivalent of one instruction being executed

Figure 5.42 Overlapping instructions

is that the technology used to make the micro-processors limits the maximum clock frequency possible. This is approximately 25–30 MHz with present technology with some new microprocessors using internal frequencies of over 60 MHz. Micro-processors are presently being designed which will use frequencies of 100 MHz and over.

The architecture of the microprocessor may place limits on the speed of execution of complete in-structions due to the number of actions that have to be performed. Each instruction consists of a fixed number of clock pulses determined by the actions that have to be performed. If the clock frequency is operating at its maximum limit, an alternative method of increasing the MIPS is to reduce the number of clock pulses per instruction. Generally this is not possible with complex instruction sets as first the operation code of the instruction is fetched from memory and then decoded to determine whether it is a two, three, four or six byte instruc-tion. If necessary, further bytes are fetched from memory. The instruction is then completely de-coded, executed and any results produced dealt with. The instruction pointer is then automatically incremented by the correct number of bytes to point to the beginning of the next instruction. Each of these actions cannot be performed until the previ-ous one has completed, see *Figure 5.41*. Each of the actions occupies a finite amount of time, generally one clock pulse per action and this prevents the reduction of clock pulses per instruction. Hence the MIPS cannot be increased in this way.

An alternative to this is used by the 8086, 80286 and 80386 family of microprocessors, which overlap the different actions of several instructions so that one instruction may be being decoded while the next is being fetched from memory, see *Figure 5.42*, which is called **pipelining**. This leads to increasingly com-plex internal architectures which in turn requires larger numbers of transistors to implement. The numbers of transistors required are becoming so

large that it is difficult to manufacture them reliably and this results in an increased cost.

The more complex the internal architecture becomes, the more difficult it becomes to operate the microprocessors at high clock speeds as each logic gate added to the path through the decoders adds at least one propagation delay to the instruc-tion execution time, see *Figure 5.43*.

Reduced Instruction Set

A different approach to the microprocessor archi-tecture is to use a much simplified and reduced instruction set. The more complex operations are then constructed out of two or more simple instruc-tions. To obtain the maximum benefit out of a reduced instruction set only two types of instruc-tions are allowed, those which operate on the inter-nal registers to perform simple logical operations and those which transfer data between memory and registers. Complex logical operations, logical opera-tions performed directly on memory locations and complex memory address generation techniques are not allowed as they complicate the instruction decoding process.

The reduced instruction set then allows the instruction decoding complexity to be significantly reduced. The reduction in the complexity of the microprocessor and its decoding should then result in a higher MIPS value. However, the drawback is

Simple decoding

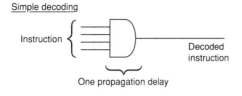

Complex decoding

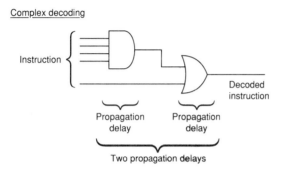

Figure 5.43 Decoding propagation delays

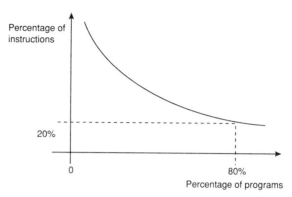

Figure 5.44 Instruction usage

that the programs become longer as the complex actions have to be constructed from several simpler instructions, instead of just using one instruction as for CISC architectures. In addition the instruction set is said to be regular, that is, the allocation of binary opcode is logical and is related to the instructions being performed. This is different from CISC devices where instructions sometimes have to be allocated to whatever binary pattern is available. Also, there are no special-purpose registers which have implicit uses such as memory pointers and so on, and all instructions can operate on all registers. Finally, there should be a large number of registers, so that all the data required can be transferred from memory into the registers, then manipulated and then the results saved, rather than having to fetch in data values from memory (using the slower memory access instructions) whenever they are required.

The aim of these concepts is to make the final execution of functionally-equivalent programs faster using a RISC architecture than using a CISC architecture.

That this aim is successful can be determined by the analysis of complex instruction set computer programs which shows that only 20% of the possible instructions are used in 80% of the programs, see *Figure 5.44*. This confirms the idea that a specially-designed microprocessor with a reduced instruction set equivalent to the 20%, would be able to execute 80% of the programs at a faster rate. The remaining

20% of the programs requiring the more complex instruction set could be executed by producing functionally-equivalent, but longer, programs.

One of the complexities that is removed in RISC architectures is the variable length instruction. Instead of allowing a variable number of bytes per instruction, depending upon the instruction, all instructions have the same length so that all instruction fetches take the same amount of time. The fixed length instructions simplify incrementing the instruction pointer and the instruction fetch cycle.

Also, memory addresses and immediate data values are included directly in the instruction, allowing them to be fetched in one bus cycle. This requires the data bus width to be the same as the instruction length, see *Figure 5.45*. This can result in the data bus being wider than the address bus for RISC architectures, whereas the reverse is usually true for CISC architectures. This differs from the

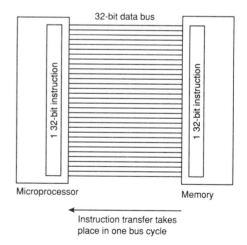

Figure 5.45 Instruction and data bus size

8086 which performs 3 bus cycles to fetch a 6-byte instruction as 3×6 words.

Load/Store Architecture

In the Load/Store architecture described above, there are only two instructions available for accessing memory:

LOAD   Transfers data from memory into a register
STORE   Transfers data from a register into memory

Complex addressing modes are not allowed such as the double indexing with offset possible with the 8086 microprocessor. Instead it is usual to only have:

(1) *Immediate*: when the data is contained within the instruction itself – this is not really a form of memory addressing as memory is not accessed; however, the result is the same as accessing memory so it is counted as such;
(2) *Memory*: data can be written to or read from a memory location, the address of which is either stored within the instruction itself, or is stored in a register.

Generally no other form of memory addressing is allowed, although sometimes it may be possible to add a constant offset to direct memory accesses, with the offset being stored in the instruction, see *Figure 5.46*.

Instruction Decoding

The fixed format of RISC instructions simplifies the decoding considerably as the instruction is already almost fully decoded. It is only necessary to perform local decoding on each set of bits, as illustrated in *Figure 5.47*. The CISC architecture hides this intermediate stage from the user but the same approach is taken by most microprocessors. The instruction is decoded into a fixed format, fixed length intermediate stage, which is then used to perform local decoding, see *Figure 5.48*. This stage can be observed in the 80286 microprocessor, as the initial decode to a wide, fixed length instruction format, is one of the pipe-lined functions.

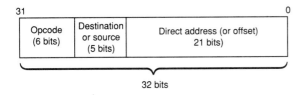

Figure 5.46 Memory offset addressing instruction

Simplified Programming Branching

As part of the simplified method of accessing data memory, only simplified methods are allowed for accessing instruction memory. Complex address calculations are not allowed, so that jumps must be made to the address given directly in the instructions, or sometimes to the address given in a register.

As part of this only a small number of conditional branching instructions will be available and hence there will only be a minimal number of flags. Some RISC devices have only one, temporary flag which is only valid after an instruction has executed and is a small exception to the 'no special registers (or flags)' rule. Others use a general-purpose register to maintain a small number of flags, but there are only a few special instructions for accessing them, and standard instructions have to be used to determine their value at selected points in the program.

Optimising assembler programs. In order to demonstrate how RISC assembler programs can be optimised, an ideal instruction set will be described and then used in several example programs to

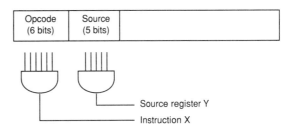

Figure 5.47 Local instruction decoding

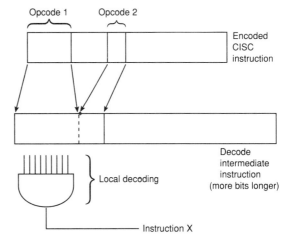

Figure 5.48 CISC instruction decoding

convey specific points. This instruction set is not taken from a real RISC device but has been designed to fit in with as much RISC philosophy as possible.

An Ideal RISC Instruction Set

For the purposes of explanation an ideal RISC device will be used which has the following characteristics:

(1) 32 registers (R0 to R31);
(2) All instructions can operate on all registers;
(3) R0 is used as the stack pointer;
(4) 32 bit data bus and hence all instructions are 32 bits long and the address bus is 32 bits long.

The following instructions are implemented:

LOAD mem,R	Loads a value from memory location 'mem' into register R
SAVE R,mem	Saves a value from register R into the memory location 'mem'
SUB Rx,Ry,Rz	Subtracts the contents of register Rx from register Ry and saves the result in register Rz
ADD Rx,Ry,Rz	Adds the contents of register Rx to register Ry and saves the result in register Rz
AND Rx,Ry,Rz	Logically ANDs the contents of register Rx to register Ry and saves the result in register Rz.
OR Rx,Ry,Rz	Logically ORs the contents of register Rx to register Ry and saves the result in register Rz
NOP	No operation, simply wastes time, no registers or memory locations are affected
CALL R	Calls a subroutine whose address is stored in register R
RETURN R0	Returns from a subroutine using R0 as the stack pointer where the return address is stored
BNZ mem	Branch to the memory location 'mem' when the results of the result of the previous instruction left a non-zero result in the destination register
JUMP mem	Jumps to the memory location 'mem'

Some of the instructions have three operands, which operate from right to left, with the first two being the source operands and the third the destination operand. For example:

    ADD R1,R2,R3

means add the contents of register R1 to the

contents of register R2 and save the result in register R3. The original contents of R3 are lost but R1 and R2 still have their original values. Any register can be used as the source and destination operands, so that the instruction:

    ADD R1,R1,R1

is the equivalent of adding the contents of register R1 to itself.

Overlapping LOAD/SAVE instructions with register-only instructions. One method of increasing the execution speed is to overlap the longer LOAD/SAVE instructions with the shorter register-only instructions. In the examples that follow, the LOAD/SAVE instructions are considered to take 10 cycles to complete and a register-only instruction takes only 4. Therefore, every time a register-only instruction is overlapped with a LOAD or SAVE, 4 clock cycles are saved, see below.

LOAD	mem1,R7	10 cycles
SUB	R1,R1,R1	4 cycles overlapped with above
	Total	10 cycles

The register-only instruction that is being overlapped must not use any of the registers being used by the LOAD or SAVE. In this example, this would be register R7. It is preferred that the compiler or assembler performs the checking to identify whether instructions can be overlapped, so that there is no need to include decoding in the RISC device to detect this. Therefore, should a LOAD or SAVE be overlapped with a register-only instruction which uses the same register, the result of the overlapping will be undefined and should be avoided at all costs.

Methods of optimising RISC programs

The following is a program specification for an assembler program for the ideal RISC.

Two values are stored in memory. The most significant bit of each value is to be masked off and the remaining values are to be added together, with the result being saved in memory.

	Non-Overlapping	
Clocks	*Instruction*	
10	LOAD	mem1,R1
10	LOAD	mem2,R2
10	LOAD	07FFFH,R3
4	AND	R1,R3,R1
4	AND	R2,R3,R2
4	ADD	R1,R2,R4
10	SAVE	R4,mem3

The 52 cycles and 7 instructions give an average of 7.4 cycles per instruction.

Overlapping now possible. Before a realistic assessment of the improvement of the effect of overlapping can be made, the sequence of instructions has to be re-ordered to maximise the possible overlap, as initially there is little scope for improvement and the only existing overlap (the third and fourth instruction) cannot be allowed as both instructions use R3.

Re-ordered program

Clocks	Instructions	
10	LOAD	07FEFH,R3
	<another register-only instruction>	
10	LOAD	mem1,R1
	<another register-only instruction>	
10	LOAD	mem2,R2
	AND	R1,R3,R1
4	AND	R2,R3,R2
4	ADD	R1,R2,R4
10	SAVE	R4,mem3
	<another register-only instruction>	

This gives 48 cycles and 10 instructions so that the average cycles per instruction has been reduced to 4.8, which is a significant improvement. The additional register-only instructions added to the program fragment would be taken from another part of the program where their removal would not cause any conflicts for the program function. If suitable instructions cannot be found then NOPs would be used instead, although they would not then be performing any useful task. An optimising compiler is preferred for this type of program re-organisation in order to obtain the maximum improvement.

Delayed Branching

When a program branch is made, a long instruction has to be used but this can usefully be overlapped with the immediately following (register only) instruction, as illustrated below:

```
CALL R31
ADD R1,R2,R3
       ;This instruction is overlapped with the CALL
```

In this example, the register-only instruction being overlapped would be the first instruction from the subroutine being called, hence the name delayed branching. This only applies to the unconditional branches which are always taken, that is, CALL, RETURN, JUMP.

Example programs

Example of branching without delayed branching.

```
       LOAD    subr,R31
       CALL    R31          ;call a subroutine
       SUB     R8,R27,R27   ;first instruction after the
                            ;subroutine return.
                            ;The subroutine
subr   AND     R1,R2,R1
       OR      R3,R2,R27
       <other instructions>
       RETURN  R0
```

The same program with delayed branching.

```
       LOAD    subr,R31
       CALL    R31
       AND     R1,R2,R1     ;first instruction taken from
                            ;the subroutine.
                            ;The subroutine
subr   OR      R3,R2,R7     ;this is now the second
                            ;instruction of the subroutine
       <The other instructions of the subroutine>
       RETURN  RO
       SUB     R8,R27,R27   ;The instruction which was
                            ;previously after the CALL is
                            ;moved to here
```

Conditional Branches

A similar method can be used with conditional branches, where the branch may or may not be taken, depending on the exact data values at that point in the program. However, it introduces a problem. If the branch is taken the immediately following register-only instruction is executed, but if the branch is not taken this means the overlapped instruction is not required either, so the overlapped instruction is not executed, that is, it is skipped, or alternatively it may be considered to be executed and then un-executed.

```
       BNZ     label
       OR      R1,R2,R3     ;This instruction is only executed
                            ;when the branch is taken.
```

Predicted conditional branching. With branch instructions it is not always worthwhile having the ability to overlap as it may not provide any additional benefit if sometimes the branch is taken and sometimes it isn't. This can be improved upon by using predicted conditional branching which seeks to identify the probability of a branch being taken (or not). This is then combined with the ability to decide whether the overlapping instruction is executed when the branch is taken, or alternatively when it is not taken. For example, when conditional branching is turned ON, the immediately following register-only instruction is executed when the branch IS taken (and has to be un-executed if the branch is not taken). When conditional branching is turned OFF, the immediately following register-only instruction is executed when the branch is NOT taken (and therefore has to be un-executed if the branch is taken).

If the predicted result of a branch is incorrect then the overlapped instruction has to be un-executed which incurs a time penalty. Predicting which state to use is not that difficult, for example in most repeated loops it would need to be ON (as the branch is nearly always taken) and for tests for error states it would be OFF (as the branch should never be taken). An optimising compiler can predict most branches but where it could not a NOP would be used so that the program execution is not affected.

Unrolling Loops

Overlapping and predicted branching can minimise loop overheads but it is much better to remove the branch instructions altogether, if possible. This is called unrolling loops, as the set of instruction is repeated in sequence a number of times.

Examples

Example of a loop before unrolling. The following loop is to be executed three times.

4		Instruction_a
4	HERE	Instruction_b
4		Instruction_c
4		Test
10		branch to HERE
	Instruction_a	;overlapped with the ;following instruction.

This requires 78 clock cycles to complete and occupies 6 instructions worth of memory space. Examples of an unrolled loop follows:

4	Instruction_a
4	Instruction_b
4	Instruction_c
4	Instruction_a
4	Instruction_b
4	Instruction_c
4	Instruction_a
4	Instruction_b
4	Instruction_c

This requires a total of 36 clocks, virtually half the previous program, but is does require 9 instructions-worth of memory. It is therefore significantly faster but also occupies much more program memory space. However, as memory space is relatively cheap RISC devices make use of optimising compilers to

unroll loops to obtain maximum instruction execution rates.

Software Interlock Checking

As already mentioned where possible software is used to determine whether various sequences of instructions will be possible.

LOAD	mem_1,R1
OR	R1,R2,R1

If the above two instructions were overlapped the dependency on R1 would mean that the result of this sequence would be undefined. (Note that this would not even be detected as a fault as the hardware logic to detect it is left out to achieve higher clock rates.)

With software Interlock checking. If the assembler or compiler being used has this software interlock checking built into it, then the above program would be converted to something such as:

LOAD	mem_1,R1
<register-only instruction not using R1>	
OR	R1,R2,R1

If a suitable register only instruction cannot be found then a NOP would be used.

Architecture

As well as all the features described previously related to the instruction set itself, RISC devices make use of several computer hardware architecture features to increase instruction execution rate.

Fixed instruction length equal to the bus width. By making the instruction length equal to the bus width all the instructions can be fetched in one bus cycle, and the logic associated with the Program Counter in the RISC can be simplified (it will always increment the PC by 1 unless a program branch is made), so that it can execute faster.

Pipelining

There are two main types of pipelining:

(1) Instruction prefetch
(2) Overlapping of instruction

With instruction prefetch, unused bus slots are used to fetch instructions before they are required. These are then stored in the instruction prefetch queue as illustrated in *Figure 5.49* and it must be remembered that the program counter is pointing to the next instruction to be fetched, not the next instruction to be executed. *Figure 5.50* shows an instruction sequence when there is no prefetching showing the three main stages of instruction execution: fetch, decode, execute without prefetch, and then showing the same sequence assuming 100% prefetch, which will be 33% faster.

The second form of pipelining overlaps instructions or parts of instructions so that multiple instructions are executing simultaneously. This is illustrated in *Figure 5.51* and shows how prefetched instructions which can overlap the decode of one instruction with the execute of the previous instruction, achieves a 66% increase in the instruction execution rate.

The drawback of pipelining, apart from the complexity, is that branches disrupt the prefetching. The program counter increments past the presently executing instruction but it cannot decode the instruction to identify branches and it wouldn't know what to do if it could. So every time a branch is taken, the contents of the prefetch queue have to be discarded, causing a temporary slowdown of the instruction execution rate, as the queue is flushed

and new instructions fetched. This is illustrated in *Figure 5.52*. This slow-down is often called a 'bubble' in the pipeline.

Demultiplexed Bus Systems

With multiplexed bus systems, the address and data signals are time multiplexed onto the same physical connections, in order to reduce the number of pin connections the microprocessor component requires, as illustrated in *Figure 5.53*. However, by using a demultiplexed bus time can be saved by not doing the demultiplexing, as illustrated in *Figure 5.54*. The disadvantage of this is that the number of physical connections is increased so that most RISC devices have large numbers of pins.

Burst-Mode Memory Access

One problem being increasingly encountered is that the RISC microprocessor is able to operate at a much higher clock rate than the memory components, and although the amount of memory accessing is reduced for RISC compared to CISC, there is still a need to improve the memory access rate as much as

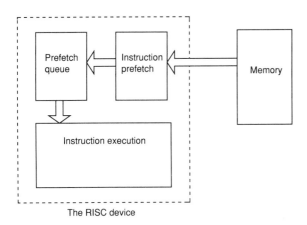

Figure 5.49 Instruction Prefetching

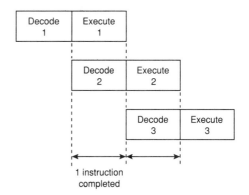

Figure 5.51 (Prefetched) overlapped instructions

Non prefetched instructions

Fetch	Decode	Execute	Fetch

With 100% prefetched instructions

Decode	Execute	Decode	Execute

33% faster instruction execution rate

Figure 5.50 Effect of prefetching instructions

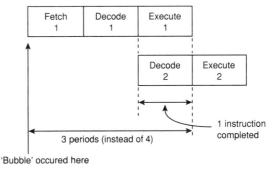

Figure 5.52 'Bubbles' in instruction pipelining

possible. One method of achieving this is to use burst-mode memory components.

Normal memory components require an address to be output for each new data value. By using burst-mode memory access, as illustrated in *Figure 5.55* only one address is output, which is the beginning of the block. The memory component then has a built-in address counter which is automatically incremented after each data access, so that the average transfer rate is significantly increased. This is only effective for blocks of memory access of consecutive memory locations and is usually limited to a maximum block size of 256 bytes (an 8-bit address counter in the memory component). However, a significant amount of computer timer is spent moving blocks of memory from one position in memory to another, so that burst-mode memory accessing can improve the system performance.

Separate program and data memory buses (called the Harvard Architecture). By having separate program and data memory buses, as illustrated in *Figure 5.56*, both instructions and data can be accessed simultaneously which can be much quicker. The drawbacks are that data and instructions cannot normally be mixed, although this is not usually much of a constraint for RISC systems, but more importantly, twice as many physical pin connections are required and twice the number of memory components are required which is more expensive.

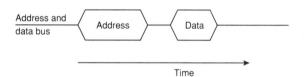

Figure 5.53 Multiplexed address and data

Figure 5.54 Demultiplexed address and data bus

Figure 5.55 Burst-mode memory access

Memory Caches

Due to the improvements in the architecture and technology used to construct the RISC devices, the required memory access time has been reduced to between 10 and 35 nanoseconds. Memory components with access times in this range are available but they are expensive and require more power and hence generate more heat. Burst mode access can make some difference but an alternative is to use a memory cache.

A memory cache is a small block of very high speed memory placed between the slower (and hence much cheaper) and larger main memory system, as illustrated in *Figure 5.57*. The aim of the cache is to keep all the instructions and data values required by the program in the cache memory, to allow high speed access. If the instruction or data is not in the cache then a cache 'miss' occurs and a slower access to main memory has to be made.

The 'hit rate' of the cache is the percentage of accesses which were able to obtain the required information directly from the high speed cache. To be useful a cache should have a minimum hit rate of at least 90% with 95% being a much more satisfactory average. It is not possible to obtain a 100% hit rate unless the cache is the same size as the main memory which would render the main memory unnecessary.

Cache operation. If the instruction fetches and data reads are in the cache then no further action is taken. If the item is not in the cache then the following process occurs:

(1) A line in the cache is discarded;
(2) A new line is fetched from the main memory containing the required item.

The result of this is that a time penalty is incurred hence the need for a hit rate of 90% or greater.

A line is a consecutive sequence of bytes of memory values (instructions or data) which can vary from one byte up to the size of the cache. If the line size is small to minimise the time penalty

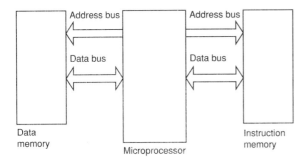

Figure 5.56 Separate data and instruction bus systems

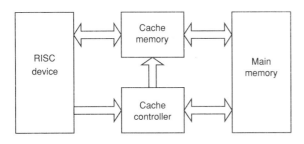

Figure 5.57 Cache memory system

incurred when updating the cache, the hit rate can drop as the required items are not in memory. If the line size is too long so that the hit rate increases, then the time penalty incurred during a miss also increases as more bytes have to be transferred from main memory to the cache. Therefore, an optimum line will be chosen for the specific system being used, with an average value being 16 bytes.

Writing to memory. If the data items being written to are already in the cache then the access takes place at cache speed (that is very fast) and the cache controller ensures that the main memory is updated with the new value, which takes much longer but is invisible to the microprocessor. Successive writes to cached data locations will fill the cache buffers so that the cache controller cannot update the main memory fast enough and a temporary halt will be made in program execution until the buffers have been cleared.

If the data value is not in cache then a write through cache is performed to the main memory, which will be at the much slower main memory access rate. This will also be a cache miss so that a cache update will also be made.

Cache controller. The cache controller has a complex function to perform and is usually at least as complex as the microprocessor itself and will have a certain amount of programmability designed into it so that it can be optimised for each specific computer system.

The main programmable elements are:

(1) The cache size itself;
(2) The line size to be used when updating the cache;
(3) The deletion algorithm used to decide which existing line of data in the cache is to be deleted when a cache miss occurs.

If the RISC has the Harvard Architecture which is the dual instruction and data bus system, then two cache controllers can be used, as illustrated in *Figure 5.58*, which is twice as expensive.

Summary

The result is that a RISC architecture enables a considerably higher value of MIPS to be attained, with the equivalent semiconductor technology used for a CISC architecture, for equivalent programs. Therefore, by using a RISC architecture for the 80% of programs for which it is more efficient than the CISC, considerable improvements in system performance are easily achievable. This is confirmed by the recent availability of RISC architectures from Motorola (88000) and Intel (80860), two of the major microprocessor manufacturers.

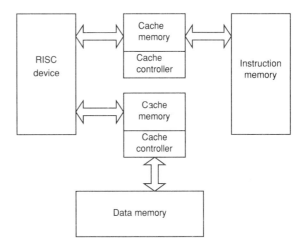

Figure 5.58 Dual cache system

These companies also produce mainstream CISC architecture microprocessors (68030 and 80386, 80486) and this illustrates that the RISC architecture is not the best solution in every situation. There is still a requirement for the more sophisticated and powerful instruction sets using CISC architectures due to the increasing use of workstations for computer-aided design and manufacture.

These need to perform complex operations on large amounts of highly structured mathematical data, at high speeds. Existing RISC architectures do not yet achieve the same system performance levels that CISC architecture can provide in this area and it is probable that both architectures will continue to be developed in the near future and then used where each is most appropriate.

SIX

Software development

6.1 INTRODUCTION

Software can be considered to be the changeable, or 'soft' part of a computer-based control system and hardware can be considered to be the unchangeable, or 'hard' part. Some systems implement software as part of the hardware, for example, by using programmable memory components in such a way that changes in the software require changes in the hardware. An alternative name used for the software is program and these two terms are used interchangeably.

The Software Design Process

The production of good quality, reliable and maintainable software is a difficult process and there are many guidelines and techniques available which will help. The choice of a particular design method is determined before the project begins so that all programmers involved are using the same one. A description of all of the techniques is beyond the scope of this book. Instead, a series of guidelines will be presented and a simple method of program development used to present the general principles and concepts.

The following nine points can be used to ensure that all of the important parameters are considered before program design begins:

(1) Involve a software engineer (if possible);
(2) Separate hardware and software;
(3) Design simple well-structured software;
(4) Define the software interfaces;
(5) Produce a problem specification;
(6) Select the programming language (preferable a HLL);
(7) Measure the performance (not always possible before the program is completed);
(8) ROM or RWM-based systems?
(9) Consider the application areas.

Involve a software engineer. The title software engineer is not often used but can be applied to anyone who applies engineering principles to the solution of software problems. As with most engineering projects, the maximum benefit is obtained by involving people with previous experience.

Separate hardware and software. Although software must have some hardware to execute on, it is preferable to design, write and test software without having the hardware available. This ensures that the interface between the software and hardware is fully defined and not assumed based on any experience of using it. This allows the software or hardware, to be changed without affecting the control function, provided the interface is maintained. It also allows the hardware to be developed in parallel if necessary, thereby saving on total project time see *Figure 6.1*.

In some situations where the hardware is an integral part of the software, it may be necessary to include some hardware details in the software definition.

Design simple, well-structured software. Although complex and sophisticated software structures are fun to produce, they are not fun to maintain. It is better to write software that uses a minimum of sophisticated structures, which is simple to use and easy to understand and maintain. This enables someone else to take over maintenance or development without any major difficulties. Only if there is a speed or size restriction would it be necessary to use complex programming structures.

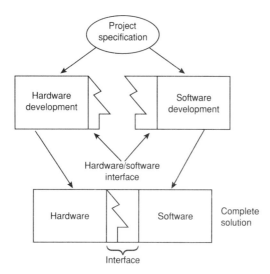

Figure 6.1 Parallel development of hardware and software

With most programs there is no real restriction on the size of the program as most computers have large blocks of memory available. If not, it is usually cheaper and simpler to add memory to a computer, rather than changing the program to make it shorter. The same is true for the speed of execution of a program, where it is much easier to obtain a faster computer than it is to make an existing program execute at a faster rate.

Define the software interfaces. One of the effects of structured programming is that different parts of the program interact at specific points in specific ways called interfaces. There are three types of interface that are of interest:

(1) The user interface;
(2) The hardware interface;
(3) The software interface.

The specification must first define how each of these interfaces is to operate and the program must then follow it exactly during implementation.

Produce a problem specification. In order to write a program to solve a problem or perform some control function, it must be defined in terms that the software engineer is able to understand. This enables the program to be written to that specification.

Selecting the Programming Language. Programming languages can be categorised into two main types:

(1) Low Level Languages (LLL);

(2) High Level Languages (HLL).

LLLs convert each program instruction directly into one computer instruction and are usually called **assemblers**. Because of the direct one-to-one conversion process it is possible to convert back from computer instructions into the LLL and this is called disassembly.

HLLs convert each program instruction into two or usually more computer instructions and are known as compiled (or interpreted) languages. The reverse process of converting from the computer instructions back into the HLL is not possible due to the one-to-many conversion.

Once the specification has been written the programming language that is going to be used is selected based upon what the software engineer perceives to be the major requirements of the problem. The language which will produce the optimum solution is chosen, selected in terms of:

(1) Ease of writing the program;
(2) The size of the final program;
(3) The speed of execution.

It should be noted that almost any software problem can be solved by using almost any computer programming language. Some just take longer and require more effort to achieve the desired result.

Why use High Level Languages ? High Level Languages are not the only type of languages that could be used, so the reasoning behind why they are to be used must be made. In general, they have the following advantages:

(1) They allow the fastest speed of development of programs;
(2) The problem orientation of the source language;
(3) They contain a useful inherent structure.

By using structured or modular programming, the following can be achieved:

(a) Each section performs a single well-defined task or a group of tasks.
(b) Program code can be re-used if it is written in a generalised form so that it can be used in a wider variety of programs. The disadvantage of this is that the more general-purpose a piece of program is, the less efficiently in terms of speed and size, it implements a specific task.
(c) Only one entry and exit to each independent section, which enables testing to be performed only at those points to verify the correctness of the module, see *Figure 6.2*.

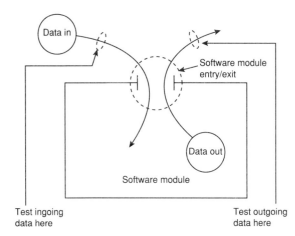

Test ingoing data here

Test outgoing data here

Figure 6.2 A single entry and exit point for each software module

(d) Standard exit methods in the event of the code module failing to complete. It is important that, should a program fail, it should do so in a structured and orderly fashion.

These guidelines are most effective when they are applied to all levels of the program structure.

To decide whether a HLL should be used, the following questions should be asked after the specification has been produced, giving answers for both HLL and LLL. The language which has the most positive set of answers, i.e. the optimum, should be selected.

(i) How easy will it be to design the program ?
(ii) How easy will it be to produce and test the program ?
(iii) How significant would a program failure be ?
(iv) How will errors be corrected or modifications made to the program during its lifetime ?
(v) Can it be kept simple ?

A program should be:

(1) *Error free:* that means that it executes without failure, produces consistent results and fault situations are detected and handled in a manner which prevents the program from crashing ;
(2) *Well defined and meets the specification:* even if a program executes it is still a bad program if it does not meet the specification;
(3) *Easy to understand;*
(4) *Easy to amend;*
(5) *Easy to test;*
(6) *Easy to operate;*
(7) *Efficient;*
(8) *Portable:* this is not so important for embedded systems.

Measure the performance. Because the basic structures underlying all programs can be described in general logic terms and then converted into a specific HLL, it is possible to compare the production of code and its execution, for the same problem, using a variety of HLLs. There are a number of what are called bench marks which can be used to make relative judgements about different programming languages and hardware configurations.

ROM or RWM-based systems ? One factor which has a significant effect on the choice of programming language selected is whether the program will be executing from ROM or from RWM. If executing from ROM, the program will be called embedded as it effectively becomes part of the hardware, as it cannot be changed without changing the hardware, i.e. the ROMs. This type of program is designed not to be changed during its lifetime and to perform a specific control function. The alternative of non-embedded programs are stored in permanent memory which could be ROM but is usually floppy or hard disks and transferred into RWM to be executed. There are two main reasons for doing this. The first is that it allows several different programs to be stored and then one selected and executed. This process can be repeated any number of times. The second reason is that it enables programs to be developed and enhanced with time, rather than being fixed as embedded programs are.

Personal Computers are a good example of the use of both embedded and non-embedded programs. The BIOS which controls the interface between the operating system and the hardware is stored in ROM, where it cannot be changed and is therefore embedded. This is not a problem as the programs are specific to the computer hardware they are being used on. Programs loaded from the disk system used are not embedded as they are transferred into RWM before they are executed and they can be updated and altered.

This illustrates an additional feature of non-embedded software, which is that it is usual to have an operating system executing on the computer hardware to control how other programs execute, see *Figure 6.3.*

Some of the many services offered by an operating system are:

(1) Real time clock;
(2) Interrupt handling;
(3) Memory manager;
(4) Some debugging facilities;
(5) Disk file management software;
(6) Program-to-program communication.

In addition, some operating systems have features which enable real-time control to be implemented and are therefore known as real-time kernels, or **multi-tasking** operating systems. These enable a non-embedded program to execute and at the same time respond immediately to specified external events. This is normally achieved using embedded programs but these have less flexibility.

Consider the application areas. There are four main categories of computer programs:

(1) Sequential operations, i.e. one after the other;
(2) Logical operations;
(3) Closed loop operations, which are repeated time after time;
(4) Numerical operations or programs, where arithmetic operations are performed on sets of numbers, the results of which have some meaning to the user. For example, a 3-D drafting package which is displaying a view of some item. When the viewpoint is changed, the positions of all the lines on the screen have to be recalculated.

The particular application area can have a direct effect on the particular programming language chosen and the method of software design used. In addition to the consideration of ideal effects which may result in the choice of the optimum language for a

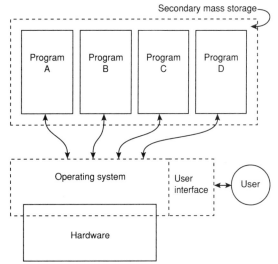

The user selects the program to be executed and the operating system fetches it from the secondary mass storage into the hardware where it is executed

Figure 6.3 Non-embedded systems

particular problem, there are several practical considerations which have to be made.

Key areas for industrial applications. When considering software solutions for industrial applications there are several important factors:

(1) Single board computer versus custom design;
(2) Interrupt handling and subroutine linkage;
(3) Compiler versus interpreter
(4) Timing;
(5) Performance measurement:
    (a) Speed of execution;
    (b) Memory requirements;
    (c) Efficiency of I/O statements;
    (d) Speed of I/O;
    (e) Speed of memory access;
    (f) Interrupt response time;
(6) Debugging;
(7) Language availability.

Software Design

Once the consideration of all the points raised previously has been made, the remaining parts of the software design process can be implemented. The development of software can be considered to fall into three parts:

(a) Specification;
(b) Implementation of the specification;
(c) Testing.

Specification. The software specification describes the actions to be performed and the limitations imposed, such as accuracy. The operation of the software is outlined functionally using generalities and should be independent of the programming language. The specification may define the interfaces between different sections as this is helpful for modular techniques of design, but it will not contain any detailed descriptions of the implementation. The aim is to produce an error-free specification and if detailed internal details are included which are hardware or software dependent, there may be problems at a later stage if the hardware or software is changed.

The aim of the specification is to produce a set of written documents which specify the complete program or software operation with all of the interfaces defined, before any programming is performed or the computer language selected. This allows all programmers working on a particular project to work to the same specific defined standard, against which they can measure the operation and performance of their programs. Once the program has been completed, the specification is used as the basis of the tests devised to ensure its correct operation. A group of programmers working on a large program can use the specification to understand how their particular part contributes to the whole.

Implementation of the specification. The design of software can be considered to be three distinct but inter-related processes:

(1) Algorithm design;
(2) Flowchart or pseudo-code design;
(3) Program writing.

The first two sections should be independent of the computer and language being used. Various computers and languages can be used, each of which has advantages and disadvantages in solving categories of problems. Computers vary from those designated as microcomputers which contain a microprocessor as the central processing unit (CPU), through to mainframe computers which implement special architectures designed to increase the number of instructions executed per second. Languages also vary between the two main types, High Level Languages, (HLL), and Low Level Languages, (LLL).

Although the design of algorithms and flowcharts should be independent of the computer language used, as a general guideline, assembly languages are better designed using flowcharts and high level languages using pseudo-code, but either process can be used for either type of language.

Algorithm Design

An algorithm is a short set of logical English-like statements which when executed sequentially will perform the required task. An example would be the tasks to be performed when walking through a closed door, as illustrated by the following algorithm.

(1) Approach the door;
(2) Turn the door handle and open the door;
(3) Go through the door;
(4) Turn and close the door;
(5) Continue journey.

The number of statements in the algorithm should be minimised and should never be more than 10 or 12. The statements themselves should make no reference to the hardware, or only general references, in order to make the solution as general purpose as possible. A general-purpose solution is a

sign of good programming as the solution can be applied to other similar problems without having to start the design process from the beginning. This leads to increased programmer output which in turn produces cheaper programs, of a higher quality and reliability as the general solutions will have had previous testing and use.

The algorithm statements may contain decisions and/or jump conditions. These generally take the form of:

IF <condition> THEN <action1> ELSE <action2>

with the ELSE <action2> being optional. Using the example of passing through a closed door, if the door had already been opened the initial algorithm would probably produce an error situation by attempting to open an already open door. This could be avoided by changing the second statement to a conditional statement:

(1) Approach the door;
(2) If the door is open then goto (3) else turn the door handle and open the door;
(3) Go through the door;
(4) Turn and close the door;
(5) Continue journey.

This solution will always leave the door closed which may be acceptable, but in some circumstances, it may be desirable to leave the door open if it was already open. This can be achieved by changing statement (4) to a conditional statement with no optional ELSE <action2>:

(1) Approach the door;
(2) If the door is open then goto (3) else turn the door handle and open the door;
(3) Go through the door;
(4) If the door was originally closed then turn and close the door;
(5) Continue journey.

The original algorithm has been improved by considering an increased set of initial conditions. These form the input data to the problem and the increased set of possible conditions prevents situations from occurring which could cause the program to fail. Further consideration of the problem may introduce other conditions requiring alternative actions which may in turn introduce other problems. It is the programmer's responsibility to consider all the possible input conditions and design suitable responses to enable the program to continue executing correctly. The ability to continue executing for all input conditions is considered to be a measure of the program's reliability. The ability to produce 'useful' results for these situations is a measure of its robustness. For large programs which have complex data input situations, 50% or more of the program may be concerned with checking the validity of the input conditions with the purpose of excluding those which are invalid and re-organising those that are correct into a more useful format. Of the remaining 50% of the program, 45% will be involved in coping with the special input data conditions which occur infrequently and in recovering from any errors caused by invalid inputs which have passed undetected through the previous input checking, or other errors caused by unknown situations. The remaining 5% of the program will be concerned with implementing the basic function required by the specification.

Pseudo-Code

An alternative to using flowcharts is to use pseudo-code. This technique also breaks down the problem into smaller and smaller sub-problems until they can be solved directly. Pseudo-code consists of English-like statements which approximate to the program language that will be used for development of the program proper. This technique is normally used when programming in High Level Languages as the pseudo-code English-like statements will often be similar to the program statements of the HLL being used. The following is a brief list of the most common statements used in pseudo-code:

(1) IF <condition> THEN <action>
(2) IF <condition> THEN <action1> ELSE <action2>
(3) WHILE <condition> DO <action>
(4) REPEAT <action(s)> UNTIL <condition>
(5) All the normal arithmetic and trigonometric functions.
(6) Any English-like statements which are used to represent more complex action.

An <action> can contain one or more simpler <actions> grouped together with a BEGIN ... END structure. For example:

```
WHILE on holiday DO
  BEGIN
    get up and have breakfast
    go to seaside and get brown
  END
```

Complex statements can be expanded as required using separate pseudo-code blocks so that the <actions> become simpler and simpler until a point is reached at which the <actions> can be directly implemented in the chosen HLL. To identify when a

complex statement is being simplified the PROCE-DURE label is used, as illustrated below:

```
PROCEDURE get up and have breakfast
BEGIN
  get out of bed
  get washed and dressed
  IF in hurry
    THEN have cornflakes ELSE have bacon and eggs
  wash up
END
```

Unlike flowcharts which are rigidly defined, pseudo-code is flexible and can be adapted to suit the solution required. This variety of solutions has many similarities to Pascal from which many of the statements have been derived, but avoids the rigid syntax restrictions of Pascal. The aim of pseudo-code is to produce a series of English-like statements organised into a logical structure, which describe the way the solution to the problem will work and can be implemented. This may be illustrated by using the central heating controller problem outlined below.

Example

As an example of producing the pseudo-code for a problem, the design of the software for a central heating controller will be outlined, see *Figure 6.4*.

The nature of the problem. As this is a fairly common situation and most people will be familiar with the use and operation of central heating, a common sense problem definition will be used. In most situations, however, it would be necessary to consult an expert in the problem area to obtain a

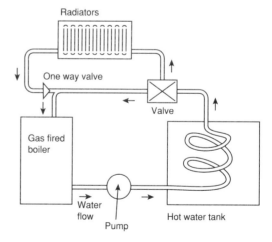

Figure 6.4 Central heating systems

comprehensive and reliable definition. The problem is defined as:

(1) It is a gas fired boiler.
(2) There is a pump for the central heating and hot water. (Note: the domestic hot water supply is heated by the same boiler as the water for the central heating but the two water systems are completely separate.)
(3) A solenoid valve is used to turn the water supply to the radiators on or off.
(4) The domestic hot water is governed by a thermostat (0 to 85° Centigrade).
(5) There is a room thermostat which measures the room temperature (0 to 25° Centigrade).
(6) When the domestic hot water temperature is below the thermostat setting the boiler is in operation (valve can be open or closed).
(7) When the room temperature is below the room thermostat setting the boiler is in operation and the valve open.

The solution. From this problem definition there are certain points to be noted which, in this particular instance, lead to the solution:

(1) If either of the temperatures drops below the appropriate thermostat setting the boiler is in operation;
(2) If the boiler is in operation the valve is only open in situations where the room temperature is below the room thermostat setting.

The above two points constitute the algorithm which can now be converted into a pseudo-code program prior to final implementation using a programming language.

```
PROGRAM central heating controller
BEGINning of the program
  REPEAT
    IF either temperature drops below the settings
      THEN turn on the boiler
      ELSE turn the boiler off
    IF the boiler is on THEN
      BEGIN
        IF room temperature is less than room
        thermostat setting
          THEN open the valve
          ELSE close the valve
      END
  UNTIL controller is reset
END of program
```

Before converting the pseudo-code into an executable program, the optimum programming language can be chosen.

6.2 COMPUTER PROGRAMMING

Once the solution to the problem has been developed using some symbolic structure this can now be transferred into the language selected. There are a variety of languages which have been developed for these processes, each of which fulfils different specific needs. The simplest is **machine code** which converts the flowchart or pseudo-code directly into the binary 0's and 1's that are directly executable by the microprocessor. This provides the greatest control over the hardware but the programs are extremely difficult to write and to change if a fault is discovered. A preferred alternative which is available for all computers, is **assembly language** which replaces the binary codes with English-like mnemonics representing the action required. These are then converted into the machine code by an assembler, which converts each mnemonic into a machine code. Because of this direct relationship between mnemonics and machine code, the reverse translation from machine code to mnemonics can also be performed, by a **disassembler**. Disassemblers are not often required as the original program source file should be available, but if this has been lost then a disassembler allows some of the original program text to be reproduced. Unfortunately because label names and comments are not converted into machine code these cannot be recovered and a program source file which does not contain labels or comments is difficult to understand.

The assembler uses the mnemonic instructions contained in the source file as its input and produces a file containing only machine code as its output, called a relocatable file. Other files may also be produced which provide the programmer with additional information. The main additional file is the listing file which contains a copy of the original source file, but with additions such as the machine code produced, linked to the appropriate mnemonic instruction, the date, time and equipment used, lists of label names, locations and initial values.

Assembly languages allow a large degree of control over the hardware itself and like machine codes, are specific to each particular type of microprocessor and CPU. Because of this, the programs become hardware-specific and cannot be transferred easily to other types of computer.

As programs are expensive to write, languages which are more general purpose and independent of the hardware have been designed and these are generally known as High Level Languages. The aim is to write the program in line with the restraints of the model of the language normally called the **syntax** so that an intermediate 'halfway code' is produced which cannot be executed but which is logical and simple. A second process called compiling is then applied which converts the mathematical model instructions into instructions for the microcomputer or computer being used. In this way, by simply changing the conversion program, it is possible for programs written to execute on one computer, to execute on a completely different type of computer. It is usual for modern **compilers** to contain both the syntax checker and compiler.

Compilers produce more than one machine code instruction from a single HLL instruction and may produce several tens of machine code instructions. Complex HLL instructions may produce several hundred machine code instructions. Also, compilers from different companies designed for the same language and for the same target microprocessors are likely to produce different sequences of machine code for exactly the same HLL instruction. This is due to the general-purpose nature of HLL and the many ways in which the conversion process can be implemented by the compiler writer. This prevents the conversion of machine code instructions back into the original HLL so de-compilers do not exist.

The conversion program which is usually called a compiler, is based upon a mathematical model which contains a large degree of error checking in three basic categories:

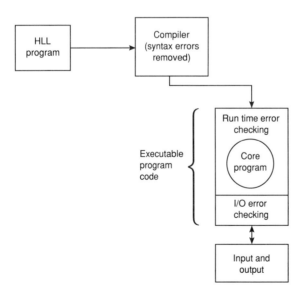

Figure 6.5 Error checking

(1) Syntax checking;
(2) Run-time errors;
(3) Input/output errors.

Syntax errors may take the form of spelling errors, instructions which break one of the rules of the model, missing characters such as statement terminators and so on, see *Figure 6.5*. Run-time errors occur when the program is executing and are generally caused by unforeseen input data combinations for which the programmer did not provide suitable responses. This type of error cannot be detected by syntax checking so, for example, a program structured to select one of ten options will produce a run-time error if an eleventh input occurs. To detect run-time errors additional code is included by the compiler as most of the potential areas of conflict can be easily identified. This extra code takes up program memory and takes time to execute, but does not contribute to the operation of the program except in error checking. To avoid a permanent overhead of extra program size and slower overall execution a program may be developed with run-time error checking included and then when confidence in the correctness of the program operation is high, the run-time checking sections can be removed using a simple instruction to the compiler.

Input and output errors occur when data and information must be passed between the computer implementation of the mathematical model of the language and the hardware of the computer. These are normally caused by the hardware configuration not matching that expected by the mathematical model. For example, there may be no disks in the the disk drives or some part of the hardware may have broken down. Generally these situations are only temporary and are controllable by the user and do not indicate that the program is wrong. However, it is usually possible to reduce the effects of these types of errors by the inclusion of input/output error recovery routines. Again, input/output error checking requires additional instructions but these are not normally removed when the program is executing correctly, because the probability of I/O errors, breakdown or human error does not diminish with the passing of time, whereas the probability of run-time errors does.

There are two main types of high level languages, interpreted and compiled. **Interpreted languages** use the original source code file as input each time the program is executed and take each statement in turn, convert it into executable instructions and then execute them. The run-time conversion process consumes additional time so that interpreted programs execute much slower than compiled programs. The advantages of interpreted programs are that program development takes place in real-time, i.e. there is no delay between adding an instruction to the program and then executing it, and that interpreters can be very small programs. This makes them suitable for use in microcomputers which only have a small amount of program memory and no disk drives. The popularity of interpreters is now declining as the price of disk drives and memory components drops so that even the cheapest microcomputer can have large amounts of program memory and a disk drive.

Compiled languages, of which Pascal and C are perhaps the most popular, use a compiler to convert the source code into the executable code file. The conversion process may take place as two separate processes, known as Pass 1 and Pass 2 or the two operations may be performed simultaneously in which case the compiler will be known as a one pass compiler. Pass 1 is a syntax check and Pass 2 converts the source program into an executable program.

Interfacing to machine code. It is possible to interface sections of program code written in assembly languages to both interpreted and compiled High Level Languages, in order to make more efficient use of the hardware of the computer. The final absolute object code must always be executable machine code. Including assembly language routines in a HLL program restricts the use of the developed programs to that specific type of computer unless the equivalent assembly language routines for another microprocessor are going to be developed.

Due to the wide range of HLLs it is not possible to outline a general structure or syntax although there are some general concepts which the majority implement. These form the basic structures available in the pseudo-code outlined previously which is why those features were included and allows a quick conversion from pseudo-code into the chosen language. In addition, the following points may be useful when attempting to select which HLL to use for a particular task.

Choosing a Language

There are some questions which the potential user should ask about a language before choosing it to solve a problem. The questions do not necessarily have an absolute right or wrong answer, but they may enable the user to identify whether the language is suitable in the particular context being used. Once the language has been chosen it will be virtually impossible to change later on due to the investment that will have been made in purchasing it, learning about it and implementing a particular problem, However, it should be noted that often these questions are not even asked because the decision will have already been made by external forces such as: 'It's what everybody else uses, so will we' or 'It's what we've always used' or 'We've got it already, so it's the one to use'. However, if there is the potential to make a choice then there are some useful questions to ask:

(1) *Maturity of the language:* Is the definition of the language stable, who has defined or standardised the language, and who has verified that the compiler you are using adheres to the standard ? For example, Pascal was designed by a lecturer teaching programming concepts to undergraduates who required a demonstration language. Therefore the language has a nice syntax and is mostly well structured as those were the main concepts being taught. However, it does not have a particularly good I/O structure as these concepts were not that important, so if the task requires considerable specialised I/O operations Pascal may not be suitable.

(2) *The language background:* what has happened since it was designed, and has it been standardised ? In the case of Pascal again, there is a British Standard definition of Pascal, the *Specification for Computer Programming Language Pascal*, ISO-7185, so that programs which adhere to the standard will be compiled correctly by all compilers which have been verified to meet that standard. This in turn has resulted in a large number of compilers being produced and many programs written in Pascal. Therefore the environment is stable, mature and likely to continue for a considerable time in the future.

(3) *Data structures available and data manipulation methods:* can the data be structured and manipulated with a variety of flexible methods ? This may be important if complex data structures are necessary to solve the program specification and to detect if transfers are attempted between incompatible data types. Pascal provides both these features by only specifying a few basic data types and then allowing the programmer to combine these basic types into as complex a data structure as required. The data type checking then extends to the user-defined data structures making Pascal a very good language as far as this requirement is concerned. It must also be pointed out that the strict data checking of Pascal can be a disadvantage, particularly if some data elements are to be used as one type in one part of the program and as a different type in a different part of the program. If this is required, the program would be better written in a different HLL.

(4) *Portability:* is the standardised version of the language implemented in compilers from a variety of different manufacturers, and/or a variety of different computers ? Portability is important for programmers as it allows general-purpose programs and sections of programs which have been written for previous problems to be re-used in later problems containing similar specifications. This improves programmer productivity and leads to cheaper programs. Pascal has these properties because it is an ISO Standard and has been available for a number of years. This particular requirement means that new HLLs must offer significant advantages before they will be widely accepted and used.

(5) *Cross-compilation:* are there compilers for the language which execute on one computer but which produce executable code for a different code for a different type of computer ? The output of cross-compilers cannot be executed by the host computer so that program verification is more difficult. Cross-compilation is necessary for programs aimed at embedded systems, such as washing machine controllers, where the microprocessor may change in different models of the washing machine, but the same program development computer must be used for all of them.

(6) *Training to write programmes in the language:* is training in writing programs for the particular language easily available and how easy is it to become 'good' (not necessarily expert) at writing such programs ?

If a new language is being considered based on the decisions made in answer to the questions outlined above, then this question becomes important. Assuming that none of the users has any experience in the new language the various factors which affect the cost and time taken for training need to be assessed. For example, if some of the existing personnel have competence in a similar type of language then it can be confidently expected that the overall

training time will be reduced. Also, the availability of training and the standard of the training schemes are important. These factors depend upon previous demand for training for that language which indicates how widespread interest and demand for that language is and also the expected ability of the trainers. A low demand may mean that the trainers are inexperienced and a very high demand may lead to a reduction in the standards of the training schemes. If the training scheme is only offered once a year this may prevent the selection of that particular language, as may the predicted time required to achieve a good level of competence in programming using the new language. A good programmer using an inappropriate language will almost certainly produce better programs than someone who is only partially trained in what is considered to be a better language. If six months experience of writing programs using the language is considered necessary for proper training because of the complexity or the new concepts involved, then the language may not be considered to be optimum at that time.

Table 6.1. Table of advantages and disadvantages

Language	Advantages	Disadvantages
Machine code	Direct control of hardware	Difficult to write Difficult to understand Difficult to change No error detection
Assembly language	English-like statements Easier to understand Some syntax checking Easier to change Quicker to produce	Requires assembler Control of hardware may be reduced slightly
High Level	Independent of hardware Syntax, run-time and I/O error checking increased Quicker to write programs More complex programs possible	Program execution may be slower Produces larger programs Compiler required Large memory and disk drives

Documentation

Every program that is written should be completely documented to ensure that the design is completed before program writing takes place and that the operation of the program can be understood by users who did not originally design the program. The algorithm and flowcharts provide some of that information but the majority of program information will be contained within the program source code as that is the only file which will be consistently maintained by all users and programmers. Therefore the following structure, illustrated in *Figure 6.6*, is advocated for all programs:

(1) Program header;
(2) Data definitions;
(3) Program code with explanations and subroutine/procedure headers.

Program header. This section of the program consists purely of comments which do not contribute anything to the execution of the program itself, but provide information to the user and other programmers concerning the way it was written, executed, designed, tested, updated and what the program is designed to do.

This will take the form of:

(1) Descriptive title (not FRED or BURT but a useful name);
(2) Author(s) name, title, and other relevant information;
(3) Where, when and on what equipment the program was written, and is to be executed upon;
(4) Revision updates, giving short explanations of the reasons for each new version;
(5) Program purpose;
(6) Program operation, and how it works. It is quite acceptable at this point to include the original algorithm, provided it is understandable.

Data definitions. Within the body of the program code, no explicit numbers, such as 27, should be used, as informative names give additional information when 'reading' the program. For example:

Days_in_week = 7 ;

They also enable any changes in constants, or numerical values to be easily made by only changing the definition at the beginning of the program, rather than trying to find the occurrences of 27, which are relevant from those which are not, throughout the program listing.

There are three categories of data definition of interest:

Constants: where labels have a fixed value associated with them which cannot be changed.

Global: variables are defined which can be altered by the program and which can be accessed by **any** part of the program.

Local: these are similar to global variables in that they can be altered under program control, but with the difference that they can only be accessed within the subroutine that they were defined within, not from anywhere else.

Program Structure

Following the data definitions is the program code, if flowcharts have been used then it is best to implement each flowchart as a separate subroutine or procedure, leading to **'nested' subroutines**. These are subroutines called from within subroutines which may contain other subroutines and so on. Nesting subroutines and procedures do result in an increased program execution time due to subroutine entry and exit times. The use of nested subroutines does not contribute directly to the program operation, but for most programs the advantage of a good structure resulting in 'good' programs, outweighs the disadvantage of longer execution times.

Normally the subroutines or procedures are written in the same order, as the flowcharts or pseudocode, with the higher levels, which are more abstract, being near the top of the program code and those which are lower down in the hierarchy dealing with the details of the program execution, being near the bottom of the source code. This is not always possible with some languages such as Pascal, which require the lower levels to appear at the top of the source program and the higher levels to appear at the bottom. There is little difference between using the two methods except to ensure that the user knows which has been used when 'reading' the program source code.

Each of the subroutines can be considered to be a

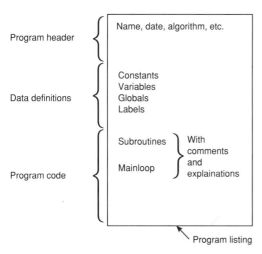

Figure 6.6 Source program structure

mini-program requiring separate subroutine headers, data definitions (if any local variables are being used) and then program code. The subroutine header need not be as comprehensive as the main program header as it is serving a different purpose. It should only contain two or possibly three sections as outlined below:

(1) Sub-routine operation description;
(2) Data passing information;
(3) Data definitions.

A short description informing the reader of the operation of the subroutine is necessary so that an assessment of its importance and usefulness can be made. It also enables the positions of any updates to be more easily identified. For example, if the data structure of a program is to be changed then the subroutine header which contained the statement 'sets up the data structure for the program' would be a better place to make changes than one which contained 'interfaces with the user to display the date and time'.

To be a useful program, most of the subroutines will perform a data processing task which may be to output data only, to accept data only, or to accept and output data. Therefore the ways in which data is transferred between subroutines must be defined in the subroutine header so that any changes will not affect this process.

There are two main methods of passing data between subroutines or procedures which are dependent on the language being used: global variables and subroutine or procedure definitions.

If High Level Languages are used it is normal to pass parameters or data via the procedure definition as this is the preferred method, being the most general purpose.

By using the procedure definition the data manipulation is localised within the specific procedure which is considered good programming practice. In addition it simplifies program testing as it is only necessary to look at data going in to and out of a subroutine to verify it is working correctly or not. If global variables are used and a wrong value is obtained, it is extremely difficult to identify the error position as it could be anywhere in the program.

6.3 DEVELOPMENT SYSTEMS

So far only the functions of software development have been discussed not the methods of performing them. Most of the functions are based upon computers or computer controlled interfaces and hardware. The systems used to produce the software are called 'development systems' as they develop the software and the hardware. There are three main types available:

(1) Mainframe environments;
(2) Dedicated systems;
(3) Personal computer add-ons.

These are illustrated in *Figure 6.7.*

Mainframe development environment

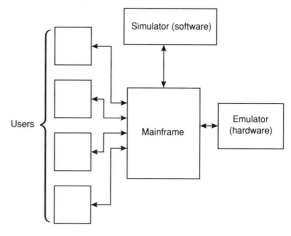

Dedicated development environment

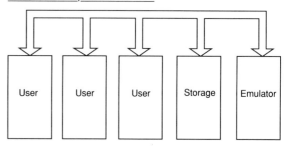

Personal computer development environment

Figure 6.7 Development Systems

Mainframe Environments

Mainframe computers are essentially multi-user time-shared computers and tend only to be used for the development of software, as it is difficult to attach target system hardware. The range of functions that are available are the:

(1) Editing of source files;
(2) Compiling of source files into relocatable files;
(3) The linking of relocatable files and library files to produce HEX files;
(4) Loading the HEX files into a simulator.

If the mainframe system does have suitable connections for downloading the developed HEX files suitable target hardware is required. This could be a SBC with a monitor or a personal computer used as a dedicated development system, see *Figure 6.7.*

Although it is possible to download from the mainframe to the target system it is not easy to transfer information back to the mainframe system.

This may seem to indicate that mainframe development systems have a serious disadvantage. However, mainframe development systems have the significant advantage of providing simultaneous multi-user access to program development facilities. The program development activities available are of a high standard and usefulness and are particularly suited for the development of High Level Language programs. This is because HLL's are designed to be as independent of the target system hardware as possible and only to use general-purpose I/O channels. Only the I/O channels need to be designed specifically for each different target system hardware arrangement and the programmer can be confident that the program will execute correctly.

Pascal is such a language and only requires the target hardware to provide:

(1) A continuous block of RWM of sufficient length to contain the program and the dynamic variables generated as the program is executing;
(2) The implementation of a file access interface;
(3) An interface to input and output ASCII characters to a VDU, often available as a specialised variation of the standard file interface of (2).

Apart from these three basic requirements, Pascal programs will execute correctly on any target hardware for which there is a compiler and often the development system being used will contain compilers for several different microprocessors. This type of compiler is termed a **cross-compiler** as it can generate absolute files for microprocessors other than the host computer, see *Figure 6.8.*

The mainframe environment is ideal for Pascal program development as there is essentially an unlimited amount of RWM available for each user and the file interfaces are sophisticated with many fail-safe characteristics. For example, automatic back-up copies of all files are made which can be retrieved if the original is corrupted. The number and size of files is essentially unlimited and there are archiving facilities for permanently saving files. For large numbers of users such as in a teaching environment, limitations on the amount of RWM available to each user and the number and size of files may be enforced to obtain the efficient use of resources.

Pascal programs developed on the mainframe use the standard I/O file interfaces and when transferred to the target hardware some problems may arise as the compilers for specific microprocessors may not implement the same file interfaces in the same way. This is because the file interface is dependent on the actual hardware components of the target system being used and these may vary from system to system. The sections of the file interface which have not been implemented must then be supplied by the user and this can lead to the introduction of non-standard Pascal I/O interfaces, optimised for a particular configuration of hardware, or which make use of a variation in the standard Pascal syntax to include extra useful facilities.

Software Interfacing. Such customisations are satisfactory for the original target hardware but problems occur when attempting to transfer the program on to a different hardware configuration, or more importantly, using a different Pascal compiler for a different microprocessor. The inability to re-use existing programs without re-writing them leads to a higher product cost with a lower quality and reliability. It was to avoid such problems that languages like Pascal were developed and the use of non-standard file interfaces for these langauges negates their advantages.

Difficulties caused by the use of non-standard I/O techniques can be reduced by performing the I/O operations through a software interface written in Pascal. The I/O operations required are written in such a way that only a small number of procedures are involved in the transfer of characters and data between the Pascal program and the file interface. These can be collected together into a special I/O module which may contain non-standard Pascal in order to obtain high levels of performance. The remainder of the program must then be written in

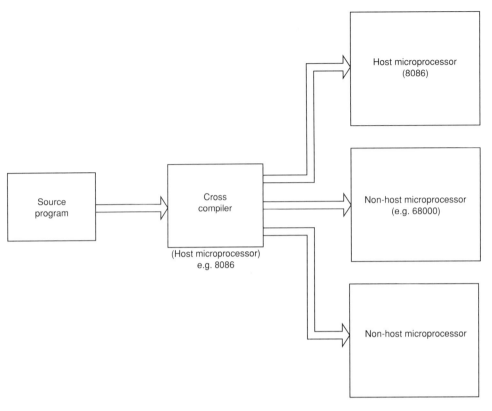

Figure 6.8   A cross-compiler

standard Pascal even if this means sacrificing some flexibility and useful features provided by the particular compiler being used. When the program is transported to a different compiler or when a different target system hardware is used, only the interface controlling the transfer of information between the software and the hardware needs to be re-written.

Once the program has been written and if possible verified on the mainframe environment, it can be transferred either to the target hardware using a download protocol such as Kermit, or loaded into a simulator. The operation of a simulator is described in the next chapter.

Downloading. When downloading from a mainframe to a target system a transfer protocol, which provides additional facilities and error checking and correction options to those available from simple checksum tests, becomes desirable. This is because program files are often of considerable size, several thousand or even several hundreds of thousands of bytes. The communication links between mainframes and the user's terminal have error rates

which lead to corruption of such large downloaded program files. The large size of programs means that it is preferrable to transfer files to an intelligent terminal, such as a personal computer (PC) with terminal emulation, using a transfer protocol. The program can then be transferred from the PC to the target using an ordinary simple serial communication link without using a sophisticated transfer protocol. This is because the communication links between the mainframe and the user's terminal are more likely to corrupt data values due to electrical interface than communication links between the terminal and target. This is mainly due to the distances involved as the probability of the communication link containing errors is proportional to the distance between the transmitting and receiving points. The mainframe to terminal link can be from several hundred metres if in the same building, to many thousands of kilometres if situated in a different country. The normal distance between the terminal and target hardware is less than 2 metres.

The downloading process is complex and requires a method of starting the transmission process, detecting the termination point and implementing some method of handshaking to ensure that the data has been transmitted and received correctly. Handshaking is necessary because other symbols which might be used to indicate the end of a file are valid data values. This can lead to difficulties in terminating the transfer and returning control of the communication link to the user's VDU and mainframe.

The Kermit protocol. This provides the necessary encoding, transmitting, handshaking, error detection and correction operations to transfer files successfully. The operation of Kermit is virtually invisible to the user but does require complete control of the terminal. The user can no longer use the terminal to access the mainframe while the transfer protocol is operating and this has the disadvantage that if the transfer is halted for some reason it can be difficult to regain control of the terminal. However, this does not happen often.

The essential functions of a transfer protocol are that the file being transmitted is split into packets of data, for example 255 bytes long, plus additional codes designed to detect any errors that occur in the transmission process. The individual packets are transmitted one at a time with the receiver checking each packet as it is received for errors. At the end of each packet the receiver sends a message back to the transmitter and if an error is detected, the message returned to the transmitter indicates this. If an error is detected the transmitter will re-transmit the packet. If the re-transmitted packet still contains errors this process is repeated a specified number of times, after which the transmission of the rest of the file is aborted as the communication link is considered to be too unreliable. If there are no errors the transmitter sends the next packet and this is repeated until the end of the file is reached. Then the protocol sends a special message indicating the end of the file has occurred and the transmission process terminates, returning control of the terminal to the user.

Once the program file has been transferred, either to the mainframe-based simulator or to the target hardware, the verification of the program continues using the appropriate methods, as outlined in the next chapter.

If the program is developed in assembler language the mainframe environment does not offer many advantages, other than providing a simultaneous multi-user environment. Programs can be produced using the same editor and then passed to an assembler and linker. Assembler program operation can-

not be verified in the same way as for HLL's unless verified in the mainframe environment, through the use of a simulator.

Dedicated Development Systems

Mainframes are used to perform many tasks other than producing embedded systems software and the hardware costs of a mainframe are large. An alternative is to use a system which has been especially designed for the purpose of software and hardware development. Such systems are termed 'dedicated development systems' and generally provide only single-user environments, as shown in *Figure 6.7*. The editor, compilers, assemblers, linkers and emulators are available to the user as for the mainframe environment but only one of them can be in use at any one time.

It is unusual to provide dedicated development systems with a simulator as they already have emulators. Emulators are superior to simulators as they allow extensive I/O operations to be performed and assuming the target hardware is available, enable real-time operation and verification of the software and hardware combination. The verifications obtained using an emulator are considerably more reliable than those obtained with a simulator so there is no advantage in supplying a dedicated development system with a simulator.

Some dedicated development systems do allow additional work stations to be linked together via a communications network to form a simple **Local Area Network** (LAN), so that some resources can be shared. The most common shared resources are printers, PROM programmers, and permanent file storage in the form of a hard disk drive. If a hard disk system is being used then the system software used by the development system is maintained on it and this enables the same version of the operating system software to be used by all users. This prevents the possibility of some users operating with outdated and possibly incompatible software development facilities.

Work stations. The terminals of dedicated development systems are referred to as 'work stations' as they are able to perform all the software development processes, such as compiling, assembling, linking, and emulation, independently of the rest of the LAN. The only requirement they have is to be able to access the hard disk to obtain copies of the appropriate programs, such as compilers. The work station contains a computer with sufficient RWM,

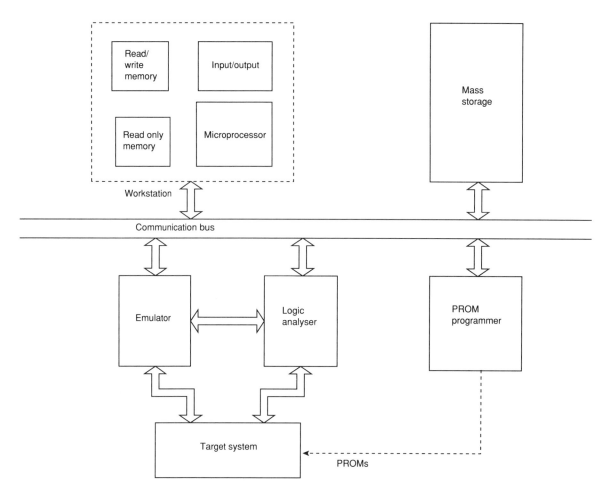

Figure 6.9 Dedicated development system

ROM and I/O functions to execute the software development process. In addition, an emulator, logic analyser and PROM programmer will be available to perform hardware and combined hardware/software verification, see *Figure 6.9*. Generally a work station will be expandable and adaptable by the addition of new printed circuit boards to perform new functions.

The ability to change the printed circuit boards extends the useful life of the dedicated development system which is important as one of the disadvantages of this type of software development system is that it is aimed at specific types of microprocessors. The useful life of dedicated development systems can be extended by making the basic chassis as general purpose as possible and then installing suitable additions to perform the required functions. Such a work station will contain a SBC with a moni-

tor, a memory board, an emulator board and a logic analyser board. In addition some of the work stations may contain a PROM programmer for permanently storing programs in ROM and floppy disk drives for local storage of files. This helps to prevent the work station from becoming obsolete when new microprocessors become available.

Personal Computer Add-ons

The third type of development system which can be used to overcome the problems of dedicated work stations is to use a general-purpose computer such as a Personal Computer (PC), with some additional software and hardware. The software performs some of the development functions and the hardware performs the remainder connected to the PC via a standard communication link such as a RS232C link.

The editing, compilation, assembly and linking are performed as software functions on a computer and operate in a very similar manner to those on the mainframe environment. Like the dedicated development work stations only one person can be using it at a time but the cost per user is much lower, because the PC is a more general-purpose and hence cheaper computer. The compilation, assembling and linking can take longer than for mainframe and dedicated work station environments although if the mainframe has large numbers of terminals active its response time is considerably degraded and the PC may then be faster. With a PC the response time is constant as it is with dedicated work stations, but for mainframes the response time increases as the number of terminals in use increases.

The hardware interface added to the PC performs the emulation and logic analysis functions and is generally specific to a particular microprocessor. The basic operations of the emulator and logic analyser remain the same, such as single step, memory and register display and alteration, but some of the more sophisticated enhancements available on dedicated work stations, such as real-time tracing of program execution may be absent. This is due to the requirement to pass all information via the communication link and the simplicity of the hardware interface. The simplicity is necessary to lower the cost in order to compete with the dedicated work stations, however, a PC with an emulator and logic analyser add-on provides almost the same facilities as dedicated work stations, but at a much lower cost per user. In addition, the PC can be made available to perform other general-purpose computer tasks when not being used as a development system.

If a mainframe environment is available as well as dedicated work stations or PCs with add-on interfaces, then utilisation of the available systems can be optimised. The mainframe environment provides multi-user access with good support for HLLs but only minimal support for assembly languages. The dedicated work stations and PCs with add-ons provide good HLL and assembly language development support, plus hardware development support but for a much more limited number of users. Therefore, where possible programs should be written, developed and verified on the mainframe environment using a simulator and then downloaded via Kermit into the work stations or PCs. The program is then re-compiled and/or re-assembled, re-linked and emulated on the target hardware, knowing that the operation of the program has already been verified. Only real-time verification whilst executing on the target hardware system remains and this is performed much more quickly than for programs that have been developed entirely on the PC. This enables the maximum use to be made of all the existing systems and increases programmer productivity.

SEVEN

HLL software design and examples

7.1 INTRODUCTION TO PASCAL

This chapter will illustrate the principles outlined in the previous chapter, through the use of several case studies. Two main examples will be used: one a simple software-only solution and one requiring some knowledge of the hardware of the computer. Only High Level Languages will be used in the design with both Pascal and C solutions developed from the same specification for the first case study and a Pascal-only solution for the second case study, to demonstrate how the software design process is independent of the final computer language used. This will also demonstrate the requirement for a detailed and accurate specification. The examples used are necessarily simple but will portray the entire design process and will illustrate most problems that occur.

The first part of this chapter provides a brief introduction to both these languages, first Pascal and then C. These introductions are not intended to provide full explanations or guides to the syntax and use of the languages, but to provide an overview and to enable simple programs to be produced. These programs will probably not be particularly elegant or efficient but they should work. They will also enable a better understanding of the case study programs to be gained.

Pascal was designed as a **block-structured language**, which promotes good programming techniques. A block-structured language is one in which the internal parts of the program can be separated into distinct sections, or blocks, which perform a specific operation, see *Figure 7.1*. Each block is self-contained which means that all the information and instructions required to perform the operation are

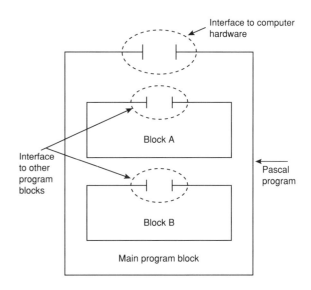

Figure 7.1 A block-structured program

contained within the block, or will be passed to the block.

The block is therefore defined by its internal operation specification, and the interface with the rest of the program. This means that a block can be replaced with a completely different block, provided that the internal operation specification and program interface remain the same.

Blocks can also be nested so that complex operations can be constructed of simpler ones, but the remainder of the program is not involved. Anything inside a block is 'invisible' to any outer blocks, but is visible to any 'inner' blocks.

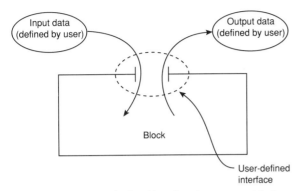

Figure 7.2   The user-defined interface for program blocks

Good Programming Techniques

The input and output of data to and from each block is always made via a single 'user-defined interface', see *Figure 7.2*. This is a user-defined interface as the program language does not define it for you. This allows flexibility.

The variables in each block are then invisible to other blocks and data can only be input and output through the user-defined interface. This enables boundary conditions to be applied to the data passed, and also enables test conditions to be imposed upon the data, if the block contains any errors.

The Pascal-to-Computer Interface

The transfer of information and data between the Pascal program and the hardware of the computer, for example, the floppy disks, keyboard, monitor, etc., is made through a standard interface, using 'files', see *Figure 7.3*. Files are contiguous sequences

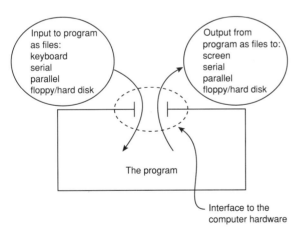

Figure 7.3   The program/file interface

of characters on which several simple operations can be performed. A file can be opened for reading and writing, after which it must then be closed. When opened, a file can be written to, either by making a new file, or adding to an existing file, or can be read from, when the file must already exist.

The standard interface is denoted by the Pascal statement:

```
PROGRAM program_name(INPUT,OUTPUT,file_1,file_2...);
{The rest of the program}
```

where:

program_name can be any sequence of characters defined by the user;

INPUT and OUTPUT are two special filenames, which must always be present, and enable the transfer of characters to the monitor (OUTPUT) and from the keyboard (INPUT);

file_1,file_2 where, if required, other user-defined filenames can be included if information is to be saved after the program has terminated, for example, on a floppy disk.

The line is terminated by the semicolon. This is the Pascal terminator character and indicates to the compiler, that it is the end of the statement. The rest of the program statements follow this line.

Example of Pascal file definitions

```
program quadratic(input,output) ;
{rest of statements}
```

Note that upper and lower case characters can be used anywhere and the compiler will ignore the difference. For example, Quadratic and quadratic will usually be considered to be the same label. However, some compilers do differentiate between two user-defined labels which are spelt the same but the case of the letters is different.

In this document, upper case characters will generally be used to indicate words which have a special meaning to the Pascal compiler, and are known as reserved words. In subsequent appearances, the reserved words may be upper or lower case for clarity.

User-defined Blocks

The remainder of the Pascal program will consist of user-defined blocks, which can be nested if required, that are called Procedures. A procedure has a similar structure to the program statement, except that the name PROCEDURE is used instead of the name PROGRAM, and that the interface is user-defined, and is between the block and the rest of the program, rather than between the program and the hardware.

Example of defining a procedure

procedure proc_name(user_defined_interface) ;
{rest of procedure statements}

A program then consists of one or more, user-defined procedures and a main block of statements. The user-defined interfaces require some data variables to operate on and these are defined at the beginning of the program.

Example of a Pascal program framework

Program quadratic(input,output) ;
   {variable definition}

procedure user_name1(user_defined_interface1) ;
   {rest of procedure statements}

procedure user_name2(user_defined_interface2) ;
   {rest of procedure statements}

BEGIN{main block}
   {user-defined combination of data variables,}
   {Pascal statements and user-defined procedures}
END.

Note: Anything within curly brackets { } is treated as a comment by the Pascal compiler and does not produce any executable program.

The main block is started with the BEGIN statement and finished with the END statement. This is immediately followed by a full stop used to indicate that it is the end of the program source code. Pascal is block-oriented and the blocks can be nested within one another to almost any level. The procedure statement is one method of creating a block, and the BEGIN..END structure is another.

The procedure block has essentially the same structure as the program statement and can consist of user-defined variables and user-defined procedures. They will contain a main loop or block delimited by BEGIN and END, which contains a user-defined combination of data variables and user-defined procedures.

Example of nesting procedure definitions

Procedure example1(user_defined_interface) ;
   {user defined variable definitions}

   procedure internal1(user_defined_interface2) ;
      {procedure internal statements}

{rest of procedure example1 statements}

BEGIN{main loop}
   {user-defined combination of procedures,}
   {variables and Pascal statements}
END ;

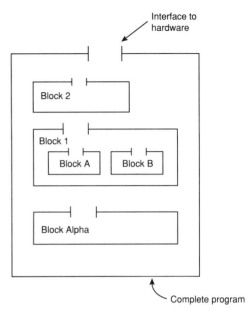

Figure 7.4 Block structures

Additional comments on procedure definitions. Procedure BEGIN . . END blocks are terminated by semicolons not full stops, as they effectively become a user-defined Pascal statement. Therefore they are terminated in the same way as all other Pascal statements.

Internally-defined procedures are optional. If they are defined they can only be used within the procedure within which they were defined. They cannot be used in any other block or the main loop because the block structure renders the internal operation of any block invisible to all other external blocks. An example is given in *Figure 7.4*, where blocks A and B can *only* be used by block1 as they are invisible to block2 and block Alpha. Similarly, only block1 and block2 can be accessed by block Alpha. If block1 is used by block Alpha this will indirectly access blocks A and B. Otherwise blocks A and B cannot be directly accessed. Only procedures defined previously in the program listing can be accessed, so that block2 could not access block1, or block Alpha.

Data Variables

To perform useful actions, a program must have some input data values, perform some actions on these, and output some data values, that is, the result, as indicated in Figure 7.5. The format the data is held in is the type of the data, and the main built-in Pascal types are:

INTEGER : All positive and negative whole numbers.

REAL : All positive and negative scientific numbers.

CHAR : All printable ASCII characters. This means that the character '1' is treated differently to the number 1.

ARRAY : A single or multi-dimensional array of some other type.

The data definitions are started by the VAR statement, and terminated by a BEGIN or PROCEDURE statement.

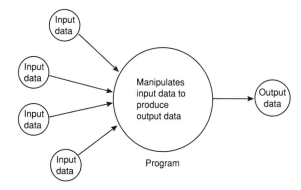

Figure 7.5 Program operation

Example of data definitions

```
VAR
user_name1 : INTEGER ;
user_name2 : REAL ;
BEGIN or PROCEDURE
```

Pascal allows almost any combination and length of characters to be used in user-defined names. This allows 'names' or 'labels' which convey meaning to be used.

Example of useful data labels

```
VAR
number_of_oranges : INTEGER ;
day : CHAR ;
```

The user-defined name is separated from the type definition by a colon, and the type specification is terminated by a semicolon. In general, *all* Pascal statements are terminated by a semicolon, apart from the main block END statement which is terminated by a full stop.

Procedure BEGIN..END blocks. The BEGIN.. END block of the procedure may contain any valid Pascal statements. The most commonly used ones are:

(1) IF <condition true> THEN <action> ;
(2) IF <condition true> THEN <action1> ELSE <action2> ;
(3) REPEAT <actions> UNTIL <condition true> ;
(4) WHILE <condition true> DO <action> ;
(5) CASE <data variable> OF
        <value1> : <action1> ;
        <value2> : <action2> ;
        <valueN> : <actionN> ;
  ELSE <actionN + 1> ;
  END ;
(6) FOR <data variable> := <initial value> TO <final value> DO <action> ;
for example :
factorial := 1 ;
FOR count := 1 TO 10 DO
factorial := factorial * count ;

Each of the <action> statements can be comprised of a separate BEGIN..END block containing more Pascal statements.

Example of a complete Pascal procedure

```
Procedure add ( var number_1 : integer ;
                var number_2 : integer ;
                var result : integer) ;
var
ch : char ;
begin
  writeln('Shall I begin') ;
  readln(ch) ;
  if ch = 'y' then
    begin
      number_1 := number_1 * number_1 ;
      number_2 := number_2 * number_2 ;
      result := number_1 + number_2 ;
    end
  else
    result := number_1 + number_2 ;
end ;{add}
```

Points of Interest.

(1) Data is input from the keyboard using the READ or READLN statement with the receiving variable enclosed in brackets. Output to the display is by using the WRITE or WRITELN statements, again with the appropriate variables or constants within brackets.

(2) The two symbols, :=, can be read as meaning 'becomes equal to', so that : A := B + C is equivalent to A becomes equal to B plus C.

(3) The four arithmetic operations are:
    +   addition,
    –   subtraction,
    *   multiplication,
    DIV integer division,
    /   real number division.

(4) The IF . . THEN statement required the condition to be true or false. Therefore the equality (ch = 'y') is used to obtain such a result. If the variable, ch, contains the letter 'y' then the equality will be true, otherwise it will be false, in which case the second <action> is initiated.

Turbo Pascal

Turbo Pascal is an easy to use variation on standard Pascal, which runs on an IBM PC/XT/AT or close compatible, under the MS-DOS operating system. It is commonly available and is a very powerful, fast and efficient implementation of the Pascal language. However, because it was specifically designed to execute on a PC some of the language constructs are non-standard to make it easier to use and to enable easy access to some of the PC hardware functions such as Input/Output ports. This does mean that programs written specifically for the PC may not compile or execute correctly if ported to other computers and other compilers. The reverse is also likely to be true, so unless the programs have been written specifically to adhere to the ISO standard easy porting of programs from one compiler to another doesn't take place. This problem can be reduced by ensuring that any non-ISO standard features of a version of a Pascal compiler used in a program, are saved in a known part of the program so that they can be easily changed. Some compilers even have a selectable warning function while they are compiling which identify the non-standard use of Pascal (even if it is allowed by that particular compiler).

7.2 INTRODUCTION TO C

C is a more difficult language to learn than Pascal, after all Pascal was defined as a teaching language, whereas C was defined as an aid to writing an operating system so is good for writing useful programs, but is more difficult to learn. For your first program, enter the following (into the Turbo C environment):

```
/* HELLO.C—Hello, World */
#include <stdio.h>
main ()
{
printf("Hello, World\n") :
}
```

The above illustrates the simplest program used to introduce the C programming language which just displays the message 'Hello World' on the computer display.

As an additional exercise, add a second printf statement containing: My name is .... Save this in a file called name_C. Now recompile and execute the program.

Programming

The purpose of any program is: to solve problems. The programmer's purpose is to:

(a) Get information into program;
(b) Keep it somewhere;
(c) Manipulate it;
(d) Output results to user.

The Seven Elements of C

There are seven basic elements of C programming, or any other language, which are listed below:

(1) Data types;
(2) Input;
(3) Operations;
(4) Output;
(5) Conditional execution;
(6) Loops;
(7) Subroutines.

Output of data and information using PRINTF.
First, the output of data and/or information will be considered so that the simplest programs can be produced. Note that the first program only performed output. Printf writes information to the screen and has the following syntax:

```
printf (<format string>, <item>,<item> . . .),
```

The format string, which must be enclosed in double quotes (" "), contains text and indicators where data values, taken from the item sequence are to be inserted. These indicators start with a % and are followed by one or two letters which indicate the data type.

Example of PRINTF

```
printf("The sum is %d \n",sum) ;
```

Note: \n indicates that a linefeed is to be performed at that point in the format string.

Some of the data types available are:

%u	Unsigned integer
%ld	Long integer
%p	Pointer value
%d	Integer
%f	Floating-point number
%e	Floating-point (exponential)
%c	Character
%s	String
%x	Integer in hexadecimal format

Field width of displayed data values. The printed length of the item can be specified by inserting a number between the % symbol and the letter indicating the data type: %4d which indicates an integer 4 characters wide.

Other output methods. There are a number of alternative output functions which are simpler to use, execute quicker, but do not have the flexibility of printf. For example: puts( ) writes a string to the screen followed by linefeed:

```
puts("Hello World");
```

An even simpler function outputs only a single character: putchar(ch) writes a single character to the screen.

Data Types

The available data types are listed below, some of which can be prefixed by the unsigned reserved word to alter their use.

$$\text{unsigned} \begin{cases} \text{short} & \text{8-bit integers} \\ \text{int} & \text{16-bit integers} \\ \text{long} & \text{32 bit integers} \end{cases}$$
$$\qquad\qquad \text{float} \quad \text{floating point numbers}$$
$$\qquad\qquad \text{char} \quad \text{characters}$$

Unsigned integers can only have positive integer values.

Other data types can be constructed from those shown above.

Example of using data definitions within a program

```
#include <stdio.h>
main( )
{
int a,b :
float ratio ;
unsigned int count ;
char question ;
}
```

Strings. Strings are not an 'official' data type but are defined as either: character array or character pointer.

Example of a character array

```
#include<stdio.h>
#include<string.h>
main( )
{
char msg[30] ;    /* an array of 30 characters */
strcpy(msg,"Hello world\n") ;
```

```
                  /*This function copies the string */
                  /*into the character array */
puts(msg) ;       /*Outputs the contents of array */
                  /*until the NULL character is */
                  /*encountered */
}
```

NULL indicates end-of-message and allows string to be any length up to 29 chars (NULL = 30th).

Example of a character pointer

```
#include<stdio.h>
#include<string.h>
main( )
{
char *msg ;       /*Defines msg as a pointer */
msg = "Hello world\n" ;
                  /*Sets msg to the address */
                  /*of the beginning of the */
                  /*String. A NULL is auto- */
                  /*matically inserted at the*/
                  /*end of the string. */

}
```

Identifiers

Identifiers, that is, the name given to labels, must start with a letter, but from then on can be alphanumeric and they are case sensitive so that CaSE is not the same as case. Only the first 32 characters are significant, that is, they are used to distinguish between different identifiers. However, more than 32 characters can be used if it is helpful to the programmer but it should be remembered that if they are different,the difference must occur in the first 32 characters. For example:

```
Last_data_entered_from_the_keyboard_one
```

and

```
Last_data_entered_from_the_keyboard_two
```

would be considered to be the same, whereas:

```
One_Last_data_entered_from_the_keyboard
```

and

```
Two_Last_data_entered_from_the_keyboard
```

would be considered to be different.

Assignment (=)

A data variable is given a specific value after it has been defined by the use of assignment. The value on the right of = is assigned to the variable on the left, for example:

```
Ratio = a/b ;
```

Assignments can be stacked. If as is common in computer programs, a number of variables have to be assigned the same value at some point in a program, it is not necessary to write out each data variable in a separate assignment statement. The assignments can be stacked as illustrated below:

```
sum = a = b ;
```

which means the same as:

```
sum = b ;
a = b ;
```

Arithmetic Operators

C has the standard arithmetic operators, which are listed below, although it doesn't distinguish between integer and real number division as Pascal does, since the compiler identifies which type of division is being implemented and performs the appropriate operation automatically:

- * multiply
- / Divide
- % modulus
- + addition
- − subtraction

Increment (+ +) and Decrement (− −). Often, there is a requirement to increment or decrement a variable by 1 and rather than use a standard add statement, a short hand form for increment and decrement is used.

```
a++ ;    /* This is equivalent to a = a +1 ; */
```

In addition, this operation can be used for pre-incrementing and post-incrementing variables, as illustrated below:

```
b = ++a ; /* a = a + 1 */
          /* Pre-increment of a before assignment */
          /* b = a */
b = a++ ; /* b = a */
          /* a = a + 1 */
          /* Post-increment of a after the */
          /* assignment */
a− − ;    /* a = a − 1 */
b = − −a ;   /* a = a − 1 */
          /* b = a */
b = a− − ;/* b = a */
          /* a = a − 1 */
c − a+b++ ;
          /* c − (a + b) */
          /* b = b + 1 */
          /* a = a */
```

Bit Operators

As well as the standard arithmetic operators C includes bit operators which manipulate the under-lying binary format representation of the data variables. This is not part of standard Pascal. The list of bit operators is given below with some examples.

$$
\left.
\begin{array}{ll}
<< & \text{shift left} \\
>> & \text{shift right} \\
\& & \text{AND} \\
| & \text{OR} \\
\wedge & \text{XOR} \\
\sim & \text{NOT}
\end{array}
\right\}
\begin{array}{l}
\text{These are not the same as} \\
\text{Boolean operators}
\end{array}
$$

These allow very low level bit manipulations to be performed as part of the STANDARD Language, most High Level Languages (HLL) do not!

Examples of bit operators

```
c = a << 4 ;        /* shift 4 bits to the left*/
c = sum >> 3 ;      /* shift 3 bits to the right*/
c = a & b ;
c = a | b ;
c = a ^ b ;
```

Combined Operators

C allows a short-hand representation of combined operators which enables two or more operators to be concatenated, as illustrated below:

```
a+= b ;        /* a = a + b */
a-= b ;        /* a = a - b */
a*= b ;        /* a = a * b */
a/= b ;        /* a = a/b */
```

Note that = can be combined with (+, −, * , %, <<, >> ,& , | , ^, − −, ++)

Address Operators

One of the properties of C is to allow the address of variables to be specifically manipulated, which is quite unusual in a HLL. Two operators are required:

```
address of    denoted by    &
indirection   denoted by    *
```

Note that indirection is what is at an address. If a variable **sum** is of type INT then **&sum** is the address of the variable and not the contents. Whereas if **msg** is of type CHAR then ***msg** is the character to which **msg** points.

Input of Data

Now that the output of data variables and information has been described, along with the manipulation of that data within a program, the input of data needs to be explained. Input of data is achieved mainly by the use of the scanf function which is similar in format to printf.

scanf(<format string>, <addr>, <addr> ...) ;

The format string is almost identical to that used in printf, but the items inserted are denoted as being addresses and not just variable names.

Example of SCANF

The following statement will input two integers and store them at the locations given by the addresses of the data variables a and b:

scanf("%d %d",&a,&b) ;

Note the use of the address operator in the item list. In the format string the two data type definitions are separated by a space, which is called a white space as it indicates that there can be any amount of spaces, returns, tabs between the inputting of the two numbers at the keyboard. The alternative is to use a comma when the two numbers have to be separated by a comma when they are entered at the keyboard, as illustrated below:

scanf("%d,%d",&A,&b) ;

Inputting Strings. As strings are saved as arrays, the array name is already an address and it is not necessary to use the address operator as they are already stored as addresses, as illustrated below:

```
#include<stdio.h>
#include<string.h>
main( )
{
char name [150] ;
printf("What is your name : ") ;
scanf("%s", name) ;   /*Note lack of & before name */
printf("Hello, %s\n",name) ;
}
```

Example Program

Multiply the two [2 × 2] matrices shown below, together and print out the result:

$$A = \begin{bmatrix} 1 & 2 \\ 3 & 4 \end{bmatrix} \quad B = \begin{bmatrix} 5 & 6 \\ 7 & 8 \end{bmatrix}$$

Write the C program to do this.

```
#include <stdio.h>
#define row 2
#define col 2
main ( )
{
   int matrix_A[row][col] ;
   int matrix_B[row][col] ;
   int result[row][col] ;
   int index ;
   char delim ;
   int index_col ;
   int index_row ;
   int line_numb ;
   printf("\nMatrix multiplication program \n") ;
   printf("This program will multiply two 2 × 2 matrices and") ;
   printf("\ndisplay the result\n") ;
   printf("\nDr R C Seals : University of Greenwich ") ;
   printf("\n 21st February 1992\n") ;
   printf("\nPress return key to continue . . .\n") ;
   delim = getch( ) ;
/* get the first matrix - matrix_A */
   printf("\nEnter the matrix, with each row on separate
        lines and the numbers\n") ;
   printf("separated by a single space\n") ;
   printf("\n") ;
   for (line_numb = 0 ; line_numb < row ; line_numb++)
      scanf("%d %d",&matrix_A[line_numb][0],&matrix_A
        [line_numb][1]) ;
   printf("\nMatrix successfully entered\n") ;
   printf("\n") ;
/*get the second matrix - matrix_B */
   printf("\nEnter the matrix, with each row on separate
        lines and the numbers\n") ;
   printf("separated by a single space\n") ;
   printf("\n") ;
   for (line_numb = 0 ; line_numb < row ; line_numb++)
      scanf("%d
%d",&matrix_B[line_numb][0],&matrix_B[line_numb]
        [1]) ;
   printf("\nMatrix successfully entered\n") ;
   printf("\n") ;
/* multiply matrix_A with matrix_B and put the answer
        into result */
   printf("\nMatrices are being multiplied\n\n") ;
   for (index_row = 0 ; index_row < row ; index_row++) {
      for (index_col = 0 ; index_col < col ; index_col++) {
         result[index_row][index_col] = 0 ;
         for (index = 0 ;index < row ; index++) {
            result[index_row][index_col] =
result[index_row][index_col] +
            (matrix_A[index_rowl][index] *
matrix_B[index][index_col]) ;
         }
      }
   }
/* display the result */
   printf("\nThe result of the multiplication is : \n\n") ;
   for (index = 0 ;index< row ; index++)
      printf(" %7d %7d
\n",result[index][0],result[index][1]) ;
   printf("\n") ;
/*sign off message */
   printf("\nThank you for using this program.\n") ;
   printf("\nPress the return key to exit from the
        program .\n") ;
   delim = getch( ) ;
}
```

GETS and GETCH. It is often required to enter text strings from the keyboard into the program for manipulation and two special functions are provided to make this a little easier.

gets – get string

This reads in everything until return is pressed, as illustrated below.

```
#include<stdio.h>
main( )
{
char name[150] ;
printf("What is your name : ") ;
gets(name) ;
printf("Hello,%s\n",name) ;
}
```

The alternative only enters a single character:

getch get character

This reads a single character from keyboard, without echoing it, unlike gets and scanf.

Relational Operators

Within conditional statements it is necessary to make comparisons between data values, such as 'a larger than b', and so on. These are called relational operators as they indicate the relationship between data variables rather than altering the data variables themselves. A list of the available operators is given below:

> greater than
>= greater than or equal to
< less than
<= less than or equal to
== is it equal to
!= Not equal to

(== should not be confused with = which means 'becomes equal to',)

Logical Operators

As well as the relational operators there are a number of logical operators which enable the logical relationship between data variables to be established. This are quite different from the bit operators described earlier. Bit operators actually alter the data variable values, but logical operators do not; they allow logical comparisons to be made. The list of logical operators is given below:

&&   -AND
|| -OR
!   -NOT

IF THEN ELSE. Within a program it is usually necessary to make decisions based on the value of data variables. For example if x is less than 10 then increment x else increment y. This language structure is described below and is called conditional execution.

if (condition) statement1 ;

or

if (condition) statement1 ;
else statement2 ;

These should be read as: 'If the condition is true then execute the statement1 (else execute the statement2)', as illustrated below:

```
if (b==0.0)
    printf("The ratio is zero\n") ;
else
    printf("It's non-zero\n") ;
```

Grouping statements. In order for many program structures to be able to execute more than one statement, multiple statements can be grouped together and then treated as if they were a single statement. This is achieved by the use of the open and close curly brackets.

```
{           beginning of group
statements go here
}           end of group
```

Example of grouping statements

```
if (direction ==0)
{
    phase = 0 ;
    state = state+2;
}
```

WHILE. The while statement repeats the execution of the specified construct (or group of constructs if they are grouped) for as long as the condition is true and has the following syntax:

```
while (condition)
    statement ;
```

Example of the WHILE statement

```
int len ;
len = 0 ;
puts("Type in sentence") ;
while (getchar( ) !='\n')
    len++ ;
/* counts length of sentence */
```

DO WHILE. An alternative to the while statement, is the do while statement. This is virtually the same as the while statement except that it will always execute the statement at least once before it checks whether the condition is true. The while statement, always checks the condition is true before executing the statement even once.

do statement while (condition) ;

Example of a DO WHILE statement

```
do
{
    printf("Hello world\n") ;
    count = count+2;
} while (getch( ) !='q') ;
```

FOR. If it is known exactly how many times a section of code has to be executed then a more efficient statement than a while (or a do while) is the for statement. The for statement is used to alter an index data variable, which may or may not be used within the statement being repeated. The index variable has an initial value and a final value specified, with the method of change to the index indicated, and has the following syntax:

```
for (exp2 ;exp2 ;exp3)
    statement ;
```

       exp1   Initialises index
       exp2   Terminating condition
       exp3   Index modification

Example of a FOR statement

```
for (indx=1 ;indx<=10 ;indx++)
    printf("time %d\n",indx) ;
```

Functions

In C, functions must return a value, that is, the function has to have a 'type' defined.

Example of defining a function

```
float get_ratio (float dividend, float divisor)
```

This defines a function to have a return data type of floating point, with a function name of get_ratio, which has two floating point parameters passed to it, called dividend and divisor.

(1) Many functions do not need to return a value, so use type void;
(2) Parameters are either constants or fixed values, to be passed in, or 'address-of' types, so that values produced by the function are saved. Note: values are not passed out via the function definition, as is the case with Pascal Procedures;
(3) Functions cannot be nested, so are always global;
(4) Function headings should be defined at the beginning of the program, the code comes later.

Example of function definition

```
#include<stdio.h>
#include<conio.h>
/* Function declarations */

void get_parms(float *p1,float *p2) ;
float get_ratio(float dividend,float divisor) ;
void put_ratio(float ratio) ;
const float INFINITY = 3.4E+38 :

/* main function : start of program */
main( )
{ float a, b, ratio ;

do {
    get_parms(&a,&b) ;
    ratio=get_ratio(a,b) ;
    put_ratio(ratio) ;
    printf("Press q to quit") ;
} while (getch( ) !='q') ; }
/* end of main */
/* function definitions */
void get_parms (float *p1,float *p2)
{ printf("\nEnter two numbers : ") ;
    scanf("%F,p1,p2) : }
float get_ratio(float dividend,float divisor)
{   if (divisor==0.0)
        return(INFINITY) ;
    else
        return(dividend/divisor) : }
void put_ratio (float ratio)
{   if (ratio==INFINITY)
        printf("The ratio is undefined.") ;
    else
        printf("The ratio is %F\n",ratio) ; }
```

Global declarations

If it is required that data variables or constants can be accessed anywhere within a program then they have to be declared as globals. This is achieved by declaring them right at the top of the program listing underneath the main( ) reserved word. Also, any constants, data types and variables defined outside of any function are *global* and can be used anywhere.

If they are defined within a function they are *local* and can only be used within that function and cannot be accessed by any other function. It is recommended that where possible all variables should be local so that if a particular variable is required within a function, it should be passed to the function as one of the parameters. This helps when trying to find errors that exist within a program as it is only necessary to test variable values as they enter functions and then the results of any functions, to identify if the fault lies within the function being tested. If global variables are used it is very difficult to identify where in a program an incorrect variable value is being generated.

However, for constants, it is recommended that all

constants are defined as globals so that they are available anywhere in the program. Constants do not introduce the same fault finding problems as global variables, because constant values cannot be changed during program execution, so if a constant does have an incorrect value, it can just as easily be determined for global as for local constants.

The Switch Statement

If a decision in a program can result in more than two possible decisions, for example if checking the value of x being one of 1,2,3,4,5,6,7,8,9, then multiple IF statements can be used, as illustrated below:

```
if (x == 1) printf("one") ;
else
   if (x == 2) printf("two") ;
      else
         if (x == 3) printf("three") ;
```

and so on.

However, there is a much more efficient alternative called the switch statement (this is equivalent to the case statement in Pascal), which has the following syntax.

Structure of Switch. Unlike most other C constructs which only allow one statement, the switch construct allows multiple statements after each matching constant.

```
switch (integer expression)
{ case constant1 : statements ; break ;
  case constant2 : statements ; break ;
  case constant3 : statements ; break ;
  default : statements
}
```

The statement operates by comparing the integer expression specified in the brackets next to the switch-reserved word, with the integer values listed after the case-reserved words. When a match is found the statements after the colon are executed, but only those statements. All the other statements after the other colons are ignored. If a match is not found then the default-reserved word is used to catch this situation and its associated statements can be executed. If all the possible integer values have been included then default is unnecessary and can be left out.

An example of using switch is given below:

```
switch (x)
{ case 1 : printf("One") ; break ;
  case 2 : printf("Two") ; break ;
  case 3 : printf("Three") ; break ;
  default : printf("Not matched") ;
}
```

Note the position of the curly brackets.

Arrays

Arrays are not a specific data type within C and are produced by adding open and close square brackets, [ ], to a variable definition, as illustrated below:

```
int array[31] ;
```

The number of elements is counted as 0 to 30, not as 1 to 31 as zero is always assumed to be the first element in the array.

If multi-dimension arrays are required then additional square brackets are included, as illustrated below:

```
int matrix[4][4] ; /* 4 by 4 array of integers */
```

Files

Files are the means by which data is permanently stored which is to be used, or is created by a program, and come in two different formats: Sequential and Random Access (which are not covered in these notes)

Sequential Files. As the name suggests sequential files are a sequence of data elements arranged in a consecutive format, as illustrated below with a file containing four data elements:

(1) Beginning of the file
(2) Second data element
(3) Third data element
(4) End of file

Data Elements

It is usual for files to contain a number of data elements where each data element occupies the same amount of memory as every other data element in that file. Data elements vary in size depending on the data type of the variable used when the data was created.

```
chars    – occupy 1 byte
integers – occupy 4 bytes
```

Data elements are accessed serially, so to read element 3, elements 1 and 2 have to be accessed first, even if they are not required. It is not possible to read past the end of a file as it causes a run-time error. Nor is it possible to reverse the direction of accessing the data to re-read an element. If it is required to access a data element which has already been passed then the file must be closed, re-opened from the beginning and then serially accessed to the correct element.

Opening a File. Before using, a file must be declared and then opened. Declaring is the process where the program is made aware that a file is going to be accessed and the name of the file is specified so that it can be used within the program.

Example of declaring a file

FILE *fptr /* This sets up a pointer to a file */

FILE is a pre-defined type and must be in capitals.

Syntax of opening a file. The function which opens the file is fopen (for file open) which has two parameters:

Fptr = fopen("filename","mode") :

The first, "filename", which must be given within the double quotes, is the actual name of the file on the floppy or hard disk system. The second parameter is the mode which indicates the type of operation that is going to be performed on that file. The two main modes are listed below:

r   read only, file must exist;
w   write only, current file deleted and new one made.

The function, fopen is a function of type file pointer and is used to link the external file with the internal file pointer (fptr).

Error. Because files are a very important part of the operation of a program and can cause run-time errors if they are not accessed properly, there are a number of special C functions for handling possible errors so that the termination of a program due to an unforeseen file error can be avoided.

If the file cannot be opened, fopen returns the **null file pointer** and this can be used to check for correct operation.

Example of opening a file

```
fptr =fopen("name.txt","w") ;
if (fptr !=NULL) printf("file open OK !") ;
else printf("Cannot open file !") ;
```

Closing files. When finished using an opened file, it should always be closed before the program ends. This flushes the file buffer, and resets the file pointer. Like fopen, fclose returns a data variable of file pointer and if the file can be closed, the NULL file pointer is returned and this can be used to check for the correct operation of fclose.

Example of closing a file

```
if (fclose(fptr) != NULL)
    printf("Cannot close file !") ;
else
    printf("The file has been closed") ;
```

The particular value of fptr is used to identify the particular file that is going to be closed. Failing to close a file can lead to loss of data as the file buffers may contain valuable data which is not saved to the actual file until the fclose operation is performed.

Writing data to files. All data is written as text and there is an automatic numeric-to-text conversion of data, which is performed by a special version of printf, called fprintf (file printf).

Syntax of FPRINTF. The format string and the item list are exactly the same as for printf, the only difference is an additional parameter, fptr, which is a file pointer which points to the specific file being used in the write operation.

fprintf(fptr,"format string",items) ;

This file *must* have been opened for writing first.

Reading data from files. All data is read as text, unless it is numeric, when there is an automatic text to numeric conversion by the special version of scanf that is used, called fscanf.

Syntax of FSCANF. The format string and item list are exactly the same as for scanf, the only difference is the addition of a third parameter, fptr, which is used to identify the specific file being used in the read operation :

fscanf(fptr,"format string",items) ;

This file *must* have been opened for reading first.

Example program using files

Write a C program which will:

(1) Read your name from the keyboard;
(2) Write it to a file;
(3) Close the file;
(4) Open the file;
(5) Read the contents of the file and display on the screen.

The following program will implement the above algorithm. There is no error checking and it is left to the reader as an exercise to add this:

```
#include<stdio.h>
main( )
{
FILE *fptrin,*fptrout ;
char name[20] ;
{
    fptrin = fopen("temp.txt","w") ;
    printf("Enter your name ") ;
    scanf("%s",name) ;
```

```
    fprintf(fptrin,"%s",name) ;
    fclose(fptrin) ;
    strcpy(name," ") ;
    fptrin = fopen("temp.txt","r") ;
    fscanf(fptrin,"%s",name) ;
    printf("%s",name) ;
    fclose(fptrin) ;
  }
}
```

End-of-File

If an attempt is made to read past the End-of-File (EOF), a run-time I/O error will occur, therefore, a program should always check for EOF before reading in order to produce a 'robust' program. This can be achieved by the fscanf function which returns a negative value when the end of file (EOF) occurs.

Example of checking for EOF

```
file = fscanf(fptr,"%s",name) ;
if (file==EOF)
   printf("No more data, end of file") ;
```

When writing to a file it is not necessary to check for EOF as each new data element is added to the end of the file and the EOF automatically moved to include it. In this way writing to files never encounters the EOF.

Example of using FEOF

In addition to using fscanf, there is a function, to specifically check for end-of-file, rather than checking the result of fscanf. This returns a non-zero value if the end of the specified file has been reached, otherwise it returns zero.

```
if (feof(fptr) !=0)
printf("Not the end of the file") ;
```

Single Character I/O

In the same way that single character input and output is possible with putch( ) and getch( ), there are special versions for reading a single character from a file, getc and writing a single character to a file, putc. Examples of using these two functions are given below.

```
ch = getc(fptr) ; /* reads a single character from a file */
putc(ch,fptr) ;   /* writes a single character to a file */
```

Checking for file errors. It is possible to specifically check for any errors during fscanf or fprintf, using the ferror function, which checks the specified file, indicated by the file pointer passed as a parameter, for any errors. If the function returns a value greater than zero then a file error has occurred, as illustrated below:

Example of using the FERROR function

```
if (ferror(fptr)>0)
   printf("A file error has occurred")
```

7.3 CASE STUDY 1: MATRIX MULTIPLICATION

The multiplication of matrices is a common problem in engineering and this program sets out to produce a simple working solution. Before starting on the design of the specification, a short revision of matrix multiplication will be given.

Multiplying two 4 x 4 Matrices

Two matrices can be multiplied together if the number of columns of the left hand matrix is equal to the number of rows of the right hand matrix, as illustrated below.

Matrix [A] 2×2 (2 rows $\times$ 2 columns)

$$[A] = \begin{bmatrix} a & b \\ c & d \end{bmatrix}$$

Matrix [B] 2×3 (2 rows $\times$ 3 columns)

$$[B] = \begin{bmatrix} e & f & g \\ h & i & j \end{bmatrix}$$

These two matrices can be multiplied together in the order:

[A] [B]   =   [Result]

$(2 \times 2)(2 \times 3)$ = (2×3)

The result will be a 2×3 matrix (2 rows, 3 columns). The centre two values can be considered to cancel each other out. The reverse arrangement of:

[B] [A]   =   [Result]

(2×3) (2×2)

cannot be achieved as the left hand matrix [B] has three columns and the right hand matrix [A] has 2 rows. These are not equal so the multiplication cannot be performed.

The multiplication is performed by multiplying each row of the left hand matrix by each row of the right-hand matrix:

$$\begin{bmatrix} a & b \\ c & d \end{bmatrix} \begin{bmatrix} e & f & g \\ h & i & j \end{bmatrix} = \begin{bmatrix} X & Y & Z \\ P & Q & R \end{bmatrix}$$

X = 1st row × 1st column

To multiply the row by the column, the corresponding elements are multiplied together and the results added to produce the answer. So the 1st row × the 1st column becomes:

$$X = (a \times e) + (b \times h)$$

This is then repeated for 1st row and 2nd column:

$$Y = (a \times f) + (b \times i)$$

and so on until all rows and columns have been multiplied.

The Specification.   The specification can be divided into three sections:

(1) Inputting the two matrices;
(2) Multiplying the two matrices;
(3) Displaying the results.

There are a variety of ways of inputting the data:

(a) From the keyboard;
(b) From a disk file;
(c) Some other communication link.

For this particular case study, the simplest solution will be used of entering the data from the keyboard. This has the disadvantage that the data has to be entered in total each time the program is executed. Entering data from a file has the advantage that it is permanently stored and can be repeatedly used if required, but the use of files makes the program more complicated. Other communication links might be used to enter the data in an embedded system such as controlling a robot.

Inputting the data.   Data will be input as integers, with each row of the matrix entered on a separate line at the keyboard. Each element will be separated by a space and the line of data values terminated by pressing the return key.

Multiplying the two matrices.   This is the simplest part of the specification to produce as the matrix multiplication is a well-defined mathematical technique and converts easily into a program. Multiply each row of the left hand matrix by each column of the right hand matrix and save the result in a new matrix.

Displaying the results. There are a variety of display options that could be chosen. For example, the original two matrices could be displayed as well as the result, or just the result could be displayed. A more general-purpose solution would be to have an output section capable of displaying any matrix and this is what has been chosen.

Each row of the matrix will be displayed on a single line on the display, with each number separated by two spaces. Each row of the matrix will be on a consecutive display line.

This has completed the specification design and this will be used to produce a program using pseudo code.

Converting the Specification into a Program Design

In line with the concepts of modular design, each of the three main sections of the specification will be converted into separate modules, combined in a main block. A possible pseudo code program is outlined below:

Example pseudo code program

```
Program multiply matrices.
Procedure get matrix (matrix)
   begin
      for the next four lines
         read line from keyboard
         save line into matrix
   end
procedure multiply (matrix A, matrix B, Result)
begin
   for each row of matrix
      display matrix (row) on the display screen
end
main loop
   get matrix (matrix A)
   get matrix (matrix B)
   multiply (matrix A, matrix B, Result)
   display (result)
end
```

There are no problems with this pseudo code program, so the specification does not require alteration. This now can be converted into a program for execution. A Pascal implementation is illustrated below. (A C implementation is given later.)

Example Pascal program listing

```
program matrix_multiply(input,output) ;
const
row = 4 ;
col = 4 ;
type
matrix = array[1..row,1..col] of integer ;
var
matrix_A : matrix ;
matrix_B : matrix ;
```

```
result : matrix ;
mat_file : text ;
procedure get_matrix(var mat : matrix) ;
var
line_numb,index_col : integer ;
delim : char ;
begin
  for line_numb := 1 to row do
    readln(mat_file,mat[line_numb,1],
        delim,mat[line_numb,2],
        delim,mat[line_numb,3],
        delim,mat[line_numb,4]) ;
end ;{get_matrix}
procedure multiply(mat_a,mat_b : matrix ;
        var result : matrix) ;
var
index_row,index_col,index : integer ;
begin
  for index_row := 1 to row do
    for index_col := 1 to col do
      begin
        result[index_row,index_col] := 0 ;
        for index := 1 to row do
          result[index_row,index_col] :=
result[index_row,index_col] +
          (mat_a[index_row,index] *
mat_b[index,index_col]) ;
end ;{for}
end ;{multiply}
procedure display(mat : matrix) ;
var
index : integer ;
begin
  for index := 1 to row do
    writeln(mat[index,1],' ',mat[index,2],'
    ',mat[index,3],' ',mat[index,4]) ;
end ;{display}
begin{main loop}
  assign(mat_file,'matfile.txt') ;
  reset(mat_file) ;
  matrix_A[1,1] := 0 ;
  matrix_B[1,1] := 0 ;
  result[1,1] := 0 ;
  get_matrix(matrix_A) ;
  get_matrix(matrix_B) ;
  multiply(matrix_A,matrix_B,result) ;
  display(result) ;
  readln(mat_file) ;
end.
```

Compiling and testing the program. Now that the program has been written it can be compiled to remove syntax errors and executed and tested.

Generating Test Data

Before testing can begin the test data has to be generated. The test data must be designed to ensure that all sections of the program are exercised and that boundary conditions are checked. For this particular program all parts are exercised for any pair of matrices which simplifies testing.

When generating test data it is always best to avoid regular values such as:

$$\begin{bmatrix} 1 & 2 & 3 & 4 \\ 5 & 6 & 7 & 8 \\ 9 & 10 & 11 & 12 \\ 13 & 14 & 15 & 16 \end{bmatrix}$$

as these sometimes can disguise some small errors in the program. The following are two general matrices that can be used for the majority of testing.

$$[A] = \begin{bmatrix} 1 & 6 & 9 & 11 \\ 4 & 16 & -5 & 0 \\ -13 & 2 & 6 & 8 \\ 7 & 3 & -6 & 2 \end{bmatrix}$$

$$[B] = \begin{bmatrix} 10 & -14 & 3 & 2 \\ 0 & 11 & 6 & -5 \\ -2 & -1 & 0 & 11 \\ 7 & 5 & 4 & 1 \end{bmatrix}$$

Note that negative numbers have been included as well as some zeros. The numbers are all 16 or less purely for this example. A full set of test matrices would include some larger numbers although it would be necessary to ensure that any results do not exceed the maximum integer value of the compiler being used.

It is now necessary to calculate the result of [A][B] and [B][A], using a different method than the computer program. In this example, the results were calculated manually.

Expected result (1)

$$[A][B] = \begin{bmatrix} 1 & 6 & 9 & 11 \\ 4 & 16 & -5 & 0 \\ -13 & 2 & 6 & 8 \\ 7 & 3 & -6 & 2 \end{bmatrix} \begin{bmatrix} 10 & -14 & 3 & 2 \\ 0 & 11 & 6 & -5 \\ -2 & -1 & 0 & 11 \\ 7 & 5 & 4 & 1 \end{bmatrix}$$

$$[C] = \begin{bmatrix} 69 & 98 & 83 & 82 \\ 50 & 125 & 108 & -127 \\ -86 & 238 & 5 & 38 \\ 96 & -49 & 47 & -65 \end{bmatrix}$$

Expected result (2)

$$[B][A] = \begin{bmatrix} 10 & 14 & 3 & 2 \\ 0 & 11 & 6 & 2 \\ -2 & -1 & 0 & -5 \\ 7 & 5 & 4 & 1 \end{bmatrix} \begin{bmatrix} 1 & 6 & 9 & 11 \\ 4 & 16 & -5 & 0 \\ -13 & 2 & 6 & 8 \\ 7 & 3 & -6 & 2 \end{bmatrix}$$

$$[C] = \begin{bmatrix} -71 & -152 & 166 & 138 \\ -20 & 194 & -31 & 52 \\ -41 & -43 & 17 & -32 \\ -18 & 133 & 56 & 111 \end{bmatrix}$$

The boundary conditions can now be derived. The full set of boundary conditions would require too much space to illustrate, so only the main ones will be included. The two main boundary conditions occur when the zero matrix [0], or the identity matrix [I], are involved, where:

$$[0] = \begin{bmatrix} 0 & 0 & 0 & 0 \\ 0 & 0 & 0 & 0 \\ 0 & 0 & 0 & 0 \\ 0 & 0 & 0 & 0 \end{bmatrix}$$

$$[I] = \begin{bmatrix} 1 & 0 & 0 & 0 \\ 0 & 1 & 0 & 0 \\ 0 & 0 & 1 & 0 \\ 0 & 0 & 0 & 1 \end{bmatrix}$$

The following are the expected results:

Expected results (3),(4) [A][I] = [I][A] = [A]

Expected results (5),(6) [A][0] = [0][A] = [A]

Test Results. The 6 sets of test data are entered into the program, the results generated and compared with the expected values.

Test Data (1)

$$\text{Expected result} = \begin{bmatrix} 69 & 98 & 83 & 82 \\ 50 & 125 & 108 & -127 \\ -86 & 238 & 5 & 38 \\ 96 & -49 & 47 & -65 \end{bmatrix}$$

The actual result of Test Data (1) is given below:

```
Matrices are being multiplied

The result of the matrix multiplcation is:

      69     98     83     82
      50    125    108  -127
     -86    238      5     38
      96    -49     47    -65

Thank you for using this program.

Press the return key to exit from the program . . .

C:\TP\BOOKPAS>
C:\TP\BOOKPAS>
C:\TP\BOOKPAS>
C:\TP\BOOKPAS>
C:\TP\BOOKPAS>
C:\TP\BOOKPAS>
```

Figure 7.6

Test Data (2)

$$\text{Expected result} = \begin{bmatrix} 41 & 296 & 26 & 138 \\ -20 & 194 & -31 & 52 \\ -41 & -43 & 17 & -32 \\ -18 & 133 & 56 & 111 \end{bmatrix}$$

The actual result is given below:

```
Matrices are being multiplied

The result of the matrix multiplcation is:

      41    296     26    138
     -20    194    -31     52
     -41    -43     17    -32
     -18    133     56    111

Thank you for using this program.

Press the return key to exit from the program . . .

C:\TP\BOOKPAS>
C:\TP\BOOKPAS>
C:\TP\BOOKPAS>
C:\TP\BOOKPAS>
C:\TP\BOOKPAS>
C:\TP\BOOKPAS>
```

Figure 7.7

Test Data (3) and (4)

Expected result = $\begin{bmatrix} 1 & 6 & 9 & 11 \\ 4 & 16 & -5 & 0 \\ -13 & 2 & 6 & 8 \\ 7 & 3 & -6 & 2 \end{bmatrix}$

Test data (5) and (6)

Expected result = $\begin{bmatrix} 0 & 0 & 0 & 0 \\ 0 & 0 & 0 & 0 \\ 0 & 0 & 0 & 0 \\ 0 & 0 & 0 & 0 \end{bmatrix}$

The actual results are given below:

The actual results are given below:

Matrices are being multiplied for Test Data (3)

The result of the matrix multiplcation is:

```
    1    6    9   11
    4   16   -5    0
  -13    2    6    2
    7    3   -6    2
```

Thank you for using this program.

Press the return key to exit from the program . . .

C:\TP\BOOKPAS>
C:\TP\BOOKPAS>
C:\TP\BOOKPAS>
C:\TP\BOOKPAS>
C:\TP\BOOKPAS>
C:\TP\BOOKPAS>

Matrices are being multiplied for Test Data (4)

The result of the matrix multiplcation is:

```
    1    6    9   11
    4   16   -5    0
  -13    2    6    8
    7    3   -6    2
```

Thank you for using this program.

Press the return key to exit from the program . . .

C:\TP\BOOKPAS>
C:\TP\BOOKPAS>
C:\TP\BOOKPAS>
C:\TP\BOOKPAS>
C:\TP\BOOKPAS>
C:\TP\BOOKPAS>

Matrices are being multiplied for Test Data (5)

The result of the matrix multiplcation is:

```
    0    0    0    0
    0    0    0    0
    0    0    0    0
    0    0    0    0
```

Thank you for using this program.

Press the return key to exit from the program . . .

C:\TP\BOOKPAS>
C:\TP\BOOKPAS>
C:\TP\BOOKPAS>
C:\TP\BOOKPAS>
C:\TP\BOOKPAS>
C:\TP\BOOKPAS>

Matrices are being multiplied for Test Data (6)

The result of the matrix multiplcation is:

```
    0    0    0    0
    0    0    0    0
    0    0    0    0
    0    0    0    0
```

Thank you for using this program.

Press the return key to exit from the program . . .

C:\TP\BOOKPAS>
C:\TP\BOOKPAS>
C:\TP\BOOKPAS>
C:\TP\BOOKPAS>
C:\TP\BOOKPAS>
C:\TP\BOOKPAS>

Figure 7.8

Figure 7.9

All the results generated are as predicted, indicating that the program is executing as required.

Correcting minor defects. Now that the program has been tested and shown to be working correctly any minor defects not affecting the operation of the program can be corrected. The most obvious minor error occurs in the layout of the columns in the result matrix displayed. These do not always align due to the different number of digits in each number and the presence of the minus sign for negative numbers. If the specification is reconsidered, which specifies two spaces between adjacent numbers, it can be seen that the misalignment cannot be avoided. It would be better to make a small adjustment to the specification so that the alignment of columns is as required rather than indicating the number of spaces between numbers. This is achieved by specifying the column width and whether the numbers are to be right or left justified.

Left justified numbers	Right justified numbers
1234	1234
–3	–3
66	66
136	136

The usual technique is to use right justified numbers.

Deciding on the column width can be a little bit more difficult. The columns should all be the same width and be wide enough to display the largest number. The largest number can be determined from the MAXINT constant built into each Pascal compiler. For Turbo Pascal this is 32,767 which is a five-digit number. In addition, a character is required for the minus sign and another to ensure at least one blank space between numbers. This gives the column width as seven characters.

A more sophisticated specification would be to require an adaptable column width two characters wider than the width of the largest number to be displayed, one for the minus sign and one as a space. This would lead to different result matrices occupying different widths which may or may not be acceptable.

The fixed column width technique will be used for this solution as it is simple and works perfectly well. The only slight drawback it has is that if the result contains only single or double digit numbers they will look spread out. However, for this solution that can be considered acceptable.

Obtaining a column width of seven, with right-justified numbers is obtained by altering the WRITELN statement in the display procedure, as follows:

```
writeln(mat[index,1] :7,mat[index,2] :7,
mat[index,3] :7,mat[index,4]7) ;
```

User Interface

A second area of improvement is the user interface. The specification did not give any indication as to what messages the program was to display as it was executing, and from the printouts obtained with Test Data (1) to (6), it can be seen that no information is displayed to help the user. The program meets the specification as given but is not user-friendly. By adding some display statements to the various parts of the program the user interface can be significantly improved.

A revised program listing is shown below which includes a simple user interface and the result is displayed in four lines of four seven figure columns with right-justified numbers.

Example program with user interface added.

```
program matrix_multiply(input,output) ;
const
row = 4 ;
col = 4 ;
type
matrix = array[1 . . row,1 . . col] of integer ;
var
matrix_A : matrix ;
matrix_B : matrix ;
result : matrix ;
mat_file : text ;

procedure get_matrix(var mat : matrix) ;
var
line_numb,index_col : integer ;
delim : char ;
begin
  writeln ;
  writeln('Enter the matrix, with each row
    on separate lines and the numbers') ;
  writeln('separated by a single space') ;
  writeln ;
  for line_numb := 1 to row do
    readln(mat_file,mat[line_numb,1],
        delim,mat[line_numb,2],
        delim, mat[line_numb,3],
        delim,mat[line_numb,4]) ;
  writeln ;
  writeln('Matrix successfully entered') ;
  writeln ;
end ;{get_matrix}

procedure multiply(mat_a,mat_b : matrix ;
        var result : matrix) ;
var
index_row,index_col,index : integer ;
begin
```

```
  writeln ;
  writeln('Matrices are being multiplied') ;
  writeln ;
  for index_row := 1 to row do
    for index_col := 1 to col do
      begin
        result[index_row,index_col] := 0 ;
        for index := 1 to row do
          result[index_row,index_col] :=
  result[index_row,index_col] +
          (mat_a[index_row,index] *
  mat_b[index,index_col]) ;
      end ;{for}
end ;{multiply}
procedure display(mat : matrix) ;
var
index : integer ;
begin
  writeln ;
  writeln('The result of the matrix
          multiplication is :- ') ;
  writeln ;
  for index := 1 to row do
    writeln(mat[index,1] :7,mat[index,2] :7,
        mat[index,3] :7,mat[index,4] :7) ;
  writeln ;
end ;{display}

begin{main loop}
  assign(mat_file,'matfile.txt') ;
  reset(mat_file) ;
  writeln ;
  writeln('Matrix multiplication program') ;
  writeln ;
  writeln('This program will multiply two
          four by four matrices and') ;
  writeln('display the result') ;
  writeln ;
  writeln('Dr R C Seals University of
          Greenwich 11th Dec 1992') ;
  writeln ;
  writeln('Press return key to continue . . .') ;
  writeln ;
  readln ;
  matrix_A[1,1] := 0 ;
  matrix_B[1,1] := 0 ;
  result[1,1] := 0 ;
  get_matrix(matrix_A) ;
  get_matrix(matrix_B) ;
  multiply(matrix_A,matrix_B,result) ;
  display(result) ;
  writeln ;
  writeln('Thank you for using this
          program.') ;
  writeln ;
  writeln('Press the return key to
          exit from the program ...') ;
  writeln ;
  readln(mat_file) ;
end.
```

Post script. It is interesting to consider the relationship between the number of lines of program and the function implemented and table 7.1 indicates how the lines are distributed between the main functions. Blank lines have been counted as they contribute to the structured layout of the program.

Table 7.1 Distribution of program lines to function

Function	Lines	%
User interface	31	31
Structured programming	51	52
Data entry	5	5
Multiplication	9	9
Data display	3	3
Total	99	100

Only 17% of the program listing is actively concerned with the fundamental function of the program which is to enter two matrices, multiply them together and display the result. The remaining 83% of the program is concerned with the user interface and the structured programming technique.

Condensed Program

If it is desirable to write as short a program as possible, many of the user interface and structured programming lines of the program can be removed as listed after Table 7.2. Functionally this program is exactly the same but has been condensed.

Table 7.2 illustrates how condensing the program alters the proportion of structured programming and user interface from 83% down to 3%. The data entry, matrix multiplication and data display sections remain virtually unchanged in the number of lines they occupy but their percentage proportion increases significantly.

Table 7.2 Distribution of program lines in the condensed program

Function	Lines	%
User interface	1	3
Structured programming	10	36
Data entry	6	21
Multiplication	8	29
Data display	3	11
Total	28	100

However, because the structured programming approach has been removed the program listing is much harder to decipher. In addition, when using the program it becomes much more difficult as the user interface has been removed.

Example condensed Program

```
program matrix_multiply(input,output) ;
var
mat_A,mat_B,res : array[1..4,1..4] of integer ;
index_row,index_col,index : integer ;
ch : char ;
mat_file : text ;
begin
  mat_A[1,1] := 0 ;
  mat_B[1,1] := 0 ;
  for index := 1 to 4 do
    readln(mat_A[index,1],ch,mat_A[index,2],ch,
        mat_A[index,3],ch,mat_A[index,4]) ;
  for index := 1 to 4 do
    readln(mat_B[index,1],ch,mat_B[index,2],ch,
        mat_B[index,3],ch,mat_B[index,4]) ;
  for index_row := 1 to 4 do
    for index_col := 1 to 4 do
      begin
        res[index_row,index_col] := 0 ;
        for index := 1 to 4 do
        res[index_row,index_col] :=
        res[index_row,index_col] +
        (mat_A[index_row,index] *
mat_B[index,index_col]) ;
      end ;{for}
  for index := 1 to 4 do
    writeln(res[index,1] :7,res[index,2] :7,
        res[index,3] :7,res[index,4] :7) ;
  readln ;
end.
```

Executing the program and checking with the same test data produces exactly the same results as the longer program. This demonstrates how it is possible to write two different programs which implement the same function and how fixed test values for ensuring they both produce the same results are important.

Comparison of Compilers and Execution Speed

To give some idea of the differences between compilers, the programs were compiled and executed using different versions of Turbo Pascal. Two parameters were measured; the final size of the executable programs and the speed of execution. To enable the speed of execution to be compared the programs had to be modified to avoid the time taken to read the data from the keyboard. This was achieved by altering the programs to read the matrices from a file rather than the keyboard and removing the 'readln' instructions.

The following listing illustrates how the condensed program was modified to achieve this. The same technique was used on all three programs. The timings were made using an 8 MHz Tandon PCA IBM-compatible PC/AT with 40 Mbyte hard disk, using

versions 3.0, 4.0 and 5.5 of Turbo Pascal. The timings were performed using a batch file to display the time before and after 10 successive executions of the programs. This is a crude technique which is not very accurate but it is easy to implement.

Example modified condensed program

```
program matrix_multiply(input,output) ;
var
mat_A,mat_B,res : array[1..4,1..4] of integer ;
index_row,index_col,index : integer ;
ch : char ;
mat_file : text ;
begin
  assign(mat_file,'matfile.txt') ;reset(mat_file) ;
  mat_A[1,1] := 0 ;
  mat_B[1,1] := 0 ;
  for index := 1 to 4 do
    readln(mat_file,mat_A[index,1],ch,
        mat_A[index,2],ch,mat_A[index,3],ch,
        mat_A[index,4]) ;
  for index := 1 to 4 do
    readln(mat_file,mat_B[index,1],ch,
        mat_B[index,2],ch,mat_B[index,3],ch,
        mat_B[index,4]) ;
  for index_row := 1 to 4 do
    for index_col := 1 to 4 do
      begin
        res[index_row,index_col] := 0 ;
        for index := 1 to 4 do
        res[index_row,index_col] :=
        res[index_row,index_col] +
        (mat_A[index_row,index]
        *mat_B[index,index_col]) ;
      end ;{for}
  for index := 1 to 4 do
    writeln(res[index,1] :7,res[index,2] :7,
        res[index,3] :7,res[index,4] :7) ;
  readln(mat_file) ;
end.
```

Table 7.3 Comparison of different compilers

	Turbo Pascal version	Program 1	Program 1 with user interface	Condensed program
Speed	3.0	0.403	1.40	0.399
	4.0	0.311	1.33	0.333
	5.5	0.315	1.40	0.333
Progam size	3.0	12,082	12,840	12,033
	4.0	3200	4512	2976
	5.5	3104	4400	2864

The results in Table 7.3 illustrate the effect of two different areas; different compilers and different program design techniques. There was a significant change between versions 3.0 and 4.0 of the compiler which resulted in a 23% decrease in the execution time and a 74% reduction in the size of the executable program 1. For program 1 with the user interface there is very little reduction in the execution time although the size of the program is reduced by 65%. This is expected as the user interface usually increases the execution time considerably, in this instance by 347% for version 3.0 of the compiler. It is also worthwhile noting that the condensed program only executes marginally faster than the structured approach of program 1 indicating that condensing a program produces no real advantage.

When program size is considered, it can be seen that there is a considerable reduction in size for all programs due mainly to a change in the compiler. For version 3.0, many of the standard Pascal functions were automatically included in the executable program, whether they were used or not. This simplifies the compiler but makes the programs longer. Version 4.0 takes a more sophisticated approach and only includes necessary routines, leading to a significant reduction in the size of executable programs. It can be seen that the condensed program is only marginally smaller than program 1 and that the program with the user interface added is 41% larger.

The change of the compiler from version 4.0 to version 5.5 has little effect on either program execution time or size. The difference in the compilers is mainly in their development environment (i.e. user interface) and the increased range of facilities. These do not directly influence these test programs in the two parameters being studied.

These figures are typical of program development and characterisation and indicate two guidelines:

(1) The use of structured design techniques usually has no effect on execution time or the size of the executable program;
(2) The user interface usually has the major influence on the execution time of the program.

These indicate why structured design techniques are nearly always used and why so much effort is put into making the user interface execute as quickly as possible.

Further Testing: Faulty Input Data

Although the programs have been tested using the specified test values and found to be functioning correctly, this does not mean that the program does not contain any errors. The test data used lies within the permitted values for correct operation, but one area that has not been tested is what

happens when faulty input data is used. For example, what happens if real numbers are entered, or non-numeric values such as letters, or a mixture of everything ?

The specification does not indicate any actions to be taken if faulty input values are used, or what possible faulty input values should be handled by the program and what should be done with them. This is a defect in the specification, although it is a common one of not defining clearly the possible faulty input data ranges and the expected program responses.

The inherent assumption in any specification is that all faulty input data values will be detected and a suitable response made to prevent the program from failing completely and then recover as much of the existing execution as possible. For example, in the matrix multiplication program, if an error was made while the second matrix was being entered the program would be expected to do at least two steps:

(1) Detect the faulty data and avoid failing;
(2) Assuming step (1) is successful and only require the faulty data values to be re-entered.

Re-entering the faulty data could mean just the individual matrix element that is faulty, or possibly the entire second matrix. This would require special data checking procedures to examine every number entered to ensure they have the correct format. This is not accomplished by the simple READLN statement and something more sophisticated would be required. Unfortunately, due to the way data is input to Pascal programs from the keyboard, it would be necessary to treat incoming data as characters rather than numeric strings to avoid the run-time errors which cause the program to abort. The character strings would then have to be converted into numeric strings by the program after they have been checked to ensure they are error free. This type of error detection is complex, difficult to implement and is usually avoided. Instead, the program is organised to minimise the probability of faulty input data, usually through the user interface being helpful and guiding the user as to what values to enter. This is coupled with some simple checking on the input data. For example, the user interface would attempt to ensure that the user only enters numbers to the matrix multiplication program, while the program would then ensure that they were within acceptable limits, such as between +100 and −100.

Once the data has been entered, further error detection and correction techniques should be used continuously throughout the program. The most robust and reliable programs are produced when the program always assumes that, whatever point is reached in the program execution, faulty data values will occur. Then the appropriate error detection and handling techniques are always implemented, particularly at sensitive points.

Typical Fault-sensitive Points

It is impossible to list every possible fault-sensitive condition that may arise in a program as they are dependent on the specific program language and layout. However, the following examples indicate the type of conditions that need to be considered.

Case statements. Case statements are particularly sensitive as they have a wide range of possible input values, but only a small number of them will be useful. Consider the situation where an integer (possible range –32,768 to +32,767) is selecting one of three actions:

```
case            integer_number of
  1 :             action_1 ;
  2 :             action_2 ;
  3 :             action_3 ;
end ;
```

For any values other than 1, 2 or 3 a run-time error will occur. This can be avoided by error checking before the routine runs and then error correction or error handling should an error still occur. The recommended technique for case statements is to use an IF THEN ELSE statement:

```
if (integer_number > 0) and (integer_number <4) then
case integer_number of
    1 : action_1 ;
    2 : action_2 ;
    3 : action_3 ;
  end
else
  begin
    writeln ('Error in integer_number') ;
    readln ;
  end ;
```

This is an example of an error handling technique, where the error is detected and an alternative action executed. The same program with error correction might be:

```
if (integer_number < 1) or (integer_number > 3)
then integer_number :=1 ;
case integer_number of
```

```
    1 : action_1 ;
    2 : action_2 ;
    3 : action_3 ;
end ;
```

Error correction techniques cannot guarantee to give faulty data values their correct value; all they do is to give an acceptable value which will allow the program to continue executing.

Most programmers would not use the above technique but would use an extension to standard Pascal to handle unspecified values:

```
case integer_number of
    1 : action_1 ;
    2 : action_2 ;
    3 : action_3 ;
  else begin
      writeln ('Error in integer_number') ;
      readln ;
  end ;
end ;
```

When using extensions to a standard language it should always be remembered that they increase the difficulty of porting the program to another compiler which probably has different extensions.

Conditional Statements. Conditional Statements are another error-sensitive point and care needs to be taken to make them robust. For example, the following program counts down to zero using a repeat until loop:

```
count := value ;
repeat
  actions ;
  count := count –1 ;
until count = 0 ;
```

This will work perfectly well in most situations, but consider what would happen if somehow count was to become negative. The loop would continue for ever or until a run-time error occurred.

This type of potential problem is avoided by never using the equals condition. This results in the program being re-written to:

```
count := value ;
repeat
actions ;
count := count –1 ;
until count < 1 ;
```

The program will execute in exactly the same way as before and exit the loop when count = 0, but it will also exit the loop if count ever becomes negative and so the loop will be executed a maximum of once for negative numbers.

Arithmetic errors. Arithmetic operations are always subject to potential errors due to the inherent limitations that digital computers have in representing numbers and the use of efficient techniques to manipulate them. The most common arithmetic fault is division by zero to produce a result of infinity which cannot be represented. The only technique for avoiding this problem is to check before the division that the number is not zero. This is easy to achieve with integers by the use of a conditional statement:

```
if numb_b <> 0 then
    result := numb_A div numb_B
else
    result := maxint ;
```

This program avoids the use of the equals sign as required by the conditional statement guideline and allows every number except zero to be used in the division. If numb_B = 0, then the error condition is detected and the best correction possible made.

Global Variables. One of the basic concepts of structured programming is to minimise the use of global variables. Global variables are variables that can be accessed anywhere within the program, whereas local variables can only be accessed from within the procedure they are defined in. The aim of minimising global variables is to prevent variable values being inadvertently changed by the wrong part of a program.

Taking the example program used in the conditional statements explanation, if the count had been a global variable then the procedure called ACTIONS could have altered its value either to prevent the loop exiting (by incrementing) or to give it a faulty negative value. However, if count is a local variable, then ACTIONS has no way of altering it, unless it is passed as a parameter to the procedure. This technique significantly reduces the possibility of errors occurring.

HLL Errors

Errors that can occur when using HLLs can be separated into four categories:

(1) Syntax errors.
(2) Functional errors.
(3) Run-time errors.
(4) I/O errors.

Syntax errors are faults in the way the language is being used to write the program. These are always detected by the compiler, assuming the compiler

to be error-free(!) and must be corrected before an executable version of the program can be produced.

Functional errors are produced by the program author who has produced a program which is syntactically correct but which does not do what is required.

Run-time errors occur when program execution produces an intermediate result or value which cannot be handled by the program. For example, if two large positive integers are multiplied together in the matrix multiplication program, the result may well be larger than the maximum allowed integer:

$$1000 \times 1000 = 1,000,000$$

Valid numbers $\rightarrow$ Invalid number

This type of error is difficult to prevent as it depends on the specific combination of numbers used. Placing restrictions on all numbers may prevent perfectly valid combinations. For example, assume all numbers must be equal to or less than 100:

$$100 \times 100 = 10\ 000 \text{ correct}$$

Also correct is :

$$1000 \times 10 = 10\ 000$$

$$500 \times 20 = 10\ 000$$

but these combinations would be prevented by the maximum value of 100 placed on all input integers.

I/O errors are caused when the program expects the hardware of the computer to perform a specific task and it fails to do so. The most common type are I/O errors associated with files, where the file may not exist, or may not contain the correct number of entries, or may not have the correct format and so on.

Most I/O errors can be avoided by using some of the language extensions which detect I/O errors before they abort the program execution. For example, in Turbo Pascal, when opening a file to read data values the following commands are used:

```
assign (f_name,'data.txt') ;
reset (f_name) ;
```

If, for any reason, the file 'data.txt' does not exist an I/O error will occur. However, by turning off the built-in I/O error checking routines:

```
assign (f_name,'data.txt') ;
{$I-} {turns off I/O error checking}
reset (f_name) ;
{$I+} {turns on I/O error checking}
```

The program will continue to execute even if the

file does not exist. However, the program must be capable of checking the I/O code produced after every I/O operation to detect when I/O errors occur, otherwise faulty data may propagate through the program. The program must then have methods of handling these situations, perhaps by asking the user for an existing filename.

Similarly, tests should always be performed so that if an unexpected 'end of file' occurs, the program detects it and handles it before an I/O error is caused.

```
count := 10
repeat
   readln (f_name,data_array[count]) ;
   count := count –1 ;
until (eof(file_name)) or (count < 1) ;
```

The example program now makes two checks at the end of every loop to check for unexpected end of file, or the end of the input data. These conditions can also be used to check what caused the loop to exit and then take the appropriate action if it was an unexpected end of file:

```
count := 10
repeat
   readln (f_name,data_array[count]) ;
   count := count –1 ;
until (eof(file_name)) or (count < 1) ;
if (count > 0) and (eof(file_name)) then
   writeln ('Unexpected end of file') ;
```

Full Test Data

If a full set of test data had been produced for the multiply program, then most of the applicable error situations would have been tested to ensure that the program responded satisfactorily. As this was not the case, any faults in the input data values will cause the program to abort.

Consequences of error reduction. Although all of the guidelines given previously increase the probability of producing error-free, reliable and robust programs they do have two consequences:

(1) Increased program size;
(2) Increased program execution time.

For most programs, increased program size is not a significant problem and most programs also execute fast enough for most users. Even if this is not the case, the preferred solution is to obtain a faster computer with more memory so that the program can be executed without altering any of the error checking and error handling. However, should this be unacceptable, the alternative is to remove some

or all of the error checking, which can be achieved in two ways:

(1) Removing the error checking and handling program statements;
(2) Altering the compiler so that the automatic inclusion of error checking routines is turned off.

The majority of the instances of faulty data and methods of handling data (correct or faulty) occur while the program is being developed, after which many of them may never occur again. The hope is that none of them will ever occur again! Therefore, once a program is fully developed they can be removed and there are two ways of doing this. The first is to go through the program listing deleting all unnecessary error detection and correction statements, or making them into comments rather than actually deleting them as illustrated below. This makes it easy to return to the program at a later date to enhance or expand it, when the error detecting and correcting statements can be easily re-activated.

```
{if (integer_number> 0) and (integer_number< 4) then}
case integer_number of
     1 : action_1 ;
     2 : action_2 ;
     3 : action_3 ;
   end
{else
   begin
     writeln ('Error in integer_number') ; readln ;
   end} ;
```

This is not a recommended technique as it results in what should technically be considered a new program requiring a full set of tests performed on it using the specified test data set.

The alternative is to alter the compiler by using what is known as a compiler switch. This is a special statement placed in the program which is not part of the HLL, or the program, but is an instruction to the compiler. There are usually several compiler switches to enable the compiler to be altered in a number of ways. The compiler switches for Turbo Pascal 5.5 are listed below and give an idea of the range of parameters that can be changed within the compiler.

Compiler Switches

{$A} – Aligns word data
{$B} – Full or partial evaluation of Boolean statements
{$D} – Debug information
{$E} – Maths coprocessor emulation
{$F} – Near or far procedure calls

{$I} – I/O checking
{$L} – Local symbol information
{$N} – Numeric processing
{$O} – Overlay code generation
{$R} – Range checking
{$S} – Stack overflow checking
{$V} – Var string checking

One of the compiler switches will turn off the extra routines and instructions automatically inserted by the compiler to detect run-time and I/O errors. This reduces the size of the program considerably and leads to faster execution.

Table 7.4 shows the effect of turning off the automatic run time and I/O error checking for the three versions of the matrix multiplication program, using the Turbo Pascal compiler version 5.5.

Table 7.4 The effect of turning off error checking

	Program1	*Program1 with user interface*	*Condensed program*
Speed			
With	0.315	1.40	0.333
Without	0.297	1.40	0.333
	(5.7% faster)	(0% faster)	(0% faster)
Size			
With	3104	4400	2864
Without	2992	4016	2784
	(3.6% shorter)	(8.7% shorter)	(2.8% shorter)

The compiler directives which have an effect on these programs are listed below showing whether they should be ON(+) or OFF(–).

{$A+}
{$B–}
{$D–}
{$F–}
{$I–}
{$O–}
{$R–}
{$S–}
{$V–}

As can be seen from the table, the effect of using compiler switches to decrease executable program size and increase execution speed is minimal. There is virtually no increase in execution speed and very little decrease in the size of the executable programs.

Much more significant improvements in executable program size and speed can easily be made by re-structuring the program, as illustrated by the

Pascal matrix multiplication programs: program1, program1 with user interface and the condensed program.

The C HLL

In order to demonstrate that the design technique is independent of the HLL used, the matrix multiply program with user interface has also been written in the C HLL (see following page).

The difference between the Pascal and C versions of the programs is in the keyboard and display handling statements. Where Pascal uses readln and writeln, C uses the more complex and sophisticated scanf( ) and printf( ).

The same test data was used on the C version of the program and the same correct results were obtained. The same user interface was created so that the user is unable to tell whether the Pascal or C version is executing as illustrated below in *Figures 7.10 and 7.11*.

```
C:\TP\BOOKPAS>

Matrix multiplication program

This program will multiply two four by four matrices
and display the result

Dr R C Seals: University of Greenwich: 11th
December 192

Press return key to continue . . .

Enter the matrix, with each row on separate lines and
the numbers separated by a single space
```

Figure 7.10

```
C:\MIXC>matmul2

Matrix multiplication program

This program will multiply two four by four matrices
and display the result

Dr R C Seals: University of Greenwich: 11th
December 1992

Press return key to continue . . .

Enter the matrix, with each row on separate lines and
the numbers separated by a single space
```

Figure 7.11

Example program written in C

```
#include <stdio.h>
#define row 4
#define col 4
main ( )
{
    int    matrix_A[row][col] ={{1,2,3,4},{0,0,0,0},{0,0,0,0},{0,0,0,0}} ;
    int    matrix_B[row][col] = {{ 1,2,3,4},{0,0,0,0},{0,0,0,0},{0,0,0,0}} ;
    int    result[row][col] = {{ 0,0,0,0},{0,0,0,0},{0,0,0,0},{0,0,0,0}} ;
    char delim ;
    printf("\nMatrix multiplication program \n") ;
    printf("This program will multiply two four by four matrices and") ;
    printf("\ndisplay the result\n") ;
    printf("\nDr R C Seals : University of Greenwich : 11th December 1992\n") ;
    printf("\nPress return key to continue ...\n") ;
    delim = getch( ) ;
    get_matrix(matrix_A) ;
    get_matrix(matrix_B) ;
    multiply(matrix_A,matrix_B,result) ;
    display(result) ;
    printf("\nThank you for using this program.\n") ;
    printf("\nPress the return key to exit from the program .\n") ;
    delim = getch() ;
}
get_matrix(matrix)
int matrix[row][col] ;
{
    int index_col ;
    int line_numb ;
    char delim ;
    printf("\nEnter the matrix, with each row on separate lines and the numbers\n") ;
    printf("separated by a single space\n") ;
    printf("\n") ;
    for (line_numb = 0 ; line_numb [*less] row ; line_numb++) {scanf("%d %d %d
%d",&matrix[line_numb][0],&matrix[line_numb][1], &matrix[line_numb][2],&matrix[line_numb][3]) ;
    }
    printf("\nMatrix successfully entered\n") ;
    printf("\n") ;
}
multiply(mat_a,mat_b,res)
int mat_a[row][col] ;
int mat_b[row][col] ;
int res[row][col] ;
{
    int index_row ;
    int index_col ;
    int index ;
    printf("\nMatrices are being multiplied\n\n") ;
    for (index_row = 0 ; index_row [*less] row ; index_row++) {
        for (index_col = 0 ; index_col [*less] col ; index_col++) {
            res[index_row][index_col] = 0 ;
            for (index = 0 ;index [*less] row ; index++) {
                res[index_row][index_col] = res[index_row][index_col] + (mat_a[index_rowl][index] *
                    mat_b[index][index_col]) ;
            }
        }
    }
}
display(mat)
int mat[row][col] ;
{
    int index ;
    printf("\nThe result of the multiplication is :- \n\n") ;
    for (index = 0 ;index [*less] row ; index++) {
        printf(" %7d %7d %7d %7d \n",mat[index][0],mat[index][1],mat[index][2],mat[index][3]) ;
    }
    printf("\n") ;
}
```

No attempt was made to use any C statements that would construct a more efficient program as the aim was to show the compatibility between the two programming languages. With a little thought it would be possible to produce a more compact and faster executing C version of this program.

7.4 CASE STUDY 2: SETUP PROGRAM FOR PC/AT

The programs developed so far have been relatively simple and independent of the computer hardware they were executing on. In order to demonstrate the design, implementation and testing of a more realistic program, a second case study will be considered. This program will only be implemented in Turbo Pascal with the C implementation being left as an exercise for the reader. In addition, the design process will only be described in sufficient detail to enable a good understanding of the program function and design to be obtained. This will result in an incomplete specification and pseudo language program. Any missing details can be supplied by the user if so desired and compared with the full Pascal program listing which is included. Finally, a full set of test data has not been included although the general guidelines for producing test data are outlined in detail in this chapter.

One part of an IBM compatible PC/AT is something called the setup which describes the basic configuration of the hardware of the computer. This indicates how many disk drives, hard disks and how much memory the PC/AT has installed, plus some other useful information about such things as the real-time clock. This information is maintained in battery-backed CMOS RWM as long as the internal battery is connected. This information is scanned by the power-on routines to obtain the correct setup. This avoids the need for dip switches on the motherboard, eliminating many of the user-induced faults found on the PC/XT which uses dip switches.

If any changes are made to the hardware the information in the CMOS RWM has to be updated before the changes will be recognised. This updating is achieved by running the setup program related to the specific PC/AT being used. For the IBM PC/AT this is contained in a program on a disk called *Advanced Diagnostics AT* which can be obtained by purchasing the *Hardware Maintenance Personal Computer Service Manual*. Other manufacturers either build this into the computer itself so that it can be activated by a special key sequence, or provide it as a program included with the computer or which can be obtained later.

The setup program designed in this case study will provide similar functions to these programs but will be written in Pascal using the Turbo Pascal version 5.5. A few extensions to the Pascal language will be used although these will be kept to a minimum so that the program can be ported to other Pascal compilers with the minimum of difficulty.

Background Information

The CMOS RWM contains 64 bytes of data which can be split into three groups:

(1) Real time clock and other status information (bytes 0–15);
(2) Hardware configuration information (bytes 16–40);
(3) Extended memory and other bytes (bytes 41–63);

In order to simplify the program and because some of the information is manufacturer-specific, only section (2), hardware configuration information, will be changed. The other two sections will have a limited display facility but they will not be changeable with this program.

Reading and writing to the CMOS RWM should be the same for all PC/ATs although some compatibles may make changes. If in doubt, it is recommended that this program is not executed on the PC/AT you are using.

Writing to the CMOS RWM. To transfer data values into the CMOS RWM two steps are necessary:

(1) Write to I/O address 070H with the CMOS RWM address to be written to;
(2) Write to I/O address 071H with the data to be written to the CMOS RWM address specified previously.

There is no confirmation that an error-free write has taken place other than to read back the data from the CMOS RWM location.

Reading from the CMOS RWM. Reading from the CMOS RWM is similar to writing and consists of two steps:

(1) Write to I/O address 070H with the CMOS RWM address to be read from;
(2) Read the I/O address 071H and the data in the CMOS RWM address specified in the first step will be obtained.

CMOS RWM address allocation. The information in Table 7.5 indicates how each byte of the CMOS RWM has been allocated.

Table 7.5 CMOS RWM allocation

Address	Allocation and use
0–13	Real-time clock
14	Diagnostic status
15	Shut-down status byte (PC/AT specific)
16	Types of floppy disks (drives A : and B :)
17	Reserved
18	Types of hard disks used (drives C : and D :)
19	Reserved
20	Number of floppy disks installed, type of display and the presence of a mathematic coprocessor
21–22	Amount of memory on the system board
23–24	Amount of extended memory installed from 0–15 Mbyte (starting at memory address 1 Mbyte)
25	Hard disk C : (extension to information in byte 18)
26	Hard disk D : (extension to information in byte 18)
27–45	Reserved
46–47	Checksum (for bytes 16–46)
48–49	Amount of extended memory installed (copy of bytes 23–24)
50	Century value (usually 019H)
51	Value set during power-on (possibly manufacturer-specific)
52–63	Reserved

Disclaimer. *The program contained in this case study is for illustration only and has only been tested on a limited number of compatible PC/ATs. The author accepts no responsibility for any damage or other loss caused by the use of a compiled version of this program. The user must accept full responsibility for this program if using a compiled version, otherwise do not compile and use this program. Copyright is retained by Dr R. C. Seals and any programs which comprise this source as a major constituent (i.e. more than 75%) must acknowledge this during program execution. Other than this, no other restrictions are placed on the use of this program or any executable versions and no royalty or any other fees are required. The disclaimer must be visible in some form to all users.*

Specification

The program will display the contents of the CMOS RWM locations in an understandable format. Bytes 0–15 and 48–63 are displayable only and cannot be altered. In addition, any reserved location will be displayable but will not be alterable.

It is expected that the user will be familiar with the terms and values described by this information and detailed explanations will not be given. A simplified menu system will be used which will execute correctly on any PC/AT standard display. The menu will not use colour but will use a limited number of the graphics characters provided by IBM. The only non-standard Pascal procedures and functions that may be used are:

```
gotoxy (x,y) ;      {for the display}
port(I/O address) ;
                    {for reading and writing to the I/O}
                    {ports}
readkey             {function for reading the keyboard}
                    {directly. Avoids characters}
                    {appearing on the screen.}
```

Byte addresses will be displayed and entered as integers and the new contents of bytes calculated from the results of making simple selections. The user should not have to enter a specific number or value at any time, only select values from menus.

The following is an outline of the menu display that will be used.

CMOS RWM Allocation and alteration

Dr R. C. Seals : University of Greenwich
11th December 1992

Main Menu

(1) Display byte contents
(2) Alter byte contents (bytes 16–26 only)
(3) Save existing byte contents to a file
(4) Load byte contents from a file
(5) Exit from this program

Display byte contents sub-menu. Option (2) will display the expanded information using further menus. Option (1) will simply display the range of byte addresses and their contents in four columns. Options (3) and (4) will indicate the transfer was successful before returning to the main menu.

Option (2) sub-menu : Expanded information

Floppy disks installed:

Drive A :   X
Drive B :   X

where X is one of:

No disk installed
5.25″ standard density (360 KBytes)
5.25″ standard density (1.2 MBytes)
3.5″ standard density (720 KBytes)
3.5″ high density (1.44 MBytes)

Hard Disks installed:

Drive C: Y
Drive D: Y

where Y is one of:

No hard disk installed
Disk type number 1–47 (numbers 1–15 also show storage capacity)

Warning

Entering the wrong disk type number
can cause physical damage and loss of data.

The disk type number describes the basic parameters of the hard disk and these allow the storage capacity to be calculated. For disk types 1–14 these are the same for most PCs, but for disk types 15–47 the parameters are PC manufacturer dependent.

Table 7.6 Disk type numbers

Type	Capacity (Mbyte)
1	10
2	21
3	32
4	65
5	49
6	21
7	32
8	32
9	117
10	21
11	37
12	52
13	21
14	44

Care must be taken when selecting this disk type number as it identifies the number of heads and tracks and if the wrong value is selected it may damage the disk or data may be lost. If you do not know what the disk type number is then do not change it. Just knowing the capacity of the hard disk is not sufficient as several similar capacities such as types 2, 6, 10 and 13 have different physical organisations.

Primary Display Type: X

X is one of:

(i)   EGA, VGA or specialised adapter
(ii)   CGA 40 column
(iii)   CGA 80 column
(iv)   MDA

EGA – Enhanced Colour Graphics Adapter
VGA – Video Graphics Adapter
CGA – Colour Graphics Adapter
MDA – Monochrome Display Adapter

Most adapters can emulate lower resolution adapters so that VGA can emulate everything, EGA can emulate CGA and MDA, and CGA can emulate MDA. Choosing a lower resolution primary display than the physical adapter is acceptable. Attempting to choose a higher resolution display will result in a blank screen or possibly damage to the display adapter and the display itself.

Maths coprocessor: installed or not installed. If a maths coprocessor is physically present in the PC but this parameter is set to not installed it will not affect the PC/AT although programs which require a coprocessor to be present may or may not execute correctly.

Indicating a mathematics coprocessor is present when it is not will usually lead to unpredictable results such as blank display, intermittent or incorrect program operation.

Main RWM Installed: N

N is one of:

(i)   256 KBytes
(ii)   512 KBytes
(iii)   640 KBytes.

Note : PC/ATs with more than 640 kbytes available will have the extra memory denoted as extended memory. They will still have 640 kbytes main RWM.

Extended Memory Installed: M

M is one of:

(1) 0.512 Mbytes
(2) 1.000 Mbyte
(3) 1.512 Mbytes
(4) 2.000 Mbytes
(5) 2.512 Mbytes
(6) 3.000 Mbytes
(7) 3.512 Mbytes
(8) 4.000 Mbytes

(9) 4.512 Mbytes
(10) 5.000 Mbytes
(11) 5.512 Mbytes
(12) 6.000 Mbytes
(13) 6.512 Mbytes
(14) 7.000 Mbytes
(15) 7.512 Mbytes
(16) 8.000 Mbytes
(17) 8.512 Mbytes
(18) 9.000 Mbytes
(19) 9.512 Mbytes
(20) 10.000 Mbytes
(21) 10.512 Mbytes
(22) 11.000 Mbytes
(23) 11.512 Mbytes
(24) 12.000 Mbyte
(25) 12.512 Mbytes
(26) 13.000 Mbytes
(27) 13.512 Mbytes
(28) 14.000 Mbytes
(29) 14.512 Mbytes
(30) 15.000 Mbytes

Pseudo-code Program

Now that the specification has been detailed the pseudo-code program can be developedand this is illustrated below:

Example pseudo-code program

```
program CMOS RWM

main block
    while not the end of the program
        begin
            display main menu
            get value selected by user
if not exit then execute selected function
        end

procedure display main menu
begin
    display basic screen layout and messages
    display main menu information
end

procedure execute selected function (option)
begin
    case option of
    1) display all byte address and contents
    2) display and alter PC information
    3) save CMOS RWM contents to a file
    4) load CMOS RWM contents from a file
end

procedure display CMOS RWM (start, stop : address)
begin
    display column headings from the start address to the stop address
        begin
            get selected CMOS RWM contents
            display address as an hexadecimal number
            display contents as an hexadecimal number (in four columns)
        end
end
```

```
procedure save CMOS RWM to a file
begin
    open file from first address to last address
        begin
            get selected CMOS RWM contents
            write contents to the file
        end
    close file
end

procedure get contents of CMOS RWM from file
begin
    open file from first address to last address
        begin
            read contents from the file
            store contents in RWM address
        end
    close file
end

procedure display and alter PC information
begin
    while not the end of the procedure
        begin
            display sub-menu
            get option selected by user
            if not exit then execute selected option
        end
end

procedure display sub menu
begin
display sub menu information
end

procedure execute selected sub option (sub-option)
begin
    case ?????????????????
    end
end

procedure display and alter PC information
begin
    1) display and alter floppy disk information
    2) display and alter hard disk information
    3) display and alter PC primary display information
    4) display and alter maths coprocessor
    5) display and alter main RWM installed
    6) display and alter extended RWM installed
    7) exit
end

procedure display and alter floppy information
begin
    while not end of floppy menu
        begin
            display floppy sub menu
            get floppy to be altered
            get altered information
            if not exit then alter floppy bytes
        end
end

procedure display and alter hard disk information
begin
    while not end of hard disk menu
        begin
            display hard disk sub menu
            get hard disk to be altered
            get altered information
            if not exit then alter hard disk bytes
        end
end

procedure display and alter PC primary display
begin
    while not end of primary display menu
        begin
```

```
            display primary display menu
            get altered value
            if not exit then alter display bytes
        end
end
procedure display and alter maths coproc
begin
    while not end of maths coproc menu
        begin display maths coproc menu
            get altered value
            if not exit then alter coproc bytes
        end
end
procedure display and alter main RWM menu
begin
    while not end of main RWM menu
        begin
            display main RWM menu
            et altered value
            if not exit then alter RWM bytes
        end
end
procedure display and alter extended RWM menu
begin
    while not end of extended RWM menu
        begin
            display extended RWM menu
            get altered values
            if not exit then alter extended RWM byte
        end
end
```

Program listing

The pseudo-code program is now sufficiently well defined to enable a well-structured Pascal program to be written. This is now given below with some sample display screens shown following in *Figures 7.12 and 7.13*.

Example program

```
program cmosrwm(input,output) ;

uses crt ;

const

unknown = 0 ;
display_bytes = 1 ;
alter_bytes = 2 ;
save_to_file = 3 ;
load_from_file = 4 ;
exit = 5 ;
exit_sub = 7 ;
floppy1_exit = 3 ;
floppy_exit = 6 ;
hard_exit = 3 ;
hard1_exit = 5 ;
display_exit = 5 ;
math_exit = 5 ;
main_RWM_exit = 5 ;
extended_RWM_exit = 5 ;

type

byte = 0..255 ;
hex = string[2] ;

var

cmos_loc : byte ;
finished : char ; index : byte ;
```

```
finish : boolean ;
next_command : char ;

value : integer ;
cmos_file : text ;
```

```
{**********************************************************}
{*     The following procedures are not part of standard Pascal     *}
{*     and if this program is ported to another compiler, they       *}
{*     will need to be adjusted.                                               *}

procedure to_xy(x,y : integer) ;

begin
    gotoxy(x,y) ;
end ;{to_xy}

procedure read_cmosram(address : byte ; var contents : byte) ;

begin
    port[$70] := address ;
    contents := port[$71] ;
end ;{read_cmosram}
procedure write_cmosram(address : byte ; contents : byte) ;
begin
    port[$70] := address ;
    port[$71] := contents ;
end ;{write_cmosram}
procedure clear_screen ;
begin
    clrscr ;
end ;{clear_screen}

function read_keyboard : char ;

begin
read_keyboard := readkey ;
end ;{read_keyboard}

{********* END OF NON-STANDARD PASCAL PROCEDURES *********}

procedure write_hex_byte(numb : byte) ;
{writes an 8 bit value of numb as hexadecimal}

var

index : integer ;
hex : array[0..15] of char ;
val_ord,val_rem : byte ;

begin
    for index := 0 to 9 do
        hex[index] := chr(ord('0') + index) ;
    hex[10] := 'A' ;
    hex[11] := 'B' ;
    hex[12] := 'C' ;
    hex[13] := 'D' ;
    hex[14] := 'E' ;
    hex[15] := 'F' ;
    write('$') ;
    val_ord := numb div 16 ;
    write(hex[val_ord]) ;
    val_rem := numb mod 16 ;
    write(hex[val_rem]) ;
end ;{write_hex_byte}

procedure display_ram(start,stop : integer) ;

var
value : byte ;
index : byte ;
ch : char ;

begin
    value := 0 ;
    to_xy(10,6) ;
    write('Address Value Address Value', 'Address Value Address Value') ;
    to_xy(10,7) ;write(' ') ;
```

```pascal
    to_xy(10,8) ;
    for index := start to stop do
      begin
        write(' ') ;
        read_cmosram(index,value) ;
        write(index :3) ;write(' ') ;
        write_hex_byte(value) ;
        write(' ') ;
        if index mod 4 = 0 then
          to_xy(10,(index div 4 + 8)) ;
      end ;
    to_xy(10,24) ;
    write('Press any key to continue') ;
    ch := read_keyboard ;
end ;{display_ram}

procedure hex_to_byte(hex_string : hex ; var bite : byte) ;

var

index : integer ;
value1 : byte ;
value2 : byte ;

begin
{get first character and convert to binary}
  case hex_string[1] of
    '0','1','2','3','4','5','6','7','8','9': value1:= ord(hex_string[1])–ord('0') ;
    else value1 := ord(hex_string[1]) - ord('A') + 10 ;
  end ;{case}
{get second character and convert to binary}
  case hex_string[2] of
    '0','1','2','3','4','5','6','7','8','9': value2 := ord(hex_string[2])–ord('0') ;
    else value2 := ord(hex_string[2])–ord('A') + 10 ;
  end ;{case}
  bite := (16 * value1)  + value2 ;
end ;{hex_to_byte}

procedure menu_shell ;

begin
  to_xy(1,1) ;
  writeln('——————————————————————————' ) ;
  writeln('| CMOS RWM Allocation and Alteration |') ;
  writeln('——————————————————————————|') ;
  writeln('|Dr R C Seals : University of Greenwich : 11/12/92|') ;
  writeln('——————————————————————————|' ) ;
  writeln('|                                                  |') ;
  writeln('|                                                  |') ;
  writeln('|                                                  |') ;
  writeln('|                                                  |') ;
  writeln('|                                                  |') ;
  writeln('|                                                  |') ;
  writeln('|                                                  |') ;
  writeln('|                                                  |') ;
  writeln('|                                                  |') ;
  writeln('|                                                  |') ;
  writeln('|                                                  |') ;
  writeln('|                                                  |') ;
  writeln('|                                                  |') ;
  writeln('|                                                  |') ;
  writeln('|                                                  |') ;
  writeln('|                                                  |') ;
  writeln('|                                                  |') ;
  write('——————————————————————————' ) ;
end ;{menu_shell}

procedure display_main_menu ;

begin
  menu_shell ;
  to_xy(10,7) ;write('Main menu') ;
  to_xy(15,9) ;write('1) Display byte contents') ;
  to_xy(15,10) ;write('2) Alter byte contents') ;
  to_xy(15,11) ;
```

```pascal
  write('3) Save existing CMOS RWM contents to a file') ;
  to_xy(15,12) ;write('4) Load CMOS RWM contents from a file') ;
  to_xy(15,13) ;write('5) Exit from this program') ;
  to_xy(10,15) ;write('Select option required ') ;
end ;{display_main_menu}

procedure get_value_selected_by_user(var val : integer) ;

var

ch : char ;

begin
  ch := read_keyboard ;
  val := ord(ch)– ord('0') ;
  if (val < unknown) or (val > exit) then
  val := unknown ;
end ;{get_value_selected_by_user}

procedure unknown_command ;

var

ch : char ;

begin
  menu_shell ;
  to_xy(10,7) ;
  write('You have made an incorrect selection.
  please press any key') ;
  to_xy(10,8) ;
  write('to continue') ;
  ch := read_keyboard ;
end ;{unknown_command}

procedure display_all_contents ;

begin
  display_ram(0,63) ;
end ;{display_all_contents}

{*************************************************************}
{******* Display PC information ****************************}
{*************************************************************}

procedure display_sub_menu ;

begin
  menu_shell ;
  to_xy(10,7) ;write('Display PC information menu') ;
  to_xy(15,9) ;
  write('1) Display and alter floppy disk information') ;
  to_xy(15,10) ;
  write('2) Display and alter hard disk information') ;
  to_xy(15,11) ;
  write('3) Display and alter PC display information') ;
  to_xy(15,12) ;
  write('4) Display and alter maths coprocessor information') ;
  to_xy(15,13) ;
  write('5) Display and alter the amount of main RWM installed') ;
  to_xy(15,14) ;
  write('6) Display and alter amount of extended RWM installed') ;
  to_xy(15,15) ;write('7) Exit from this program') ;
  to_xy(10,17) ;write('Select option required') ;
end ;{display_sub_menu}

procedure get_option_selected_by_user(var opt : integer) ;

var

ch : char ;

begin
  ch := read_keyboard ;
  opt := ord(ch) - ord('0') ;
  if (opt < unknown) or (opt> exit_sub) then
  opt := unknown ;
end ;{get_option_selected_by_user}

{**** procedures which actually alter the CMOS RWM contents ******}
{********** procedures which alter floppy information *************}
```

```
procedure display_floppy_menu(var number_of_floppies : byte) ;

var

{number_of_floppies : byte ;}
floppy_types : byte ;

begin
    number_of_floppies := 0 ;
    floppy_types := 0 ;
    menu_shell ;
to_xy(10,7) ;write('Existing floppy selection :-') ;
read_cmosram(20,number_of_floppies) ;
number_of_floppies := number_of_floppies div 64 ;
read_cmosram(16,floppy_types) ;
to_xy(10,9) ;write('Floppy A : ') ;
to_xy(10,11) ;write('Floppy B : ') ;
case number_of_floppies of
    0 : begin
            floppy_types := floppy_types mod 16 ;
            to_xy(20,11) ;write('Not installed') ;
            to_xy(20,9) ;
            case floppy_types of
                0 : write('No drive present') ;
                1 : write('5.25" Standard density (360 KBytes)') ;
                2 : write('5.25" High density (1.2 MBytes)') ;
                3 : write('3.50" Standard density (720 KBytes)') ;
                4 : write('3.50" High density (1.44 MBytes)') ;
                else ;
            end ;{case}
        end ;
    1 : begin
        to_xy(20,9) ;
            case (floppy_types div 16) of
                0 : write('No drive present') ;
                1 : write('5.25" Standard density (360 KBytes)') ;
                2 : write('5.25" High density (1.2 MBytes)') ;
                3 : write('3.50" Standard density (720 KBytes)') ;
                4 : write('3.50" High density (1.44 MBytes)') ;
                else ;
            end ;{case}
            to_xy(20,11) ;
            case (floppy_types mod 16) of
                0 : write('No drive present') ;
                1 : write('5.25" Standard density (360 KBytes)') ;
                2 : write('5.25" High density (1.2 MBytes)') ;
                3 : write('3.50" Standard density (720 KBytes)') ;
                4 : write('3.50" High density (1.44 MBytes)') ;
                else ;
            end ;{case}
        end ;
    2,3 : begin
            to_xy(20,90) ;
            write('3 and 4 floppies not yet implemented') ;
        end ;
    else ;
    end ;{case}
to_xy(10,15) ;write('Available selections are :-') ;
to_xy(15,17) ;write('1) Alter floppy A :') ;
to_xy(15,18) ;write('2) Alter floppy B :') ;
to_xy(15,19) ;write('3) Exit from this menu') ;
end ;{display_floppy_menu}

procedure get_floppy_selected(var floppy : integer) ;

var

ch : char ;

begin
    ch := read_keyboard ;
    floppy := ord(ch) - ord('0') ;
    if (floppy < unknown) or (floppy > floppy1_exit) then
    floppy := unknown ;
end ;{get_floppy_selected}
```

```
procedure get_altered_floppy_information
            (floppy : integer ;var new : integer) ;

var

ch : char ;

new_floppy : integer ;
previous_selection : integer ;

begin
    previous_selection := 0 ;
    new_floppy := 0 ;
    to_xy(10,15) ;write('Available selections are :-') ;
    to_xy(15,17) ;write('1) No floppy installed') ;
    to_xy(15,18) ;write('2) 5.25" Standard density (360 KBytes)') ;
    to_xy(15,19) ;write('3) 5.25" High density (1.2 MBytes)') ;
    to_xy(15,20) ;write('4) 3.50" Standard density (720 KBytes)') ;
    to_xy(15,21) ;write('5) 3.50" High density (1.44 MBytes)') ;
    to_xy(15,22) ;write('6) Exit from this menu') ;
    while not (new_floppy = floppy_exit) do
        begin
            previous_selection := new_floppy ;
            ch := read_keyboard ;
            new_floppy := ord(ch) - ord('0') ;
            if  (new_floppy [*less] unknown) or
                (new_floppy [*greater] floppy_exit) then
            new_floppy := floppy_exit ;
            to_xy(20,7 + (2 * floppy)) ;
            case new_floppy of
                1 : write('No drive present') ;
                2 : write('5.25" Standard density (360 KBytes)') ;
                3 : write('5.25" High density (1.2 MBytes)') ;
                4 : write('3.50" Standard density (720 KBytes)') ;
                5 : write('3.50" High density (1.44 MBytes)') ;
                else ;
            end ;{case}
        end ;{while}
    new := previous_selection ;
end ;{get_altered_floppy_information}

procedure alter_floppy_contents(numb_floppies:byte;floppy,new:integer);

var

old_numb : byte ;
floppy_value : byte ;

begin
    old_numb := 0 ;
    floppy_value := 0 ;
    new := new - 1 ;{adjusts menu selection to match drive }
    if (new = 0) and (numb_floppies [*greater] 0) then
        begin
            numb_floppies := numb_floppies - 1 ;
            read_cmosram(20,old_numb) ;
            old_numb := old_numb mod 64 ;
            old_numb := (64 * numb_floppies) + old_numb ;
            { write_cmosram(20,old_numb) ;}
        end ;
        read_cmosram(16,floppy_value) ;
    case floppy of
        1 : begin
                floppy_value := floppy_value mod 16 ;
                floppy_value := (new * 16) + floppy_value ;
                { write_cmosram(16,floppy_value) ;}
            end ;
        2 : begin
                floppy_value := floppy_value div 16 ;
                floppy_value := (16 * floppy_value) + new ;
                { write_cmosram(16,floppy_value) ;}
            end ;
    end ;{case}
end ;{alter_floppy_contents}

procedure display_floppy_information ;

var
```

```
floppy : integer ;
new_parameter : integer ;
numb_floppies : byte ;

begin
    floppy := unknown ;
    numb_floppies := 0 ;
    new_parameter := unknown ;
    while not (floppy = floppy1_exit) do
        begin
            display_floppy_menu(numb_floppies) ;
            get_floppy_selected(floppy) ;
            if not (floppy = floppy1_exit) and
                not (floppy = unknown) then
            begin
                get_altered_floppy_information(floppy,new_parameter) ;
                alter_floppy_contents(numb_floppies,floppy,new_parameter) ;
            end ;
        end ;{while}
end ;{display_floppy_information}

{******** end of floppy procedures *****************************}
{*********** procedures which alter hard disk ********************}

procedure display_hard_types(x,y,which : integer ; hard_type : byte) ;

var

extension : byte ;

begin
    extension := 0 ;
    to_xy(x,y) ;
    case hard_type of
        0 : write('Hard disk drive not installed ') ;
        1 : write('Type 1 (10 MBytes) ') ;
        2 : write('Type 2 (21 MBytes) ') ;
        3 : write('Type 3 (32 MBytes) ') ;
        4 : write('Type 4 (65 MBytes) ') ;
        5 : write('Type 5 (49 MBytes) ') ;
        6 : write('Type 6 (21 MBytes) ') ;
        7 : write('Type 7 (32 MBytes) ') ;
        8 : write('Type 8 (32 MBytes) ') ;
        9 : write('Type 9 (117 MBytes) ') ;
        10 : write('Type 10 (21 MBytes) ') ;
        11 : write('Type 11 (37 MBytes) ') ;
        12 : write('Type 12 (52 MBytes) ') ;
        13 : write('Type 13 (21 MBytes) ') ;
        14 : write('Type 14 (44 MBytes) ') ;
        15 : begin
                read_cmosram(25 + which,extension) ;
                write('Type ',extension) ;
            end ;
        else ;
    end ;{case}
end ;{display_hard_types}

procedure display_hard_menu ;

const

C = 0 ;{which hard disk}
D = 1 ;

var

hard_types : byte ;
which : integer ;
hard_C,hard_D : byte ;

begin
    which := C ;
    hard_C := 0 ; hard_D := 0 ;
    hard_types := 0 ;
    menu_shell ;
    to_xy(10,7) ;write('Existing Hard disk selection :-') ;
    read_cmosram(18,hard_types) ;
    to_xy(10,9) ;write('Hard disk C : ') ;
```

```
    to_xy(10,11) ;write('Hard disk D : ') ;
    hard_C := hard_types div 16 ;
    display_hard_types(20,9,C,hard_C) ;
    hard_D := hard_types mod 16 ;
    display_hard_types(20,11,D,hard_D) ;
    to_xy(10,15) ;write('Available selections are :-') ;
    to_xy(15,17) ;write('1) Alter hard disk C :') ;
    to_xy(15,18) ;write('2) Alter hard disk D :') ;
    to_xy(15,19) ;write('3) Exit from this menu') ;
end ;{display_hard_menu}

procedure get_hard_selected(var hard : integer) ;

var

ch : char ;

begin
    ch := read_keyboard ;
    hard := ord(ch) - ord('0') ;
    if (hard [*less] unknown) or (hard [*greater] hard_exit) then
        hard := unknown ;
end ;{get_hard_selected}

procedure get_altered_hard_information(hard:integer;var new:integer) ;

var

ch : char ;

begin
    to_xy(15,17) ;write(' ') ;
    to_xy(15,18) ;write(' ') ;
    to_xy(15,19) ;write(' ') ;
    to_xy(10,15) ;
    write('Select the hard disk ',chr(ord('B') + hard),' : TYPE (1 to 47) ') ;
    readln(new) ;
    if (new < unknown) or (new > 47) then
        hard := unknown ;
end ;{get_altered_hard_information}

procedure alter_hard_contents(hard,new : integer) ;

var

new_type : byte ;

begin
    new_type := 0 ;
    case hard of
        1 : begin
            if new < 16 then
                begin
                    read_cmosram(18,new_type) ;
                    new_type := new_type mod 16 ;
                    new_type := (16 * new) + new_type ;
                    { write_cmosram(18,new_type) ;}
                end
            else
                begin
                    read_cmosram(18,new_type) ;
                    new_type := new_type mod 16 ;
                    new_type := (16 * 16) + new_type ;
                    { write_cmosram(18,new_type) ;}
                    { write_cmosram(25,new) ;}
                end ;
            end ;
        2 : begin
            if new < 16 then
                begin
                    read_cmosram(18,new_type) ;
                    new_type := new_type div 16 ;
                    new_type := (16 * new_type) + new ;
                    { write_cmosram(18,new_type) ;}
                end
            else
                begin
                    read_cmosram(18,new_type) ;
                    new_type := new_type div 16 ;
```

```
                new_type := (16 * new_type) + 15 ;
                   { write_cmosram(18,new_type) ;}
                   { write_cmosram(26,new) ;}
              end ;
         end ;
       else ;
   end ;{case}
end ;{alter_hard_contents}

procedure display_hard_information ;

var

hard : integer ;
new_parameter : integer ;

begin
   hard := unknown ;
   new_parameter := unknown ;
   while not (hard = hard_exit) do
      begin
         display_hard_menu ;
         get_hard_selected(hard) ;
         if not (hard = hard_exit) and not (hard = unknown) then
            begin
               get_altered_hard_information(hard,new_parameter) ;
               alter_hard_contents(hard,new_parameter) ;
            end ;
      end ;{while}
end ;

{*********** end of hard disk procedures **********************}
{********* procedures for altering the primary display ***********}

procedure display_display_menu ;

begin
   menu_shell ;
end ;{display_display_menu}

procedure get_display_value(var display : integer) ;

var

ch : char ;

begin
   ch := read_keyboard ;
   display := ord(ch) – ord('0') ;
   if (display < unknown) or (display > exit) then
      display := unknown ;
end ;{get_display_value}
procedure alter_display_selected(disp : integer) ;
begin
end ;{alter_display_selected}

procedure display_display_information ;

var
display : integer ;

begin
   display := unknown ;
   while not (display = display_exit) do
      begin
         display_display_menu ;
         get_display_value(display) ;
         if not (display = display_exit) then
            alter_display_selected(display) ;
      end ;{while}
end ;{display_display_information}

{******** end of display procedures ***************************}
{********* procedures to alter math coprocessor information *******}

procedure display_math_menu ;

begin
   menu_shell ;
end ;{display_math_menu}
```

```
procedure get_math_value(var math : integer) ;

var

ch : char ;

begin
   ch := read_keyboard ;
   math := ord(ch) - ord('0') ;
   if (math < unknown) or (math > exit) then
      math := unknown ;
end ;{get_math_value}

procedure alter_math_selected(maths : integer) ;

begin
end ;{alter_math_selected}

procedure display_math_coproc_information ;

var

math : integer ;

begin
   math := unknown ;
   while not (math = math_exit) do
      begin
         display_math_menu ;
         get_math_value(math) ;
         if not (math = math_exit) then
            alter_math_selected(math) ;
      end ;{while}
end ;{display_math_coproc_information}

{******** end of math coprocessor procedures *****************}
{********* procedures to alter main RWM installed ***************}

procedure display_main_RWM_menu ;

begin
   menu_shell ;
end ;{display_main_RWM_menu}

procedure get_main_RWM_value(var main : integer) ;

var

ch : char ;

begin
   ch := read_keyboard ;
   main := ord(ch) - ord('0') ;
   if (main < unknown) or (main > exit) then
      main := unknown ;
end ;{get_main_RWM_value}

procedure alter_main_RWM_selected(main : integer) ;

begin
end ;{alter_main_RWM_selected}

procedure display_main_RWM_installed ;

var

main_RWM : integer ;

begin
   main_RWM := unknown ;
   while not (main_RWM = main_RWM_exit) do
      begin
         display_main_RWM_menu ;
         get_main_RWM_value(main_RWM) ;
         if not (main_RWM = main_RWM_exit) then
            alter_main_RWM_selected(main_RWM) ;
      end ;{while}
end ;{display_main_RWM_installed}

{******** procedures to alter extended RWM installed ************}

procedure display_extended_RWM_menu ;
```

```pascal
begin
   menu_shell ;
end ;{display_extended_menu}

procedure get_extended_RWM_value(var extended : integer) ;

var

ch : char ;

begin
   ch := read_keyboard ;
   extended := ord(ch) – ord('0') ;
   if (extended < unknown) or (extended > exit) then
   extended := unknown ;
end ;{get_extended_RWM_value}

procedure alter_extended_RWM_selected(extended : integer) ;

begin
end ;{alter_extended_RWM_selected}

procedure display_extended_RWM_installed ;

var

extended_RWM : integer ;

begin
   extended_RWM := unknown ;
   while not (extended_RWM = extended_RWM_exit) do
      begin
         display_extended_RWM_menu ;
         get_extended_RWM_value(extended_RWM) ;
         if not (extended_RWM = extended_RWM_exit) then
            alter_extended_RWM_selected(extended_RWM) ;
      end ;{while}
end ;{display_extended_RWM_installed}

{****** end of extended RWM procedures ***********************}
{********* end of procedures which actually alter RWM contents ****}

procedure execute_selected_option(opt : integer) ;

begin
   case opt of
      0 : unknown_command ;
      1 : display_floppy_information ;
      2 : display_hard_information ;
      3 : display_display_information ;
      4 : display_math_coproc_information ;
      5 : display_main_RWM_installed ;
      6 : display_extended_RWM_installed ;
      else unknown_command ;
   end ;{case}
end ;{execute_selected_option}

procedure display_PC_information ;

var

option : integer ;

begin
   option := unknown ;
   while not (option = exit_sub) do
      begin
         display_sub_menu ;
         get_option_selected_by_user(option) ;
         if not (option = exit_sub) and not (option = unknown) then
            execute_selected_option(option) ;
      end ;{while}
end ;{display_PC_information}

{***************************************************************}
{******** end of display PC information ********************}
{********** save contents to a file **********************}

procedure save_contents_to_file ;

var
```

```pascal
address : integer ;
value : byte ;
ch : char ;

begin
   assign(cmos_file,'cmosrwm.dat') ;
   rewrite(cmos_file) ;
   writeln(cmos_file,'CMOS RWM contents') ;
   writeln(cmos_file) ;
   for address := 0 to 63 do
      begin
         read_cmosram(address,value) ;
         writeln(cmos_file,value) ;
e     nd ;
close(cmos_file) ;
menu_shell ;
   to_xy(10,7) ;
   write('The CMOS RWM contents have been saved to a file called :') ;
   to_xy(15,9) ;
   write('CMOSRWM.DAT') ;
   ch := read_keyboard ;
end ;{save_contents_to_file}

{************* load contents from a file *********************}

procedure load_contents_from_file ;

var

address : integer ;
value : byte ;
ch : char ;

begin
   menu_shell ;
   to_xy(10,7) ;
   write('The CMOS RWM contents are being loaded from a file called :') ;
   to_xy(15,9) ;
   write('CMOSRWM.DAT') ;
   assign(cmos_file,'cmosrwm.dat') ;
   reset(cmos_file) ;
   readln(cmos_file) ;
   address := 0 ;
   repeat{until address > 63 or eof(cmos_file)}
      readln(cmos_file,value) ;
         { put_to_port(address,value) ;}{Leave this out until tested}
      address := address + 1 ;
   until (address [*greater] 63) or eof(cmos_file) ;
   close(cmos_file) ;
   to_xy(10,7) ;
   write('The CMOS RWM contents are being loaded from a file called :') ;
   to_xy(10,11) ;
   write('Press any key to continue') ;
   ch := read_keyboard ;
end ;{load_contents_from_file}

{************* end of main menu procedures *********************}

procedure execute_selected_value(val : integer) ;

begin
   case val of
      0 : unknown_command ;
      1 : display_all_contents ;
      2 : display_PC_information ;
      3 : save_contents_to_file ;
      4 : load_contents_from_file ;
      else begin
         to_xy(10,15) ;
         write('Unknown selection : make another choice') ;
      end ;
   end ;{case}
end ;{execute_selected_value}

begin
   value := unknown ;
```

```
while not (value = exit) do
  begin
    display_main_menu ;
    get_value_selected_by_user(value) ;
    if not (value = exit) and not (value = unknown) then
       execute_selected_value(value) ;
  end ;{while}
clear_screen ;
writeln('Thank you for using this program') ;
end.
```

Sample Display Screens

```
             INITIAL USER MENU
    ─────────────────────────────────────

      CMOS RWM Allocation and Alteration
    ─────────────────────────────────────

      Dr R C Seals: University of Greenwich:
                11th December 1992
    ─────────────────────────────────────

    Main menu:

    1)   Display byte contents
    2)   Alter byte contents
    3)   Save existing CMOS RWM contents to a file
    4)   Load CMOS RWM CONTENTS from a file
    5)   Exit from this program

    Select option required
```

Figure 7.12 Initial user menu

```
      CMOS RWM Allocation and Alteration
    ─────────────────────────────────────

      Dr R C Seals: University of Greenwich:
                11th December 1992
    ─────────────────────────────────────

    Existing floppy selection:

       Floppy A: 5.25"  High density   (1.20 MBytes)
       Floppy B: 3.50"  High density   (1.44 MBytes)

    Available selections are:

    1)   Alter floppy A
    2)   Alter floppy B
    3)   Exit from this menu
```

Figure 7.13 User menu for selecting floppy disks installed

Summary

From the two case studies it is possible to understand that the major part of any program design is in the production of the specification and the testing of the final program to ensure that it meets the specification. Implementing the specification is generally the easiest part, provided a structured design technique is followed, as each part is simple and easy to understand and correspondingly easy to implement as a program.

Index